Refrigeration and Air-conditioning Technology

Macmillan Texts for Industrial, Vocational and Technical Education

Refrigeration and Air-conditioning Technology

Norman Cook

Macmillan Education
Between Towns Road, Oxford OX4 3PP
A division of Macmillan Publishers Limited
Companies and representatives throughout the world

ISBN 0-333-60958-1

First published 1995

www.macmillan-africa.com

Illustrations by 1-11 Line Art

Cover illustration reproduced with permission of Carrier

Printed and bound in Malaysia

2008 2007 2006 2005
10 9 8 7 6 5 4

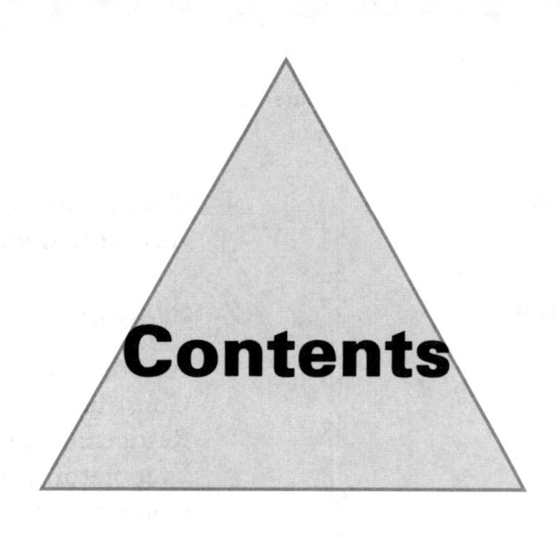
Contents

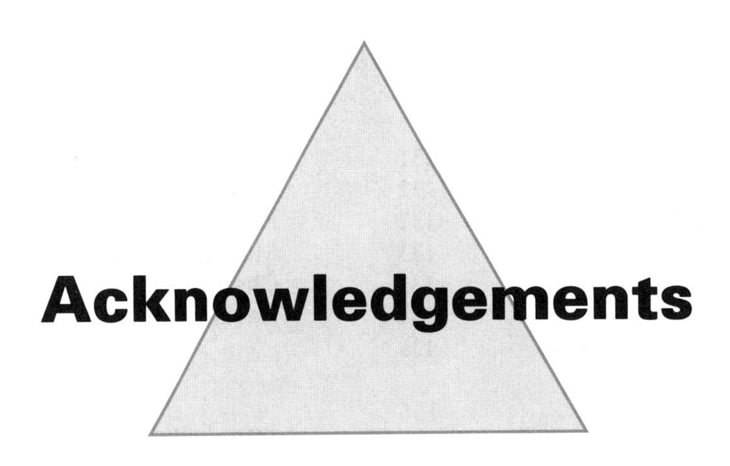

Acknowledgements

Thanks are due to my wife Brenda Cook for her help in preparing the typescript and also to John Waugh I Eng, ACIBSE, for his assistance in the area of noise control and other aspects of air conditioning.

Norman Cook

1 Introduction

People need food to live and one problem with food is that it starts to spoil quite quickly. This applies to vegetables, such as peas, beans, potatoes, which come from plants and also to meat which comes from dead animals.

Food spoils because it is attacked by very small creatures called germs. One important type of germ is called bacteria. Bacteria are so small that many millions can live in a glass of water. While animals are alive, bodily mechanisms control bacteria but once they are dead there is nothing to stop bacteria increasing in number. The same principle applies to plants. If food is not kept fresh, if food is not preserved, the number of bacteria can double very quickly. Large numbers of bacteria can make food taste unpleasant. They can also make it poisonous. If you eat spoilt food you can get food poisoning and it can cause serious illness or death.

Bacteria are not the only forms of germ. Moulds and yeasts can cause food to spoil. Moulds are made up of small plants which can grow very quickly. Yeasts are different types of small plants. Yeasts can grow quickly too. Some yeasts are used to make bread and beer. However, other yeasts cause food to spoil.

One way in which people in the past stopped food from spoiling was by cooking it. For example, fruit can be preserved by making jam. The fruit is cooked with sugar until jam is produced. It is the sugar in the cooked fruit that stops the germs from increasing. Jam can be kept for much longer than fresh fruit.

Another way of stopping food from spoiling is by pickling. Pickling is preserving in vinegar or some other liquid, such as brine. Pickling stops germs from increasing. The pickled food is placed in jars with lids, so the air cannot get to them. Air will carry in fresh germs.

Vinegar is a chemical that helps to preserve food. Modern chemicals used to preserve food are called preservatives. Preservatives are often used in soft drinks to stop them from spoiling. Other preservatives are used in bread to stop moulds from growing. Some preservatives are used to stop fruit juice from changing colour. Today many foods sold in shops contain preservatives. However, there are people who claim that some preservatives are just as dangerous as food poisoning because these preservatives can cause illness too.

Cereals can be preserved by making them into breakfast foods. Corn flakes are preserved by cleaning the corn and then cutting it up into small pieces. The pieces are then cooked in a special way. After cooking the corn is made into flakes and then toasted.

Milk can be kept from spoiling by pasteurisation. Pasteurisation involves the heating of milk to kill some of the germs. The temperature is not so high that all the germs are killed. Pasteurisation can only protect the milk for a short time and then the germs return. Other drinks, such as beer and wine can be protected by the same means.

Many varieties of food can be preserved by canning. Canned food is cooked before it is canned. Cooking kills germs because high temperatures kill germs. The cooked food is put into cans when it is still at a high temperature. The ends of the can are then closed so that air cannot enter. If air gets into the cans the food will spoil.

Vegetables are often preserved by dehydration. Dehydration means taking the water out of something to make it dry. Peas are often preserved by dehydration. Germs find it difficult to increase where there is no water. That is how dehydrated food is preserved. The peas are heated to drive away the water, then they are packed in airtight packets to stop the water in the air from re-entering.

A modern way of killing germs is by using **radioactivity**. Radiation from a radioactive material can destroy bacteria but the problem is that it can also damage the food itself. Scientists are working on ways of using radiation without damaging food. Perhaps one day they may succeed. At present some countries allow radiation to be used on food but others do not.

We have seen that germs are killed by high temperatures. Low temperatures, unless they are very low, do not normally kill germs, but they do stop them from multiplying and growing. This is how the refrigeration of food works. It is not easy to say when people first found that food is preserved by low temperatures but the inhabitants of Siberia noticed long ago that dead furry elephants called mammoths remained trapped in ice without changing for many years. People in other parts of the world noticed that food stayed fresh longer in the winter than in the summer. For this reason food cupboards or larders were often built on the cold north side of houses. Sometimes ice was gathered in the winter and stored underground or in a shed. Blocks of ice were packed with sawdust or other material between them to stop them from melting. Food kept near the ice was preserved.

During the last century, the stored ice was used in iceboxes. A block of ice was placed inside the icebox, preferably at the top. Warm air from the food on the shelves lower down rose to the level of the ice, cooled and dropped down again, so cooling the food. This process is called convection (see Chapter 3). As the ice melted the water was led away using a funnel. This is shown in Figure 1.1.

One disadvantage of using ice for refrigeration is that the lowest temperature that can be achieved is 0°C. In theory frozen salt water or brine could be used to produce temperatures as low as about −20°C but this was not done often. Frozen carbon dioxide, or dry ice, can produce even lower temperatures and it was used to store ice cream. Another disadvantage is that as the block of ice becomes smaller, the amount of refrigeration goes down, until eventually, the block has to be replaced.

The difference between the icebox and the modern refrigerator is that the ice box needs ice to be placed inside it and does not generate its own low temperatures, whereas the refrigerator is a mechanical device that can produce low temperatures in a controlled way. Another simple refrigeration device is the food cooler. Food or drink is placed in a metal box, usually tin, and the box is placed in a pan containing water. A cloth is placed over the box so that the ends of the cloth dip in the water. The cloth absorbs the water and becomes wet. The water from the wet cloth evaporates, evaporation causes cooling (see Chapter 3) and food in the tin box remains cool (see Figure 1.2).

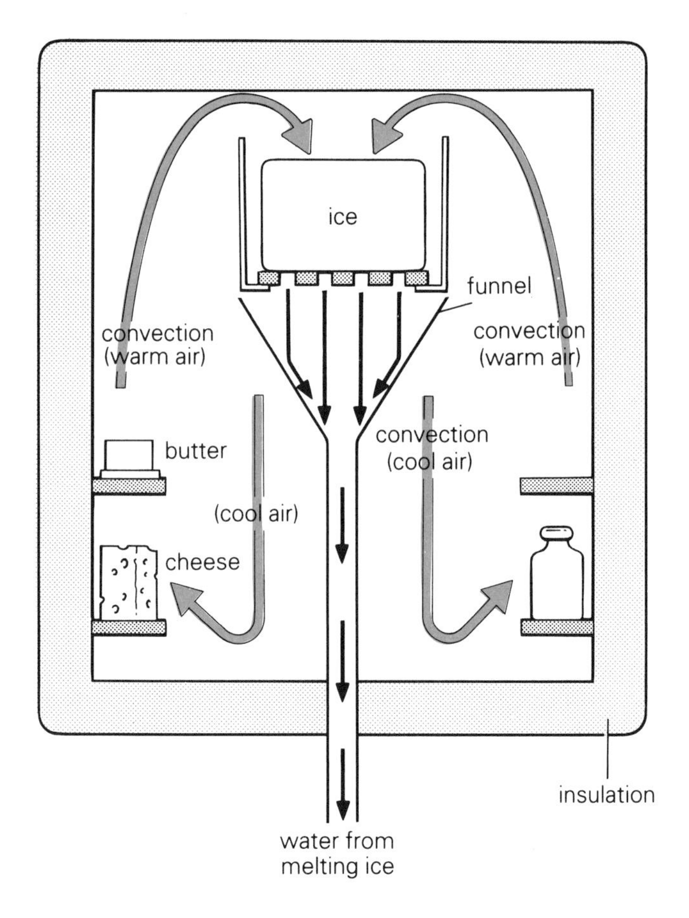

Figure 1.1 An icebox.

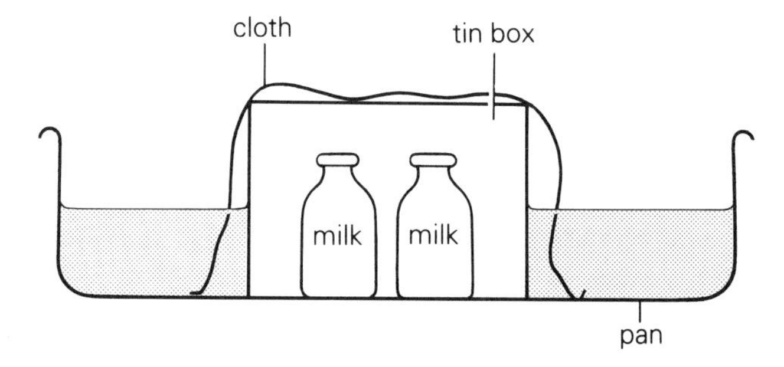

Figure 1.2 A food and drink cooler.

In hot countries, people cool drinking water by putting it in porous vessels. Some of the water soaks through the pores and evaporates and in this way the rest of the water is cooled. Milk bottle coolers are porous vessels working on the same principle. The milk bottles are placed in the porous vessel which stands in a pan of water.

Since the earliest times, people have tried to make themselves comfortable under hot and humid conditions. One way was to open windows and doors to allow in outside air. Of course this method is still used today, where there is no air conditioning. Opening windows and doors to allow air to move from place to place is called ventilation. Moving air helps people to sweat and this cools them down and makes them comfortable. This type of ventilation can help to keep people cool but it also allows in dirt, dust and fumes. These cause a great deal of discomfort in industrial and other polluted areas. In some places noise can be a problem. Open windows allow traffic noises and other noises to pass from the street into the house.

Fans have been used for a long time in order to keep people cool. The first fans were made of rigid leaves and then came fans of stiff paper or some other material. These were held by hand and moved to produce a current of air over the face. This helped sweat to evaporate from the face and caused cooling. More recently, electric fans have been used for ventilation. Electric fans have an electric motor inside them in order to make metal blades go round. These metal blades cause a steady current of air which helps evaporation from the skin to take place.

In the Middle East long ago some large buildings were designed to have a kind of air conditioning. Usually these buildings had a tower with large openings or air vents at the top. The wind blew through these vents and down into an underground tunnel. The walls of the underground tunnel were wet so that evaporation took place. This caused the walls of the tunnel to cool by the time it reached the house. Figure 1.3 shows such a building. The air which had passed through the house escaped through the windows and doors. Some air escaped through another vent in the tower. This simple air conditioning produced good cooling in the hot summers of the Middle East. One problem, however, was that dust and fumes could still enter the building. There were no filters as in scientific air conditioning. Also there was no way of keeping the building at a comfortable temperature both summer and winter.

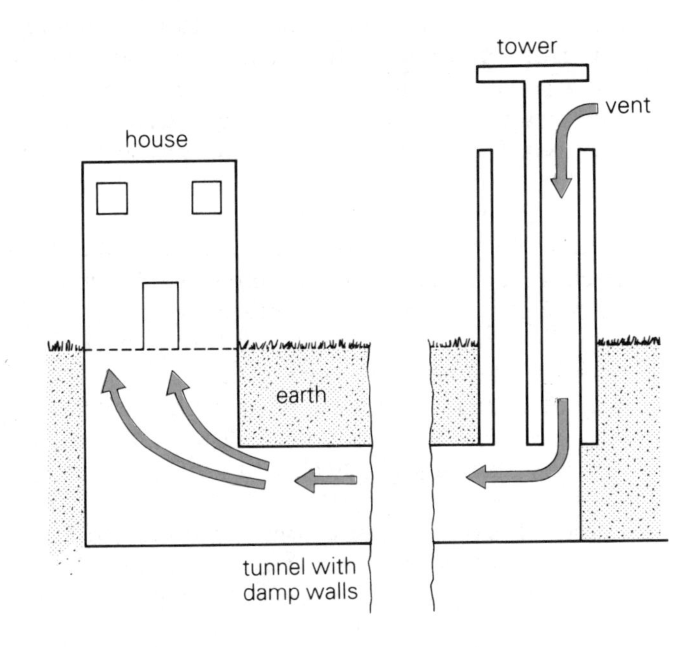

Figure 1.3 Simple air conditioning.

When mechanical refrigeration was first developed during the last century the equipment was heavy, expensive and clumsy and its use was limited to industries such as meat preservation and ice making. Gradually, however, refrigeration techniques improved and their use increased. Today, most homes in the western world are equipped with refrigerators and many have freezers for the frozen storage of food.

The majority of people in the West live in towns and do not grow their own food. The only way in which an urban population of this sort can be supported is by storing large quantities of food using mechanical refrigeration. Refrigerated transport is needed to move frozen food from storage centres to shops and supermarkets. This is done by means of refrigerated trucks which carry their own refrigeration equipment. Refrigerated ships are used to transport meat and other foods across the oceans from one country to another. Food is not only stored in frozen form. Various types of fruit, for example apples and pears, cannot be frozen and need to be stored in cold stores at temperatures above the freezing point of water. In shops and supermarkets certain foods are sold from refrigerated display cabinets in order to keep them fresh for the customer.

It is not only food that needs to be refrigerated and transported. Refrigeration is also important in other industries, too. For example, liquefied gases at low temperatures are important in many industrial processes. Liquid nitrogen is used to make steel and to refine copper and also to make hydrogen from petroleum. It is used for many other purposes, too, such as the manufacture of ammonia for refrigerators. Liquid nitrogen is used for putting out forest fires, because the nitrogen stops oxygen from getting to the fire and the low temperature helps stop the burning.

Liquid oxygen is used in the manufacture of steel. Steel is made from iron and other materials at very high temperatures. Liquid oxygen is sprayed into the furnace, this makes the fire burn brighter and the temperature increases. Hard steel, used in aircraft manufacture, becomes very hot when it is cut and it needs to be cooled down. This can be done by spraying the steel with a fine mist of dry ice.

Liquid oxygen is sometimes transported from the plant where it is manufactured to the factory where it is used by a pipeline. Such pipelines are insulated to keep out heat and can be up to several kilometres long. Where pipelines are not available and there is no refrigerated transport, Dewar flasks are often used. These are larger versions of the Thermos flask used for holding hot and cold drinks (see Chapter 3).

Liquid gases are often transported overseas by means of ships known as tankers. The liquid gas is pumped into a large tank which is part of the tanker. This tank is like a Dewar but it has a special insulating material instead of a vacuum around the tank. Tanks using the special insulating material are more efficient than Dewar flasks, because heat takes longer and the liquid gas remains cool longer. When the tanker gets to a port and delivers its load, tanker trains and tanker trucks can be used to take the liquid gas to its destination.

Refrigeration and refrigerated products are very much part of life in a modern industrial country. With them the standard of living of people increases. Without them life would be more difficult and not so convenient.

Modern air conditioning came about as a result of the invention of mechanical refrigeration. Air is cooled by means of refrigeration equipment and then pumped by means of a fan into the air-conditioned space which can be a house, a shop, a school, a factory or an office building. Air conditioning which is designed to make people comfortable is comfort air conditioning but air conditioning is also used where clean air is necessary for industrial processes. Filtering is used to remove particles of dust from the atmosphere both in comfort and industrial air conditioning. Moisture control is also very important.

In recent years, special air-conditioning systems have been developed for nuclear submarines and for space ships. Nuclear submarines can stay under water for several months. Outside air cannot be used and so oxygen for breathing is produced using special units. To stop carbon dioxide building up and killing the crew special chemicals are used which absorb the gas. The manned space satellites which orbit the earth and the space modules that have travelled to the moon have similar air-conditioning problems to nuclear submarines. This is because there is no air in space and so air cannot be taken in from outside. Space suits, used for walking in space and on the moon also have their own air conditioning to produce a comfortable temperature and humidity. They also have a means of removing carbon dioxide (see Figure 1.4).

In future, men will travel to the planets and perhaps even to the stars. Very large space ships will be needed for these journeys. The air-conditioning systems will be very large because of the number of people in the crews. For these very long journeys it is possible that plants will be taken on board the space ship. The plants will be there to take in carbon dioxide and to give out oxygen. In this way journeys of many months or even years could be made.

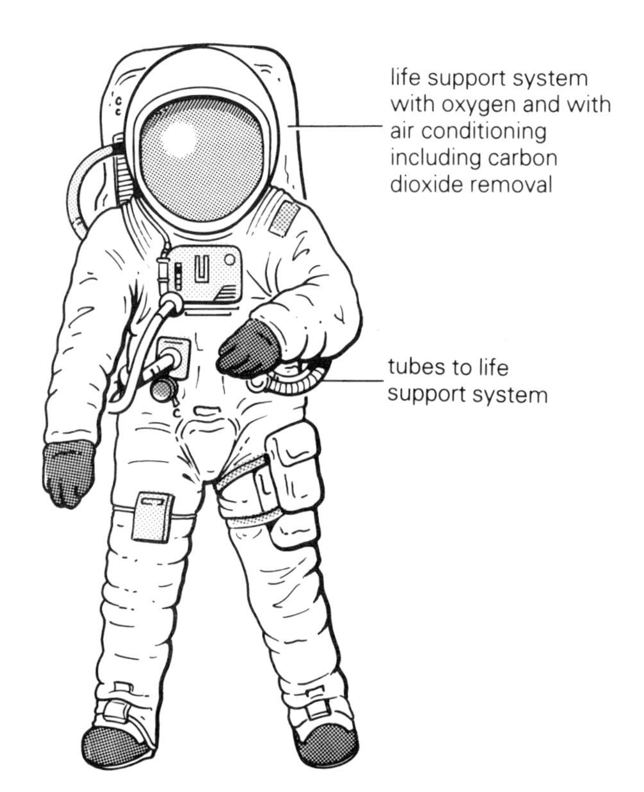

Figure 1.4 A space suit.

Air conditioning is an important part of the world in which we live, particularly in countries with hot climates. In future its use will increase as more discoveries are made.

Worldwide, there are many careers that can be pursued in the fields of refrigeration and air conditioning. Many universities include the subjects as part of their engineering degree course. Courses for technicians are run at technical colleges and places of further education. Some companies run apprenticeship schemes for young people in which practical training is provided, particularly in those areas in which the firm specialises.

Careers include research and development, designing refrigeration and air-conditioning systems, draughting, production engineering, working on machines to produce refrigerator parts, maintenance work and repair work. Some engineers work at installing refrigeration and air-conditioning systems in shops, supermarkets, offices, hospitals and other buildings. The career that you go into will be determined by your qualifications, experience and personal qualities such as initiative and determination.

The aim of this book is to cover the subject matter of refrigeration and air conditioning in a clear, concise and logical way. Chapter 2 is given over to safe working practice and first aid. This is included because safety in the workplace is of prime importance.

The early chapters cover the basic physics of the behaviour of matter and of electricity. This is done in order to lay a simple theoretical basis for refrigeration principles later in the book. Next comes a section on the behaviour of liquids and gases, and on refrigeration cycles to enable the student to understand the reason why heat is extracted from one part of the system and rejected from another. Thermoelectric refrigeration, which is done entirely without gases and vapours, is included in these chapters.

The section on the behaviour of moist air, or psychrometry, leads on to a discussion of air-conditioning systems for the home, the office and industry. The central chapters deal with the main working components of refrigeration systems, in terms of the core information necessary to understand their function.

Working fluids, or refrigerants, are covered as are lubricating oils. The final section of the book is heavily biased towards practical aspects of the subject and project-based examples are given.

Throughout the text are many worked examples to enable students to become familiar with the subject matter. *Revision exercises and questions* are included at the end of each chapter and the answers to these are given at the back of the book, under the heading *Answers to questions and answering hints.* Every chapter has a summary, placed towards the end, which briefly covers the important points. This summary is headed *Check your understanding*. Key concepts are marked throughout the book and following the Answers section at the end these are listed alphabetically under the heading *Key words.*

2 Safe practice

Introduction

Modern refrigeration equipment is driven by a compressor which in turn is powered by electricity. Circuits that control refrigeration systems are also electrical and moreover, many tools used by the modern technician, such as drills and power saws, are driven from an electrical supply. A knowledge of electrical safety principles is vital for technicians who want to progess in their careers and to avoid injury. A knowledge of dangers from other sources, such as from chemicals used in refrigeration, is also important.

Electrical conduction by the body

The human body is a conductor of electricity but the ability to conduct varies from person to person. The electrical resistance that a person has also depends upon such factors as whether the skin is wet or dry and across what part of the body resistance is measured (see Chapter 4 for the meaning of resistance and an explanation of electrical current). With dry skin a person may have a resistance of about 10 000 Ω, measured from finger tip to finger tip on opposite hands. If the supply voltage is about 250 V r.m.s. (see Chapter 4) then the current is given by:

$$I = \frac{V}{R} = \frac{250}{10\,000} = 0.025 \text{ A or } 25 \text{ mA}$$

This is the r.m.s. current that passes through the body from hand to hand. Currents of this size cause muscular contractions making it difficult for the casualty to let go of the conductor. The heart is a muscle and large currents cause the heart to stop. In addition, large electric currents cause burns to the body. For some people a current of 25 mA could be fatal, but usually a greater current is required before death occurs. If the hands are wet the resistance could drop to as little as 100 Ω, the current would then increase to 2.5 A, which is a current high enough to nearly always cause very severe injuries and death.

> ▲ Electrical plugs, sockets, switches and electrical equipment should be kept away from places where they may get splashed with water.

Earthing

Many pieces of electrical equipment have circuits mounted inside a metal box or on a metal chassis. This case or chassis should be connected to earth through the mains plug. The mains socket outlet has an electrical lead that is connected to a water pipe that eventually goes under the ground. In some cases the lead connects directly to a rod which has been pushed into the ground. The potential or voltage of the earth is 0 V so that when the equipment is plugged into the mains, the case or chassis is connected to earth. Now suppose that a

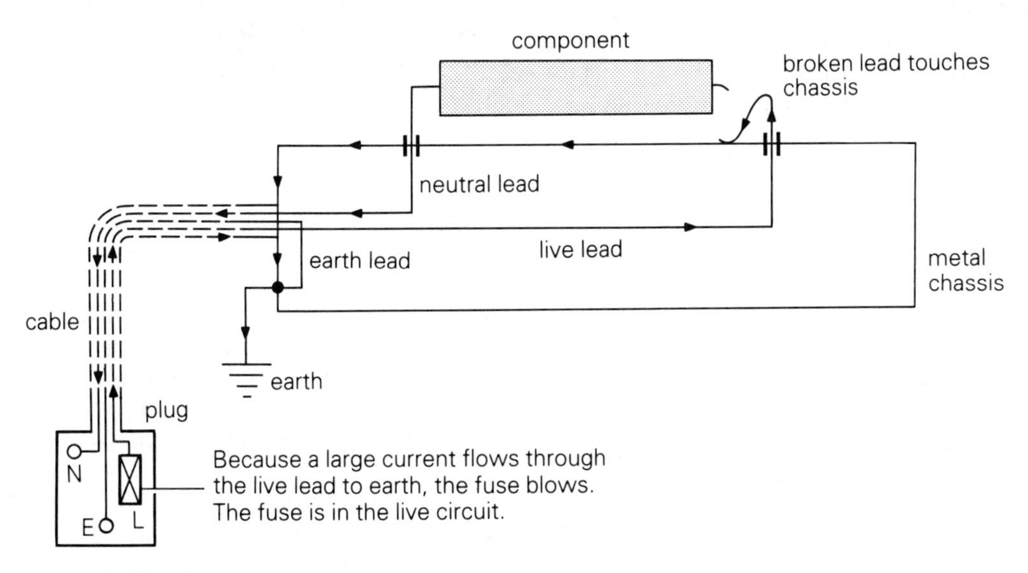

Figure 2.1 An earthed chassis.

fault occurs in the equipment and one of the leads in the circuit touches the earthed chassis, as shown in Figure 2.1.

The voltage of the component will be high as it is touching the chassis directly, so the contact resistance is almost zero. Therefore a large current flows from the supply to the zero volts of earth. If the fuse (see below) has been chosen correctly it will melt or blow. This disconnects the equipment from the mains so making it safe. Figure 2.2 shows someone touching faulty equipment that has not been earthed. A current passes through the body causing an electric shock.

If the electric shock is fatal the person is said to have been electrocuted.

Fuses

Fuses are safety devices which are designed to melt or blow when the current becomes too high.

> It is important that fuses of the correct value or rating are chosen otherwise someone may be electrocuted.

Another hazard is that if a fuse of too high a rating is used, delicate components may overheat and a fire may result.

Fuses are rated according to the current they can take. In order to work out a fuse rating it is first necessary to work out the current that the equipment takes, from the power rating in watts and the supply voltage. Once this has been done a fuse is chosen of value just greater than the equipment current. Electrical plugs for use with the mains are fitted with a fuse and, when the plug is wired to the equipment, this is sometimes the only fuse that the equipment has. However, electrical equipment sometimes has its own fuse supplied and installed by the manufacturers. Manufacturers' specifications should be consulted to find the values of these fuses.

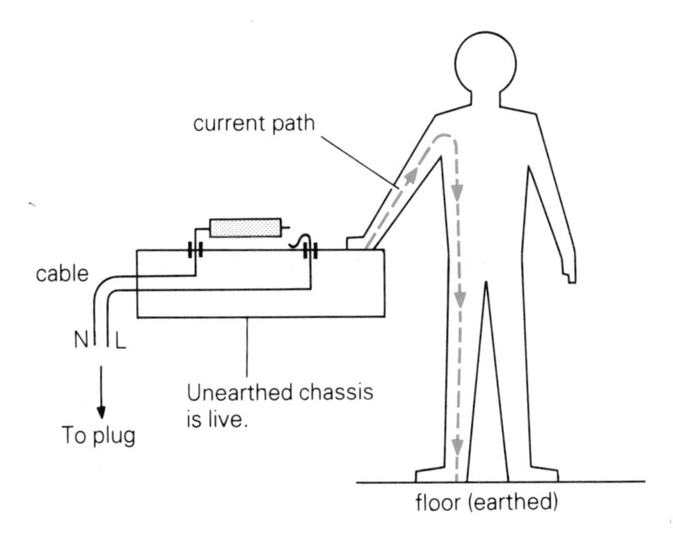

Figure 2.2 Touching faulty equipment.

EXAMPLE 2.1

A heating element for an air-conditioning circuit has a power rating of 1 kW with a supply voltage of 250 V. Which plug fuse should be chosen for the element: (i) 13 A, (ii) 10 A or (iii) 5 A?

The power (P), voltage (V) and current (I) are related by the formula $P = VI$ (see Chapter 4).

Solution

The current in the element is given by $I = P/V$, so that $I = 1000/250 = 4$ A (1 kW = 1000 W).

13 A, 10 A and 5 A are all greater than 4 A. However, a 13 A fuse would allow a current of 13 A to flow in the element if a fault should occur. This could burn out the element and a fire could occur. The same principle applies to the 10 A fuse. The 5 A fuse is the correct fuse as this would allow a current of 4 A through the element, and even a slightly greater one without overheating. If a fault occurs and the current goes above 5 A, then the fuse will blow and there will be no fire.

Selection of cables

Fires can also be caused by using the wrong cable for the equipment. It is no use using a cable that is only capable of taking a current of 3 A if it is to be used for a 2 kW compressor, as such a compressor will take a current of 8 A. In this kind of situation a fire could result, or the insulation on the outside of the cable might melt, giving the equipment-user an electric shock. Reels of PVC-coated wires and cables are available from the manufacturer who will state the current ratings for each thickness. PVC is an insulating material.

Use of power tools

Power tools are electrically operated drills, saws, sanders and so on which are used by all mechanics and technicians, including those who work in refrigeration and air conditioning. Every year there are many accidents involving power tools, particularly with the portable types, where there are no guards and screens.

There are many reasons for the accidents including carelessness and lack of attention on the part of users and lack of maintenance of the tools. Another factor is their use by staff who have not been properly trained.

You should be particularly careful of the type of clothes that you wear when using power tools. Ties, for example, can be dangerous as they can wrap around rotating drill shafts. Any loose clothing such as scarves, unbuttoned jackets and loose shirt cuffs can cause the same problems. Long hair worn loosely can catch in machinery and drag you into a dangerous situation if the working parts of the machine are moving quickly. Hair can be torn out and, more seriously, head injuries and even brain damage can occur.

To avoid problems caused by loose clothing, a proper overall, which covers the whole of the body, should be worn. For working on machinery that produces metal splinters or dust, special safety goggles are necessary. Any dust produced will be breathed in by the machine user and so a mask that absorbs dust will prevent diseases caused by dust in the throat and lungs. The industrial oils that are used with some machinery can cause skin diseases and so, when using such machines, a barrier cream that protects the hands should be used. Sometimes it is necessary to wear gloves. Long hair should be tied back or else a cap, that completely covers the hair, can be worn.

Gas cylinders

When a technician or mechanic does repairs on a refrigeration or air-conditioning system, it is often necessary to use gas cylinders, for example, refrigerants R12, R22, R134a (see later chapters), ammonia (also a refigerant) and nitrogen. **Refrigerants** are the fluids used in refrigeration systems and it is they that circulate to produce low temperatures. Safety precautions should be observed when using cylinders.

Gas cylinders should be kept in upright positions in a properly-constructed store. Some refrigerants are **flammable**; that is, they catch fire easily and others are **toxic**, or poisonous. Ammonia is both flammable and toxic. Cylinders of toxic and flammable gases should not be left in the working area overnight, as they may leak. Such cylinders should be left in a well-ventilated store. They must not be heated as the high temperature may cause fire. Large cylinders should not be carried by hand but

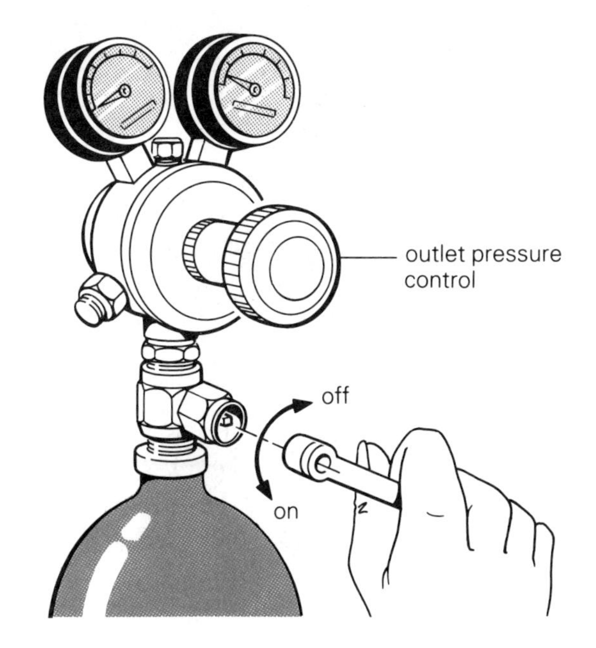

Figure 2.3 A valve tool.

moved by means of a cylinder trolley. Always use the correct tool when opening the cylinder valve as pliers, pincers and hammers can damage the valve, so releasing dangerous gas. See Figure 2.3.

When a refrigerant cylinder is being used in the working area always make sure that the area is well ventilated to dispose of fumes. Open doors and windows. The process of filling a refrigeration system with refrigerant from a cylinder is called **charging**. When you are charging a system a certain amount of refrigerant loss, or **discharging**, can occur.

 Never discharge refrigerant in the region of an open flame.

If you normally smoke, do not do so when you are using refrigerant. Make sure that there are no boilers, with pilot lights, in the room.

Brazing is the joining of metals together at high temperatures, using a brazing torch. Separating a brazed joint is called unbrazing. Before unbrazing a joint, discharge all the refrigerant from the system and, using the cylinder, allow nitrogen in. Nitrogen is an inert gas; that is, it is non-flammable, even at high temperatures, so there is no danger of fire. The nitrogen is also dry, which means that there is no water to produce a bad joint as sometimes happens when a refrigeration system is contaminated with moisture.

Dangerous chemicals

There are many chemicals that the refrigeration technician has to use that can be dangerous if not used properly. Even mercury, used in thermometers, barometers and manometers (see Chapter 3) is poisonous. Spilt mercury should be cleaned up at once and droplets that have got into places difficult to get at should be sprinkled with sulphur.

Some solvents used to clean the surfaces of evaporators and condensers (Chapters 11 and 12) are flammable and should not be used in the presence of a naked flame such as a cigarette, a pilot light or any other source. Open a window or find some other way of improving the ventilation when you are using these solvents, so that the fumes are not breathed into the lungs. Usually, manufacturers give instructions for the use of their own (proprietary) brand of cleaner, so make sure that you follow the instructions.

The refrigerant is made to circulate in a refrigeration system by a type of pump known as a compressor. Compressors contain oil that must be replaced from time to time. After you have removed the compressor from the system, pour out the oil into a glass jar or some specially-designated container. Do not be tempted to use any container that may be available such as a waste bin or saucepan. Sometimes, when problems have occurred the used compressor oil is contaminated and it will cause acid burns if it splashes on the skin. Such chemicals are said to be **corrosive**.

Disposal of waste chemicals

Small amounts of waste chemicals can be washed down the sink with large amounts of water. However, this should never be done with very toxic or very flammable materials. If you have any doubts, or want to dispose of large quantities of waste, contact your local environmental health officer. There are also private companies which specialise in the disposal of waste.

Lifting heavy objects

Some of the equipment used in refrigeration and air conditioning is heavy and can only be moved with difficulty. In some cases, lifting equipment is available and heavy objects should be moved by using this equipment. Where there are gas cylinder trolleys, these should be used. However, despite this, there will be times when you need to lift heavy objects. The worst way to do this is by bending forward, holding the object in the arms and then straightening the back. This method of lifting can cause injuries to the spine and injuries to the abdominal wall, known as a hernia. Heavy objects should be lifted with a straight back, as shown in Figure 2.4.

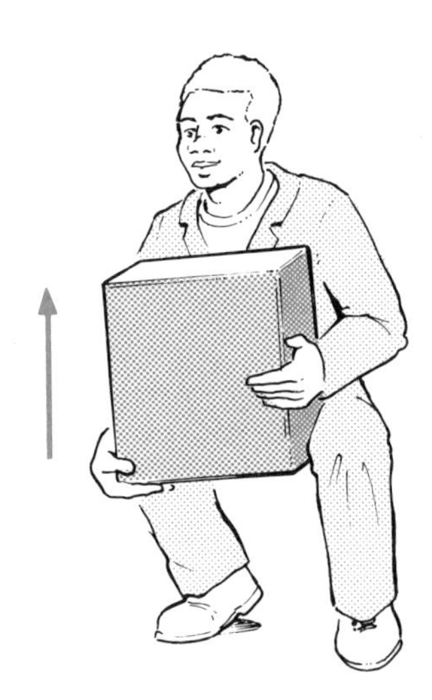

Figure 2.4 Lifting with a straight back.

Hazard warning signs

During your career as a technician or mechanic you will be admitted to buildings where there are electrical, chemical or radioactive hazards. There may be hazards in your own place of work and you may be responsible for the safety of others. As we have seen above, you may have to deal with hazards of your own as you work on equipment. It is important, then, that you can identify hazard warning signs. Those shown in Figure 2.5 are recognised within the European Community and some associated countries. Similar signs exist elsewhere in the world.

Biohazard

A biohazard label is used for areas where dangerous biological materials are stored. This might include germs, such as bacteria and viruses.

Corrosive

The term corrosive refers to chemicals such as acids and strong alkalis, such as caustic soda, which can burn the skin and chemically attack any surface that they come in contact with. This includes contaminated oil from a compressor.

Harmful or irritant

Some substances irritate the skin and cause red marks. In some cases, skin diseases can be caused. Examples are cleaning fluids and detergents.

First aid

Even in the best run work place, injuries may occur from time to time. When an injury does occur a knowledge of first aid is essential. After all it may be you lying injured one day! *First aid* is the treatment of an injured person, the casualty, in the best way possible, until a doctor or some other qualified person arrives.

As a first aider you should, as quickly as possible, assess the situation and try to find what is wrong with the casualty. Give the appropriate treatment straight away and then stay with him until medical help arrives.

Electric Shock

The casualty's heart and breathing may have almost stopped and there may be burns.

Switch off the current and remove the plug. If this cannot be done, push the casualty away from contact with the electricity using something like a wooden broom which does not conduct electricity.

Once the casualty has been disconnected from the electricity quickly examine him. If he is not breathing, start *artificial respiration*. Respiration means breathing, so that artificial respiration is artificial breathing. You do the breathing for the casualty. If his heart has stopped, start resucitation with *heart compressions* and *inflations* (see the section headed *Resucitation*).

Figure 2.5 European Community hazard warning signs.

Treat any burns that you can find.

However, the first thing to do is to start artificial respiration.

Mouth-to-mouth respiration

With the casualty on his back, push the chin upwards with one hand and press the forehead downwards with the other. This opens the air passage that runs from the casualty's mouth to his lungs, or the *airway* as it is called. Remove any foreign bodies, such as pieces of food, loose teeth and vomit. Open your mouth and breathe in (Figure 2.6(a)).

Pinch the casualty's nostrils together and place your lips around his mouth (Figure 2.6(a)).

Blow gently into his lungs and at the same time look along his chest and watch it rise. This process is called an *inflation* (Figure 2.6(b)).

Remove your mouth, breathe out and watch the casualty's chest fall. Do another inflation (Figure 2.6(c)).

Check his *pulse* to make sure his heart is beating. A pulse is a small pressure variation that you can feel when you place your finger tips on the inside of the wrist. It is caused by the beating of the heart (Figure 2.6(d)).

If his heart is beating give between 12 and 16 inflations every minute until he starts breathing

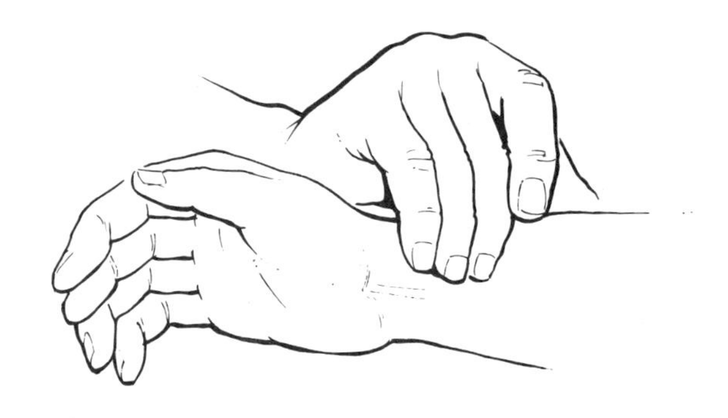

Figure 2.6 (a)–(c) Mouth-to-mouth method of artificial respiration; (d) feeling for a pulse.

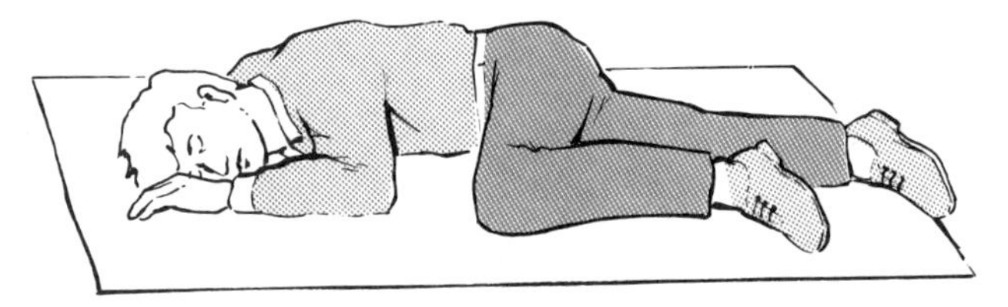

Figure 2.7 The recovery position.

again. Even if he does not start breathing, continue the process as the oxygen you are giving him may keep his body alive until a doctor arrives.

Once the casualty is breathing normally and his heart is beating, place him in the **recovery position**.

The recovery position

Kneel by the side of the casualty and hold his head tilted back so that his airway is open, then turn it to one side. Carefully roll him on to his side and bend his upper leg so that his thigh is up by his chest. Then, protecting his head with your hand, roll him on to his front. The final position is shown in Figure 2.7. Note that the head remains tilted to keep the airway open.

The recovery position is only to be used where the casualty is both breathing and has a heartbeat. If there is no pulse then you need to start *resuscitation.* Resuscitation means restoring or bringing the casualty back to a better state of health.

Resuscitation

Kneel by the side of the patient and find the lower half of the breastbone. This is the place where the ribs end and the soft part of the body begins.

Place both your hands on the lower half of the breastbone and, keeping your back and arms straight, press the breastbone down towards the spine for between about 4 and 5 cm (1.5 to 2 inches). Then release the pressure. This is called a *heart compression* (see Figure 2.8).

Do this fifteen times and then give two inflations. Repeat the process, giving 80 compressions per minute.

When the pulse has restarted and the casualty is breathing, place him in the recovery position. Even if the pulse does not start and there is no breathing, continue the process until a doctor arrives.

The descriptions given above referred to a

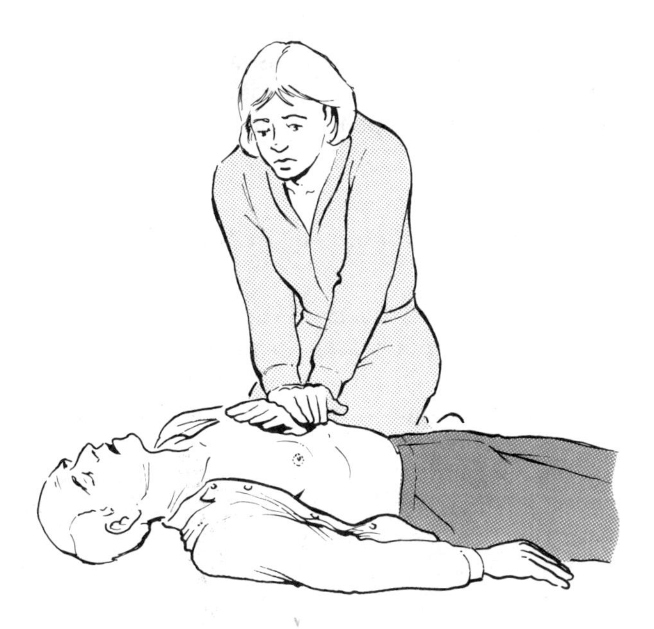

Figure 2.8 Compressions.

patient who was suffering from electric shock. However, it applies to all situations where someone has been injured and is unconscious. However, there will be changes to the procedure if, for example, there are broken bones. For a complete explanation of first aid it is better to read a first aid book or, better still, to take a first aid course.

Burns

A casualty suffering from electric shock may have burns. Burns may have other causes, too. For example, in refrigeration work, parts such as condensers may become overheated and damage the skin if touched. Very cold surfaces in freezers can cause damage similar to that caused by heat and these are called freezer burns. Wash the burn with cold running water for at least 10 minutes. Do not touch the burn.

Do not remove burnt clothing as this may be stuck to the skin.

Cover the burn with a clean dressing but do not cover burns to the face. Do not stick the dressing to the skin with sticking plaster.

Arrange for hospital treatment.

Technicians working in refrigeration and air conditioning may suffer burns caused by corrosive chemicals, such as contaminated compressor oil or some other source. Wash away the chemical as quickly as possible using running water. Carefully remove contaminated clothing. Continue to treat as for burns.

We have dealt with the treatment for burns; and often burns are caused by fire. Fire is another hazard that you may have to deal with in the workplace. Cleaning fluids should be safe if treated properly but someone might be careless and use them while smoking a lighted cigarette. Electrical fires can start if someone has used the wrong fuse.

Fighting fires

Factories and work places should be equipped for fighting fires. Buckets containing sand are useful for fighting small fires. Sand from the bucket is thrown on to the fire in order to smother it. Fire blankets, which are made of a non-flammable material, can also be used to smother small fires.

Fire extinguishers are devices that squirt a liquid at high pressure on to a fire in order to put it out. Water fire extinguishers are common but they are not suitable and are dangerous for use on electrical fires or for solvent fires caused by cleaning fluids. These are the most likely types of fire that the refrigeration technician or mechanic has to deal with.

The carbon dioxide fire extinguisher is the best general purpose extinguisher and can be used on both electrical and solvent fires. The instructions for use are normally on the side of the extinguisher. Remove the pin and press the trigger. Direct the jet of cold carbon dioxide on to the fire by using the plastic horn (see Figure 2.9). A cloud of solid carbon dioxide (dry ice) settles on the fire and puts it out. Carbon dioxide extinguishers are black.

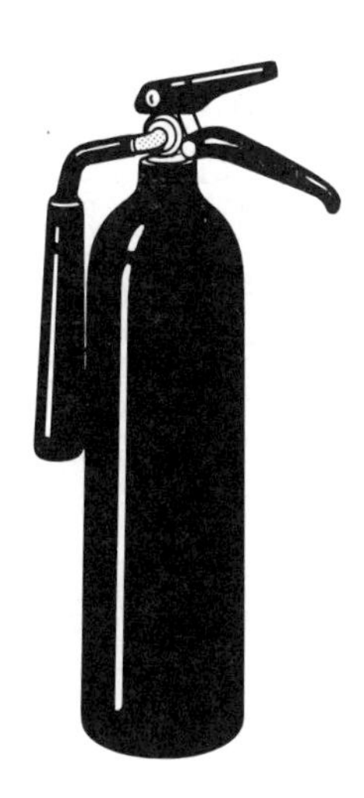

Figure 2.9 A carbon dioxide extinguisher.

There are other types of fire extinguisher, too, but they are beyond the scope of this book. More information can be found in books on fire fighting and safety. When you are fighting a fire aways make sure that you can escape if necessary. If in doubt, if the fire is large or if the fire looks like getting out of control, sound the alarm and call the fire brigade.

CHECK YOUR UNDERSTANDING

- The human body is a conductor of electricity.
- An electric current through the body causes muscular contractions and the heart is a muscle. A current may also cause burns.
- Electrical equipment is earthed to make it safe.
- Fuses are safety devices which melt when the current becomes too high.
- Cables should be selected so that they are capable of withstanding the current taken by equipment, without overheating.
- Care should be taken when operating power tools.
- Gas cylinders should be correctly moved and operated.
- The correct procedure should be adopted when handling and disposing of dangerous chemicals.
- Hazard warning signs on equipment should be noted and precautions followed.
- First aid should be applied to casualties suffering from electric shock or other injuries.
- Artificial respiration should be used if the casualty is not breathing.
- Heart compressions should be used if the casualty's heart has stopped beating.
- Once the casualty is breathing normally and his heart is beating, place him in the recovery position.
- Treat any burns that the casualty has.
- Fires can be fought using sand, fire blankets or fire extinguishers, depending on the type of fire.

REVISION EXERCISES AND QUESTIONS

1. What reactions occur in the body when a large electric current passes through it?
2. An appliance is rated at 500 W and the voltage is 250 V. Which value fuse is most suitable: (i) 1 A (ii) 3 A or (iii) 5 A?
3. If a component at mains live potential touches an earthed metal chassis, what should happen if the fuse has been correctly chosen?
4. Why should a piece of copper wire or a bent paper clip not be used to replace a fuse?
5. What are the hazards associated with the user having long hair when he is using power tools?
6. Why should an inert gas such as nitrogen be used when brazing refrigerator pipe, during repair work?
7. What hazard might occur if a cable with too low a current rating is used on a piece of equipment?
8. Why must oil removed from a compressor be treated with special care?
9. What are *chemical hazard warning signs*?
10. What injuries can result from a worker not lifting a heavy object properly?
11. What method is generally recognised as the best way to perform artificial respiration?
12. What is the *recovery position*?
13. Explain how resuscitation is performed in order to restart breathing and heart beat.
14. Why is the water fire extinguisher unsuitable for putting out an electrical fire?

3 Behaviour of matter

Introduction

An understanding of the basic physics of the behaviour of matter is needed before the refrigeration principles can be fully understood.

Units

Until recently the most widely used sets of units, for all branches of engineering, including refrigeration and air conditioning, in the English speaking world were the Imperial system and its US equivalent. These both used the foot, for distance, the pound for mass and weight and the second for time. This system is now being phased out in favour of metric units, although it is still widely used in the USA.

Because of the decline of the Imperial system, the units used in this book are the most advanced of the metric systems, the **SI units (Système International)** which are recognised by nearly all scientific and engineering organisations throughout the world. The **basic SI units** are:

Mass	kilogramme (kg)
Length or distance	metre (m)
Time	second (s)
Electric current	ampere (A)
Temperature	kelvin (K).

In addition, there are the **derived units** which depend on the basic units and come from them. For example, the unit of speed (m/s) comes from the metre and the second. The unit of force (N) comes from the metre, the kilogramme and the second. There are large numbers of derived units but some important ones are:

Speed or velocity	m/s
Acceleration	m/s^2
Force	newton (N)
Pressure	N/m^2 or pascal (Pa)
Work or energy	joule (J)
Power	watt (W).

Other derived units will be introduced, as necessary, in the appropriate places in the book.

There are also a number of multiples and submultiples to be used with the units. The common submultiples and their meanings are:

micro (μ) or 10^{-6}, × 1 millionth;
milli (m) or 10^{-3}, × 1 thousandth;
centi (c) or 10^{-2}, × 1 hundredth.

The common multiples are:

kilo (k) or 10^3, × thousand;
mega (M) or 10^6, × million.

Thus, 15 μm is 15 millionths of a metre; 3 mA is 3 thousandths of an ampere; 10 cm is 10 hundredths of a metre; 5 kg is 5000 g (g is gramme); 4 MJ is 4 000 000 J.

Many concepts, such as those of pressure and energy are very important in refrigeration. However, before we get on to these we must define some of the more basic concepts upon which they depend.

Speed and velocity

Speed is defined by the relationship:

$$\text{speed} = \frac{\text{distance}}{\text{time}}$$

Velocity is speed in a defined direction. However, in the problems set in this book, direction is usually unimportant, so the term speed will be used to mean both speed and velocity.

EXAMPLE 3.1

A car travels a distance of 50 m in 2 s. Calculate the average speed of the car.

Solution

$$\text{Average speed} = \frac{50}{2} = 25\ \text{m/s}.$$

Acceleration

Acceleration is concerned with change of speed and is defined by the relationship:

$$\text{acceleration} = \frac{\text{final speed} - \text{initial speed}}{\text{time taken}}$$

EXAMPLE 3.2

The car in Example 3.1 increases its speed from 25 m/s to 37 m/s in a time of 4 s. Calculate the acceleration.

Solution

$$\text{Acceleration} = \frac{37 - 25}{4} = \frac{12}{4} = 3\ \text{m/s}^2.$$

Force

When a **force** is applied to an object or body, the object is made to accelerate. For example, if you kick a football, the football accelerates because your foot has produced a force on the ball. The size of a force depends on the mass of the body and the size of the acceleration:

$$\text{force} = \text{mass} \times \text{acceleration}$$

The unit of force is the **newton (N)**. A newton is the force that gives a mass of 1 kg an acceleration of 1 m/s^2.

EXAMPLE 3.3

A footballer kicks a football of mass 0.7 kg, causing an acceleration of 15 m/s^2. What is the size of the force exerted by the man's foot?

Solution
Force = 0.7 × 15 = 10.5 N.

A football exerts a force of its own if it is kicked against something, for example, a wall. In just the same way, the molecules, or minute particles that make up a gas, strike the walls of their container and cause a force. This in turn sets up a pressure.

Weight is also a force. It is the force exerted by the earth's gravity on an object or body. Most objects, if they are allowed to fall, will start to accelerate. Light objects, such as feathers, will be affected by the air and so tend to be blown by the wind.

However, with solid bodies, such as lead masses, air resistance is negligible and the acceleration is about 10 m/s^2. This acceleration, known as the **acceleration due to gravity** or the **acceleration of free fall**, is about the same all over the earth's surface and is given the symbol g. If m is the mass of a body and W its weight, then:

$$\text{weight} = \text{mass} \times \text{acceleration of free fall}$$

or

$$W = mg$$

EXAMPLE 3.4

The mass of a man is 70 kg. If the acceleration due to gravity is 10 m/s^2, what is the man's weight?

Solution
Weight = 70 × 10 = 700 N.

Note that mass and weight are different things.

Mass is measured in kilogrammes (kg), whereas weight is measured in newtons (N). The weight of an astronaut varies according to where he is in space, because weight depends on gravity. However, his mass remains the same.

Density

Density is a property of a material; it is the mass per unit volume, so that:

$$\text{density} = \frac{\text{mass}}{\text{volume}}$$

Solid materials and liquids have much higher densities than gases.

For example, aluminium has a density of 2700 kg/m^3, copper 8900 kg/m^3, water 1000 kg/m^3 and air 1.3 kg/m^3. Solid materials with a density less than that of water float on water. Cork has a lower density than water, so cork floats. Density decreases with temperature so that warm air rises above cold. Because of this change of density with temperature, it is normal to quote densities at some standard temperature, such as 20°C.

Air conditioners pass large quantities of air into the room or building that is being air conditioned, so the properties of air, including the density, are important.

EXAMPLE 3.5

An air conditioner passes 2 m^3 of air every second into a room. If the density of the air at the working temperature is 1.3 kg/m^3, calculate the mass of air delivered to the room in 1 s.

Solution

Mass = density × volume
= 1.3 × 2 = 2.6 kg in 1 s.

Specific volume

The **specific volume** of liquids and vapours is important to engineers working in refrigeration and air conditioning. The word 'specific' used in this way in science and engineering always means 'per unit mass' or 'divided by mass'. Thus specific volume is volume per unit mass:

$$\text{specific volume} = \frac{\text{volume}}{\text{mass}}$$

The unit is the m^3/kg or L/kg. 1 m^3 = 1000 L, where L is the litre.

Because

$$\text{density} = \frac{\text{mass}}{\text{volume}}$$

then

$$\text{specific volume} = \frac{1}{\text{density}}$$

Specific volume is an important property of refrigerants. A refrigerant is the working fluid used in refrigeration. For example, a well-known refrigerant in its liquid form has a specific volume of 0.75 L/kg while the vapour at the same temperature and pressure has a specific volume of 75.0 L/kg. Therefore, a kilogramme of the vapour has a hundred times the volume of the liquid. More information on properties of refrigerants is given in Chapters 6 and 14. 1m^3 = 1000 L, where L is the litre.

Pressure

The air is made up of very small particles called molecules. Most are nitrogen molecules and some are oxygen. Other important substances in the air are carbon dioxide (CO_2) and water vapour. Air molecules move randomly or haphazardly from place to place very fast and they collide with objects which are placed in their path. This means forces are exerted on everything in the earth's atmosphere or air. The forces caused by the bombardment of air molecules set up an atmospheric pressure all over the earth. **Pressure** depends on two things, force and area:

$$\text{pressure} = \frac{\text{force}}{\text{area}}$$

Pressure is exerted by liquids and solids as well as gases. The SI unit of pressure is the N/m^2 or **pascal (Pa)**.

EXAMPLE 3.6

A large water tank, used for the storage of water refrigerant, has a base which measures 2 m by 3 m. If the height of the tank is 2.5 m and it is completely filled with water, calculate the pressure exerted by the water on the base of the tank. The density of water is 1 t/m^3. 1 t or 1 tonne = 1000 kg. (The tonne is the metric ton.) The acceleration of free fall = 10 m/s^2.

Solution
Area of the base = $2 \times 3 = 6$ m^2.
Volume of the water = area of base × height
$= 6 \times 2.5 = 15$m^3.
Therefore, the mass of the water =
density × volume = $1000 \times 15 = 15\,000$ kg.
Weight of the water = $mg = 15\,000 \times 10$
$= 150\,000$ N
(remember, weight is a force).

$$\text{Pressure exerted on the base} = \frac{\text{weight}}{\text{area of base}}$$

$$= \frac{150\,000}{6}$$

$$= 25\,000 \text{ N/m}^2 \text{ (or Pa).}$$

This answer can also be written as 25 kPa because $k = 1000$.

Weather forecasters generally use a unit of pressure known as the **bar** for measuring pressure changes in the atmosphere. Atmospheric pressure is usually about 100 000 Pa and 1 bar is defined as 100 000 Pa. To avoid using fractions, weather forecasters often express the pressure in millibars (mbar): 1000 mbar = 1 bar.

A high atmospheric pressure might be 1040 mbar, and a low pressure 960 mbar. The bar is also used to express pressure in refrigeration systems.

Barometers

A **barometer** is an instrument for measuring atmospheric pressure. The simplest form of barometer is the mercury type. This consists of a glass tube open at one end and closed at the other. The tube is filled with mercury and then the open end is placed in a reservoir of mercury. The pressure of the air pushes down on the reservoir and supports a column of mercury in the glass tube. There is a vacuum above the mercury and the height, h, of the column is a measure of atmospheric pressure. This is shown in Figure 3.1.

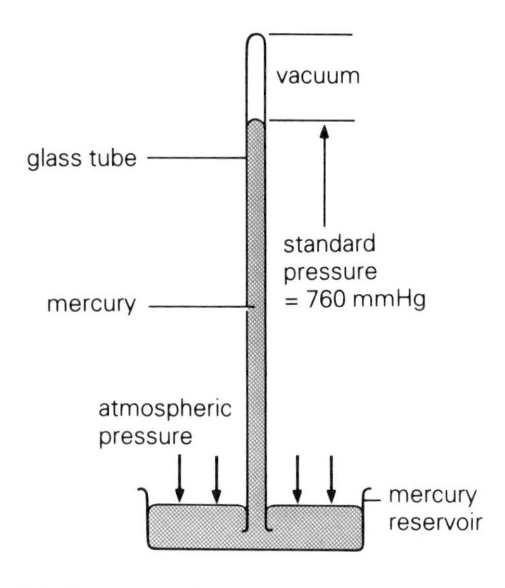

Figure 3.1 A mercury barometer.

When $h = 760$ mm of mercury the air pressure has a value called **standard pressure**. Standard pressure is sometimes written as 760 mmHg where Hg is the chemical symbol for mercury.

On most days the atmospheric pressure is either above or below standard pressure, which is an average value taken over a long period.

The mercury column height can be converted into pascals by using the formula:

$$P = Dgh$$

where D is the density of mercury, g is the acceleration of free fall and h is the height of the mercury column.

EXAMPLE 3.7

On a fine day the height of the mercury column on a barometer is found to be 770 mmHg. Calculate the atmospheric pressure: (i) in pascals, (ii) in bars and (iii) in millibars. The acceleration of free fall at the earth's surface = 10m/s^2. The density of mercury = 13 600 kg/m^3.

Solution
In order to get the pressure in pascals, the SI unit, all the quantities in the formula must be in SI units, so that 770 mmHg must be written as

$770/1000 = 0.77$ mHg or 0.77 metres of mercury. Remember, 1000 mm = 1 m.

i) Pressure $= 13\,600 \times 10 \times 0.77$
$= 104\,720$ Pa
$= 105\,000$ Pa, to 3 significant figures.

ii) $105\,000/100\,000 = 1.05$ bar.

iii) $1.05 \times 1000 = 1050$ mbar.

Using the same formula it can be shown that standard pressure is equal to 103 400 Pa (taking $g = 10\,\text{m/s}^2$). However, taking a much more accurate value of g it can be shown that the value is actually 101 396 Pa. The standard atmospheric pressure adopted for psychrometric measurements in air conditioning is 101 325Pa (see *The psychrometric chart* in Chapter 8).

A perfect vacuum contains no molecules of any sort. It is just empty space. However, a real vacuum will contain a small number of molecules and these will exert a pressure. For example, if the space at the top of the mercury column has a small quantity of air introduced into it, the mercury will be pushed down. Suppose the height of the column is now 710 mmHg but the real atmospheric pressure is 760 mmHg, then the space is said to be under a vacuum of 710 mmHg. This is because the pressure is less than atmospheric by that amount. The air inside exerts a pressure of 50 mmHg.

In refrigeration it is sometimes necessary to produce and then measure a high vacuum. For example, during repair work, in order to remove water, air and other impurities from a refrigeration system, the system is connected to a vacuum pump and evacuated as completely as possible. A high vacuum is one in which there are very few molecules and so the pressure is measured in micrometres of mercury (μmHg). A pressure of 60 μmHg = 60/1000 = 0.06 mmHg. This gives a vacuum of $760 - 0.06 = 759.94$ mmHg.

Pressure gauges

Pressure gauges are instruments which are used to measure the pressure of the refrigerant in different parts of a refrigeration system. There are two main types in use: the **manometer** and the **Bourdon gauge**.

MANOMETERS

A manometer is a U-tube full of mercury which is attached at one end to the pressure to be measured.

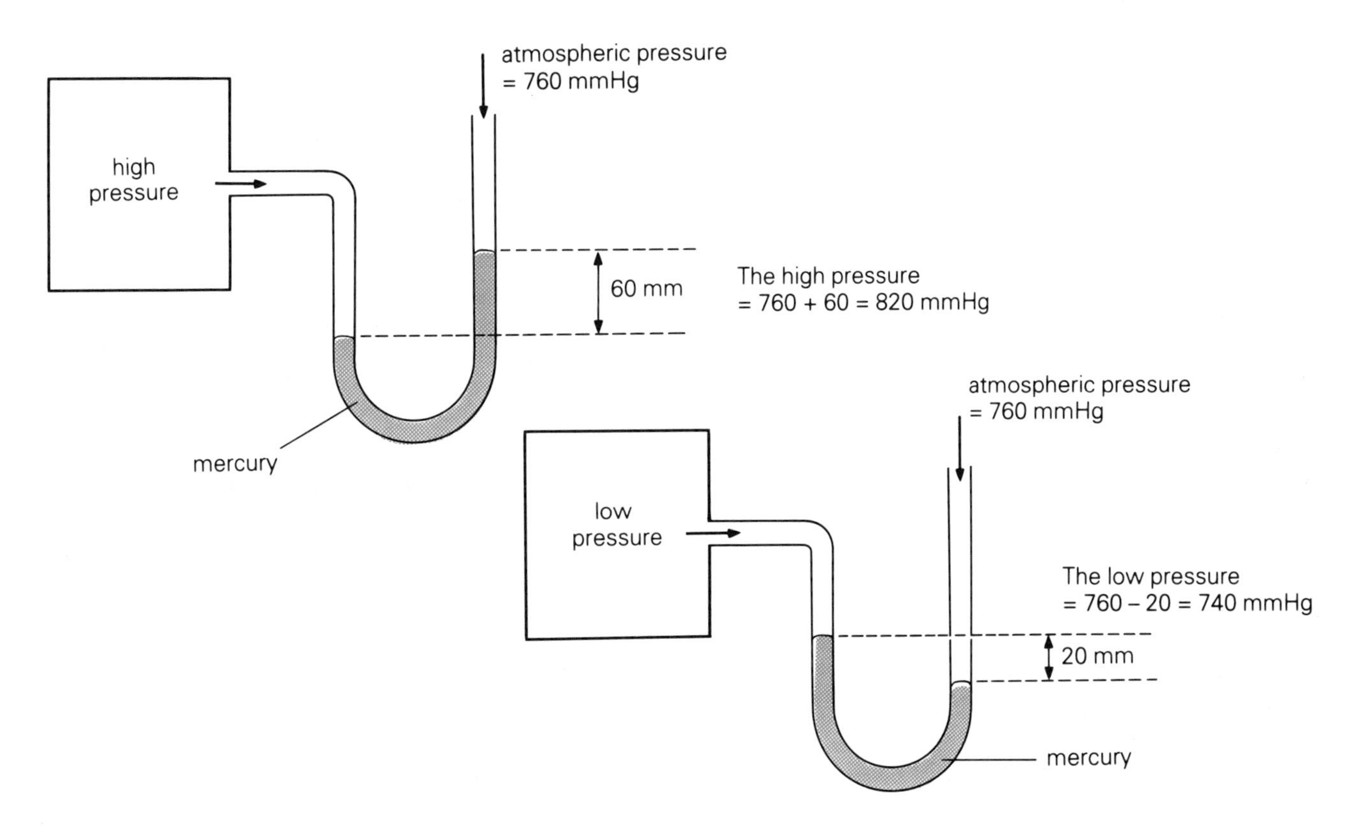

Figure 3.2 The manometer.

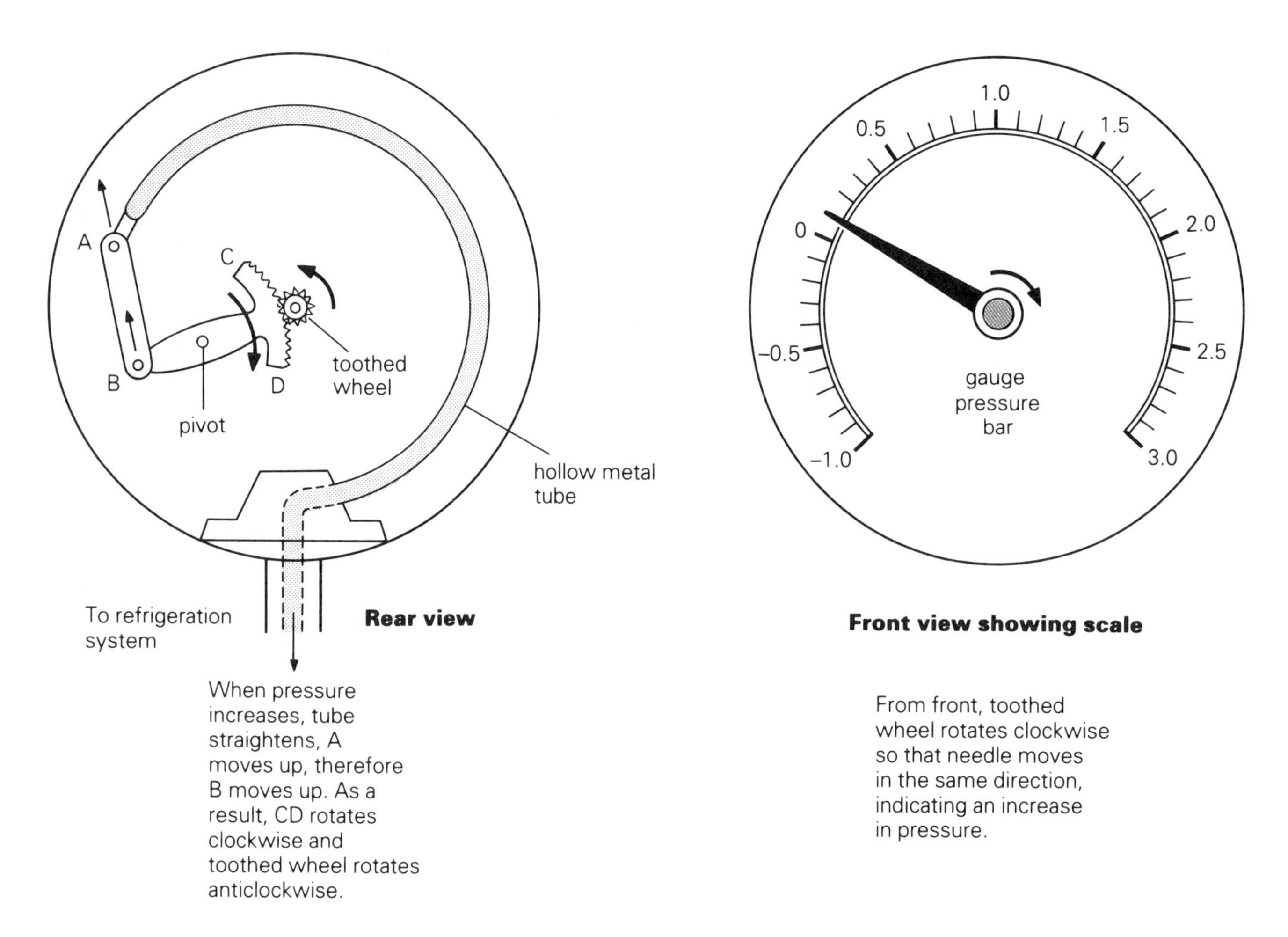

Figure 3.3 A compound bourdon gauge reading down to −1 bar and up to 3 bar.

The other end is open to the atmosphere. A pressure greater than atmospheric applied to one side of the tube pushes up the mercury level on the other side. The difference in levels gives the pressure in millimetres of mercury above atmospheric. A pressure less than atmospheric produces a reduction in mercury level on the other side. The difference in levels gives the pressure in millimetres of mercury below atmospheric. These two situations are shown in Figure 3.2.

BOURDON GAUGES

A Bourdon gauge consists of a hollow metal tube bent into a curve. The pressure of the vapour tends to straighten the tube and this causes a pointer to move across a scale (see Figure 3.3).

Bourdon gauges are calibrated in such a way that they read zero at atmospheric pressure and so when they are used in a refrigerator system they only indicate the difference between refrigerant pressure and atmospheric pressure. This pressure is known as **gauge pressure**. In order to find the total, or **absolute pressure**, the gauge pressure must be added to the atmospheric pressure.

It is important to distinguish between gauge pressure and absolute pressure. To do this it is usual to write the letters G or A after a pressure, as necessary. For example, 8 bar G for gauge pressure or 9 bar A for absolute pressure.

Bourdon gauges can also be used to read pressures less than atmospheric and this type is called a **vacuum gauge**. **Compound gauges** read both above and below atmospheric and these are useful during commissioning and maintenance work (see Chapters 23 and 24). The **system analyser** has both a high and a low pressure gauge. The high pressure gauge often has a red scale, while the low pressure gauge is often blue and has a vacuum scale in addition to the low pressure scale (see Figure 3.4).

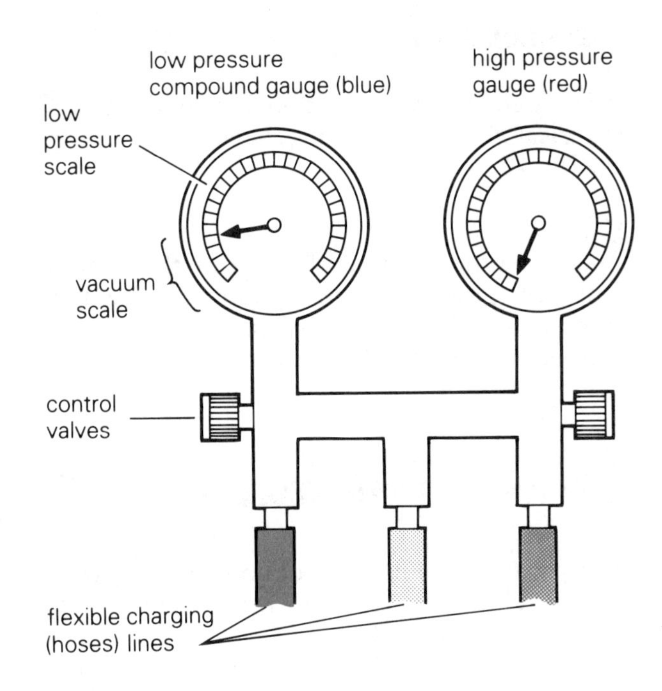

Figure 3.4 A system analyser (manifold gauge set).

EXAMPLE 3.8

A pressure gauge in a refrigeration system reads 2.5 bar. If the atmospheric pressure is 1 bar, what is absolute pressure?

Solution
Absolute pressure = gauge pressure + atmospheric pressure
= 2.5 + 1 = 3.5 bar.

EXAMPLE 3.9

A vacuum gauge in part of a refrigerator reads −3.5 kPa. If the atmospheric pressure is 1 bar, what is the absolute pressure in that part of the system?

Solution
1 bar = 100 kPa, therefore the absolute pressure
= 100 − 3.5 = 96.5 kPa.

EXAMPLE 3.10

A pressure which is less than atmospheric causes a difference of 50 mm in the mercury levels of a manometer. Calculate the pressure and the degree of vacuum if the atmospheric pressure is 760 mmHg.

Solution
Pressure = 760 − 50 = 710 mmHg.
Vacuum = 50 mmHg.

Work and energy

Work is done when a force is applied to a body and the body moves through a distance. Provided that the distance moved is in the same direction as the force then:

work done = force × distance moved

Work is measured in **joules (J)** or kilojoules (kJ).

EXAMPLE 3.11

A large refrigerator of mass 500 kg is lifted through a height of 15 m to the top floor of a building. Calculate the work done, taking g as 10m/s^2.

Solution
The weight of the refrigerator = mg
= 500 × 10 = 5000 N.
Work done = 5000 × 15 = 75 000 J or 75 kJ (remember weight is a force).

Energy is the capacity to do work. For example, the large refrigerator in Example 3.11 has the capacity to do work as the result of its position at the top of the building. This type is energy is called **potential energy (P.E.)**. The potential energy is equal to the work done in getting the body into position in the first place, so that in this case it equals 75 kJ relative to the ground:

potential energy = weight × height

or

$P.E. = mgh$, where m is the mass of the body, g is the acceleration of free fall and h is the height of the body.

Another form of energy is **kinetic energy (K.E.)**. This is the capacity of a body to do work because of its movement:

$$\text{kinetic energy} = \frac{1}{2} \times \text{mass} \times (\text{speed})^2$$

EXAMPLE 3.12

A refrigerated truck of mass 2 t is moving at a speed of 20 m/s. Determine the kinetic energy of the truck. 1 t = 1000 kg.

Solution

$$\text{Kinetic energy} = \frac{1}{2} \times 2000 \times 20^2$$
$$= 1000 \times 20 \times 20$$
$$= 400\,000\,\text{J or } 400\,\text{kJ}.$$

Energy conversion

There is another form of potential energy which is concerned with the attraction of atoms and molecules for one another. Energy appears in a number of forms with names like *heat energy*, *chemical energy*, *nuclear energy*, *elastic energy* and *electrical energy*. These are all examples of either potential energy or kinetic energy and sometimes both, appearing on a microscopic scale.

Energy can be converted from one form to another. For example, a battery converts chemical energy to electrical. A filament lamp converts electrical energy to light and heat.

> Energy can neither be created nor destroyed, only converted from one form to another. This statement is known as the **Law of Conservation of Energy**.

Power

Power is the rate of doing work or the rate of using energy:

$$\text{power} = \frac{\text{work}}{\text{time}} \text{ or } \frac{\text{energy}}{\text{time}}$$

The unit of power is the **watt (W)** or kilowatt (kW). A knowledge of electrical power is necessary in refrigeration and air conditioning.

EXAMPLE 3.13

A fan used in an air conditioner is rated at 350 W of electrical power. How much electrical energy is used in 10 minutes?

Solution

Energy = power × time. To obtain the answer in joules the power must be in watts, and the time in seconds. 10 min = 10 × 60 = 600 s.

Energy = 350 × 600 = 210 000 J or 210 kJ.

Temperature

Temperature is a measure of how hot something is. It depends on the average kinetic energy of the molecules of the body.

The everyday scale of temperature is called the **Celsius** (or sometimes centigrade) scale. On the Celsius scale the melting point of ice is taken as 0°C. This is called the lower fixed point. The boiling point of water is 100°C. This is the upper fixed point, so there are 100 degrees between the fixed points.

The SI unit of temperature is the **kelvin (K)**. (See basic SI units at the beginning of this chapter.) The zero on the kelvin scale (0K) is called absolute zero. It is the temperature at which all the molecules of a body stop moving, so that their kinetic energy is zero. The melting point of ice on the kelvin scale is 273K and the boiling point of water 373K. As in the Celsius scale, there are 100 degrees between the two fixed points. This means that the size of the Celsius degree is the same as the kelvin. Absolute zero on the Celsius scale is −273°C. Kelvin temperature can be found from Celsius by means of a simple formula:

$$T = \theta + 273$$

where T is the Kelvin temperature and θ the Celsius temperature.

The Celsius temperature can be found from kelvin by using the formula:

$$\theta = T - 273$$

However, because the size of the Celsius degree is the same as the kelvin, temperature rise in degrees Celsius is the same as temperature rise in kelvin.

Temperature is measured by means of a thermometer. The most common thermometer is the mercury in glass type.

EXAMPLE 3.14

i) The temperature of the refrigerant in a refrigeration system varies between −10°C and 40°C. Convert these two temperatures to kelvin.
ii) Express 450K in terms of degrees Celsius.

Solution
i) $T = -10 + 273 = 263$K.
   $T = 40 + 273 = 313$K.
ii) $\theta = 450 - 273 = 177$°C.

Heat

Heat is that form of energy which flows from a body at high temperature to one at low temperature. When heat flows into a substance it normally raises the temperature. Heat that causes a rise in temperature is called **sensible heat**.

Sensible heat is so called because it can be sensed using a thermometer or even the hand.

Heat capacity is the heat required to raise the temperature of a body by 1°C. Specific heat capacity (c) is the heat capacity per unit mass and it is a property of the material that makes up the body. The unit of specific heat capacity is kJ/kg K. The sensible heat required to warm up a body is given by the relationship:

$$Q = mc(\theta_2 - \theta_1)$$

where Q is the heat flowing into the body in kilojoules, m is the mass in kilogrammes, c is the specific heat capacity in kJ/kg K and $(\theta_2 - \theta_1)$ is the temperature rise in degrees Celsius or kelvin.

EXAMPLE 3.15

Water is the refrigerant in certain types of absorption refrigerator (see Chapter 7). Calculate the heat necessary to raise the temperature of 500 g of water in the generator of the refrigerator from 10°C to 40°C. The specific heat capacity of water = 4.2 kJ/kg K.

Solution
Heat required = 0.5 × 4.2 × (40 − 10)
= 63 kJ.

The mass of 500 g is expressed in kilogrammes (500 g = 500/1000 = 0.5 kg).

When a body cools there is a drop in temperature and the same formula can be used to calculate heat loss.

EXAMPLE 3.16

5 kg of meat is cooled in a refrigerator from 37°C to 7°C. How much heat does the refrigerator extract from the meat, which has a specific heat capacity of 3.0 kJ/kg K?

Solution
Heat extracted = 5 × 3 × (37 − 7)
= 450 kJ.

If a liquid is left with its surface open to the atmosphere it will normally evaporate. This means that those molecules with the greatest kinetic energy will escape into the atmosphere and the liquid will gradually convert into a vapour or gas (see Figure 3.5).

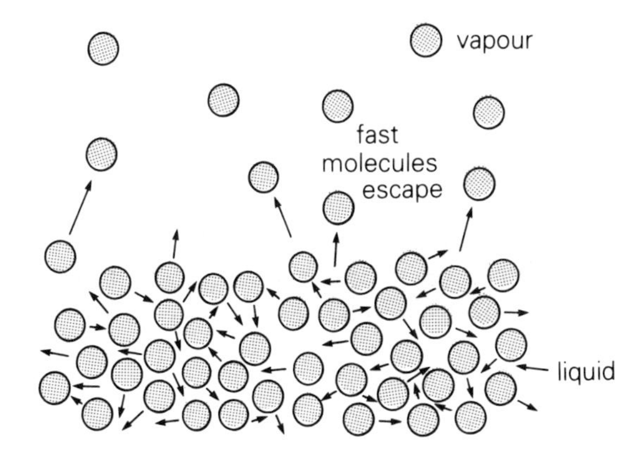

Figure 3.5 Evaporation.

Because the temperature depends upon the kinetic energy of the molecules in the liquid, the liquid will cool. Most refrigerators work on the principle of cooling by evaporation.

If the liquid is now heated by means of, say, a Bunsen burner the rate of evaporation will increase until the liquid reaches its **boiling point**. The heat necessary to raise the temperature to the boiling point is sensible heat. At the boiling point all of the heat energy supplied by the Bunsen burner will go into converting the liquid into a vapour and there is no further temperature rise. This type of heat in which there is a change of state is called hidden or **latent heat**. It is hidden because there is no change in temperature.

The latent heat required to convert a liquid into a vapour without a change in temperature is called the **latent heat of vaporisation**. The **specific latent heat of vaporisation** is the latent heat per unit mass and the value is different for every liquid. For water (steam) it is 2260 kJ/kg.

Latent heat is also required to convert a solid into a liquid at the same temperature. This is the **latent heat of fusion. Specific latent heat of fusion** is different for every solid and the value for ice is 336 kJ:

latent heat = specific latent heat × mass

Air conditioning systems have to produce air of a suitable moisture content and so water is converted to steam and some of the steam is converted back to water to get the amount right.

EXAMPLE 3.17

i) What is the amount of heat required to convert 5 kg of water into steam at boiling point?
ii) What is the amount of heat required to convert 15 kg of ice into liquid water at melting point?

Solution

i) Latent heat of vaporisation = specific latent heat of vaporisation × mass = 2 260 000 × 5
= 11 300 000 J
= 11 300 kJ.
ii) Latent heat of fusion = specific latent heat of fusion × mass = 336 000 × 15
= 5 040 000 J
= 5040 kJ.

Heat transfer

The flow or movement of heat is important in refrigeration, because a refrigeration system contains sections where heat is taken in and sections where heat is rejected. Heat transfers from high to low temperature and it can do this in three ways. These are **convection**, **conduction** and **radiation**.

Convection

Density is not constant for a given material but varies with temperature. As the temperature increases bodies get larger, or expand (volume increases) and the density goes down. If air is heated by a source of heat such as a fire or a radiator, the density of the air above the source of heat decreases. In a room this air then rises to the ceiling and gradually cools as it moves across the ceiling. The density increases and the air then falls down. Convection currents are set up in which the heat is transferred throughout the room, instead of just staying near the source. Convection currents are shown in Figure 3.6.

Food is cooled inside a domestic refrigerator by convection. At the top of a refrigerator is the freezing compartment in which ice and frozen goods may be kept. The air at the bottom of the refrigerator is warmer than the freezing compartment and so warm air rises. When it gets to the freezing compartment it cools, the density increases and the air current moves back to the bottom part of the refrigerator. In this way, the whole interior of the refrigerator is cooled (see Figure 3.7).

Conduction

There are two main types of material which are important in any discussion of conduction. These are heat conductors and heat insulators. Heat transfers through conductors mainly by means of the movement of free electrons (see Chapter 4, *Electrical principles*). Metals, which are good conductors of heat, are also good conductors of electricity. Heat travels very badly through insulators but the heat that does travel moves by the vibration of molecules. Plastics (polymers) are insulators and these are often used to prevent heat from entering a refrigerator. Poor heat conductors are also poor electrical conductors.

Radiation

Heat travels from the sun to the earth, through the vacuum of space, by means of electromagnetic radiation. Radiation is the only way that heat can travel through a vacuum. Movement through a vacuum would be impossible with convection and conduction as they both need a substance through which to travel.

Electromagnetic radiation consists of waves that travel very fast: 300 000 km/s. They travel from the sun to the earth in about 8 minutes and keep the earth from freezing to the temperatures of outer space. These waves vary in length, and electro-

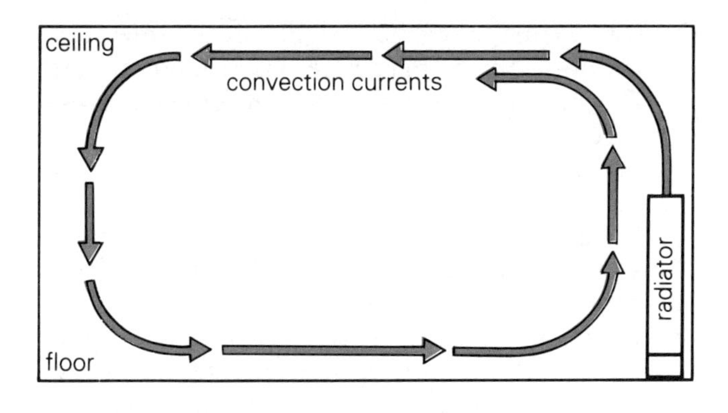

Figure 3.6 Convection currents in a room.

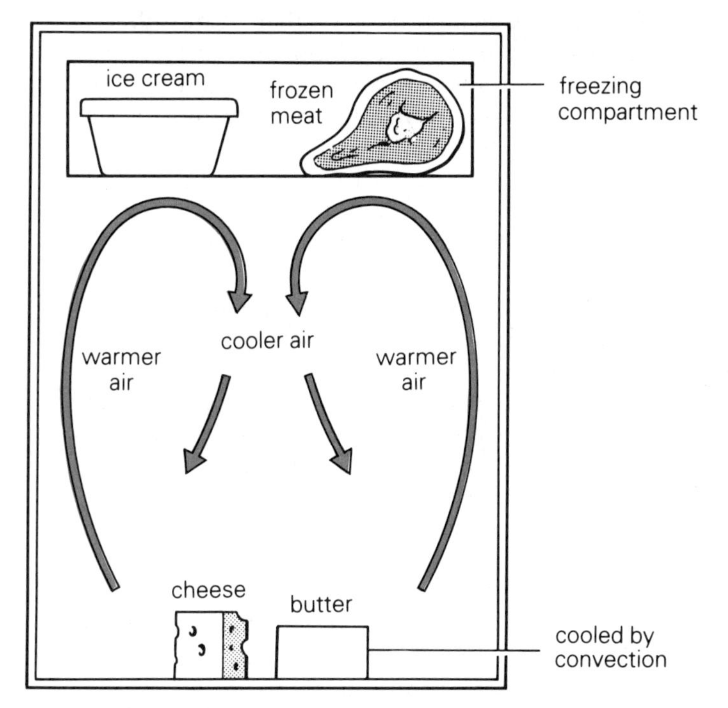

Figure 3.7 Cooling by convection in a refrigerator.

magnetic radiation has been divided into groups according to the wavelength. Radio waves, for example, are electromagnetic and they have long wavelengths. Others are, in decreasing order of wavelength: infrared, visible light, ultraviolet, X-rays and γ-rays, which are the shortest. Hot objects emit mainly infrared radiation which is invisible and usually some visible light. None of the electromagnetic waves can be seen, apart from light.

Radiation can be stopped from entering a cool body and heating it up by means of mirror-like reflecting surfaces. For example, a *Dewar* or *Thermos flask*, which is used to store cool liquids, has

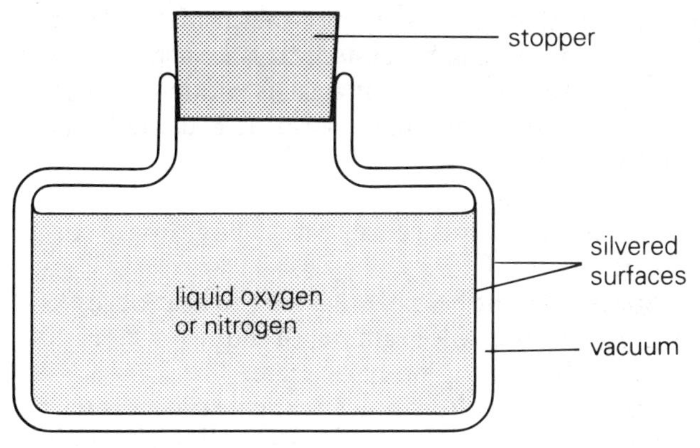

Figure 3.8 The Dewar flask.

reflecting surfaces which reflect away outside heat and so stop the liquid from heating up. Dewar flasks can also store hot liquids (see Figure 3.8).

Doctors and scientists use Dewar flasks as a temporary store for gases such as liquid nitrogen and liquid oxygen which have been refrigerated to very low temperatures.

CHECK YOUR UNDERSTANDING

- Basic and derived SI units are the modern units of scientific measurement.
- Speed = distance/time.
- Acceleration = change of speed/time.
- Force = mass × acceleration.
- Weight is a force.
- Density = mass/volume.
- Specific volume = volume/mass.
- Pressure = force/area.
- Barometers and pressure gauges measure pressure.
- Manometers measure change of pressure.
- Work = force × distance.
- Energy is the capacity to do work.
- Potential energy is the energy of position and kinetic energy is the energy of motion.
- Energy can neither be created nor destroyed, only converted from one form to another. This is the Law of Conservation of Energy.
- Power = rate of doing work or work/time or energy/time.
- Temperature is a measure of how hot something is and it depends on the average kinetic energy of the molecules of the body or space being measured.
- Temperature is measured by means of a thermometer.

- Heat is that form of energy that transfers from a hot to a cold body. Sensible heat is heat that causes a temperature rise. Latent heat is hidden heat that causes a change of phase without causing a temperature rise.
- Specific heat capacity is the heat required to raise the temperature of one kilogramme of a substance by 1°C.
- Specific latent heat of steam is the heat necessary to convert one kilogramme of liquid water into steam at the boiling point of water.
- Specific latent heat of ice is the heat necessary to convert one kilogramme of ice into liquid water at the melting point of ice.
- Convection is the transfer of heat in a liquid or gas by moving currents which arise because of changes in density in the liquid or gas.
- Conduction is the transfer of heat by electron movement and by atomic vibration.
- Radiation is the transfer of heat by means of electromagnetic waves.

REVISION EXERCISES AND QUESTIONS

1 A car travels a distance of 45 m in 3 s. Calculate the average speed of the car.

2 The car in Question (1) increases its speed from 20 m/s to 35 m/s in a time of 5 s. Calculate the acceleration.

3 A footballer kicks a football of mass 0.5 kg, causing an acceleration of 12 m/s^2. What is the size of the force exerted by the footballer's foot?

4 The mass of a woman is 60 kg. If the acceleration due to gravity is 10 m/s^2, what is her weight?

5 An air conditioner passes 3 m^3 of air every second into a room. If the density of the air at the working temperature is 1.3 kg/m^3, calculate the mass of air delivered to the room in 1 s.

6 A large rectangular-based water tank has a base which measures 2.5 m by 2 m. If the height of the tank is 3 m and it is completely filled with water, calculate the pressure exerted by the water on the base of the tank. The density of water is 1 t/m^3. 1 t or 1 tonne = 1000 kg (the tonne is the metric ton). The acceleration of free fall = 10 m/s^2.

7 On a fine day the height of the mercury column on a barometer is found to be 750 mmHg. Calculate the atmospheric pressure:
i) in pascals,
ii) in bars, and
iii) in millibars.
Density of mercury = 13 600 kg/m^3, acceleration of free fall = 10 m/s^2.

8 A pressure gauge in a refrigerator system reads 3.5 bar. If the atmospheric pressure is 1 bar, what is the absolute pressure in the system?

9 A vacuum gauge in part of a refrigerator reads −4.5 kPa. If the atmospheric pressure is 1 bar, what is the absolute pressure in that part of the system?

10 A pressure which is less than atmospheric causes a difference of 40 mm in the mercury levels of a manometer. Calculate the pressure and the degree of vacuum if the atmospheric pressure is 760 mmHg.

11 A large air conditioner of mass 400 kg is lifted through a height of 20 m to the top floor of a building. Calculate the work done, taking *g* as 10 m/s^2.

12 A refrigerated truck of mass 5 t is moving at a speed of 15 m/s. Determine the kinetic energy of the truck.

13 A fan used in an air conditioner is rated at 450 W of electrical power. How much electrical energy is used in 15 minutes?

14 The temperature of the refrigerant in a refrigeration system varies between −5°C and 45°C. Convert these two temperatures to kelvin, given that 0°C = 273K.

15 8 kg of meat is cooled in a refrigerator from 40°C to 6°C. How much heat does the refrigerator extract from the meat, which has a specific heat capacity of 2.5 kJ/kg K?

16 i) What is the amount of heat required to convert 7 kg of water into steam at boiling point?
ii) What is the amount of heat required to convert 12 kg ice into liquid water at melting point?
Specific latent heat of steam = 2 260 000 J/kg.
Specific latent heat of ice = 336 000 J/kg.

17 Distinguish between *convection* and *conduction* as means of heat transfer.

18 By what means can heat travel through a vacuum?

4 Electrical principles

Introduction

A knowledge of electrical principles is important for the technician working in refrigeration or air conditioning. This is because refrigeration systems work from a compressor that is operated from an electric motor. Control circuits contain electrical components and many tools are electrically powered. Electricity is also important because atoms themselves are electrical in nature.

Atomic structure

All objects are made up of very small particles known as **atoms**. These atoms are so small that a million could fit across the thickness of a sheet of paper. Atoms consist of even smaller particles, some of which carry electric charges. There are two types of electric charge, positive (+) and negative (−). One particle which is part of the atom is the **electron**. Electrons carry a negative charge and they move in orbit around the positive part of the atom, which is called the **nucleus**. Normally, an atom has exactly as much negative charge as positive and so it is said to be **neutral**. There are over a hundred different types of atom and Figure 4.1 shows some of them.

Sometimes an atom loses one or more of its electrons from its orbits. When this happens the atom is said to be **ionised** and it has a positive charge. An atom with a positive charge is a **positive ion**. A knowledge of the ionisation of atoms is important in understanding electric filters used in air conditioning.

Because of their electrons, atoms can join together with other atoms to form **molecules**. For

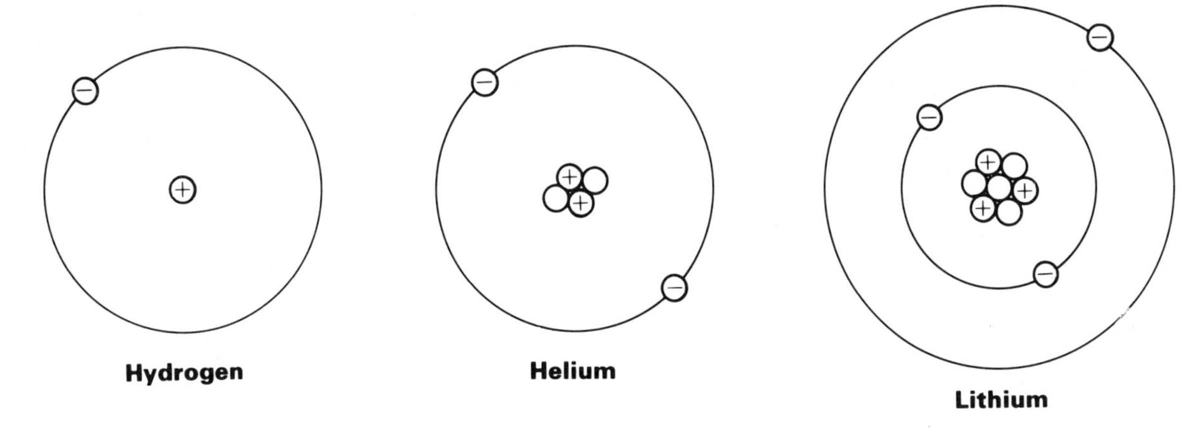

Figure 4.1 Examples of atoms.

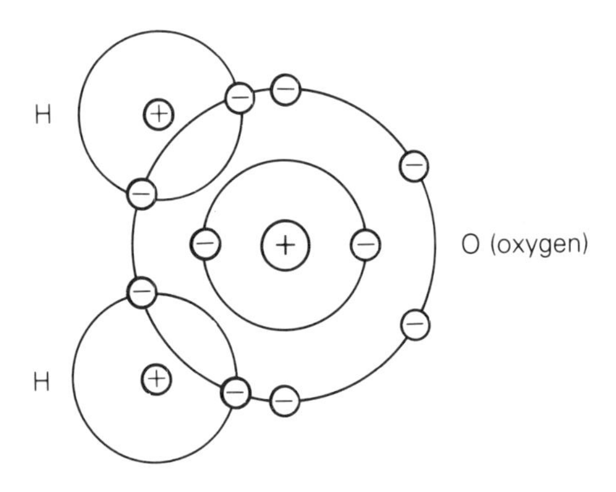

Figure 4.2 A water molecule, H_2O.

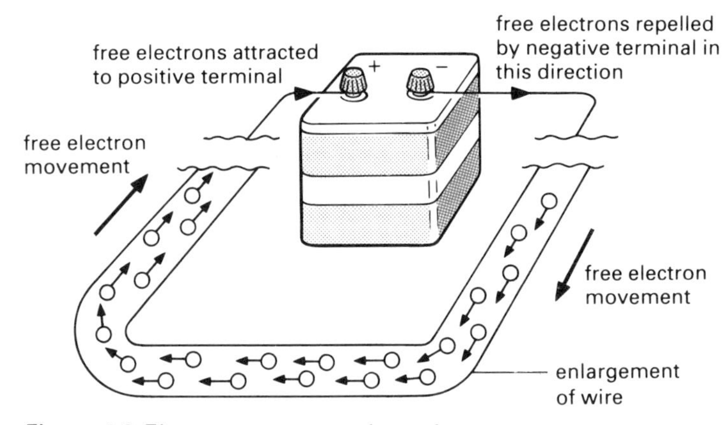

Figure 4.3 Electron movement in a wire.

example, two atoms of hydrogen join with one of oxygen to form a water molecule by sharing their electrons. Figure 4.2 shows a water molecule.

Current electricity

Technicians need a knowledge of current electricity in order to understand some of the components and circuits used in refrigeration work. They also need to understand the principles of fuses and electrical safety in general.

Batteries are devices containing chemicals which generate an **e.m.f.** or **electromotive force**. An e.m.f. causes an **electric current** to flow in a circuit that is connected to the generating device. It does this by converting chemical energy to electrical energy. The negative electrode of a battery has electrons collected on its surface, while the positive electrode lacks electrons. Circuit connections are made to terminals which are fixed to the ends of the electrodes. E.m.f. is measured in **volts (V)** and this value is marked on the body of the battery.

Let us see what happens when a metal wire is connected to the terminals of a battery. Metals have electrons inside them which have broken away from the atoms of the wire and so can move independently. These electrons are free electrons and they can move anywhere inside the wire. The positive terminal of the battery attracts these free electrons while the negative terminal repels them. This means that electrons move inside the wire from the negative terminal to the positive terminal. An electric current is said to flow in the wire. Figure 4.3 shows the movement of electrons inside a wire as a result of an e.m.f.

As electrons flow through a wire they collide with the atoms of the wire. The atoms impede the electron flow and set up an electrical **resistance**. If the resistance of the wire is increased (by increasing its length) the current decreases. Resistance is used in a circuit to control the flow of current.

> ▲ Do not connect a short wire between the terminals of a battery. This can damage the battery and you may even burn your fingers.

Resistors, which are electric components specially made to have a particular resistance value, are sometimes made of wire. Such resistors are called wirewound resistors. There are other types of resistor too, such as carbon resistors.

Figure 4.4 shows a **circuit diagram** in which a current from a battery flows through a resistance. This resistance can be that of a resistor or of something else in the circuit.

Circuit diagrams use **circuit symbols** to make circuits easier to understand. For example, there are thousands of different types of batteries manufactured throughout the world and each one looks different but there is only one circuit symbol.

The arrows show the direction of **conventional current** from positive to negative. The only real flow in the circuit is that of electrons from negative to positive but the convention was made before the discovery of the electron and it is still in force today. A convention is made by a group of top scientists whose job it is to establish standards. The arrows on a circuit diagram always show conventional flow unless it is otherwise stated. The term current used on its own means conventional current.

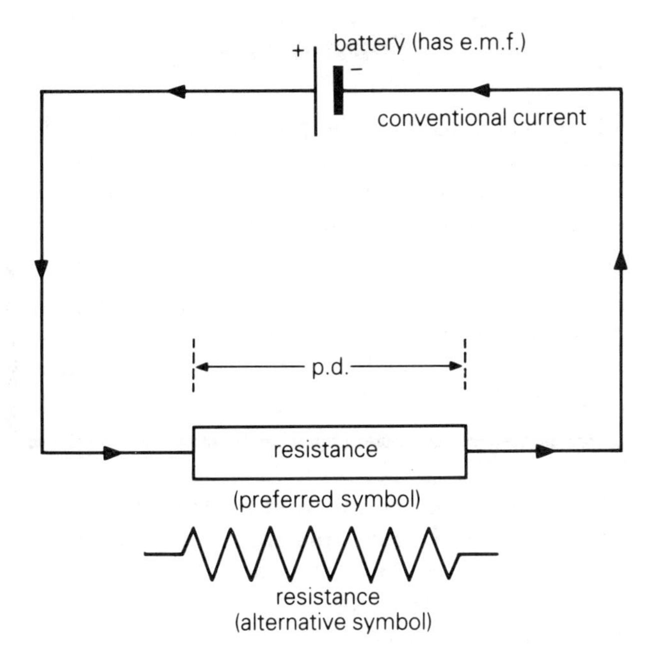

Figure 4.4 A simple circuit.

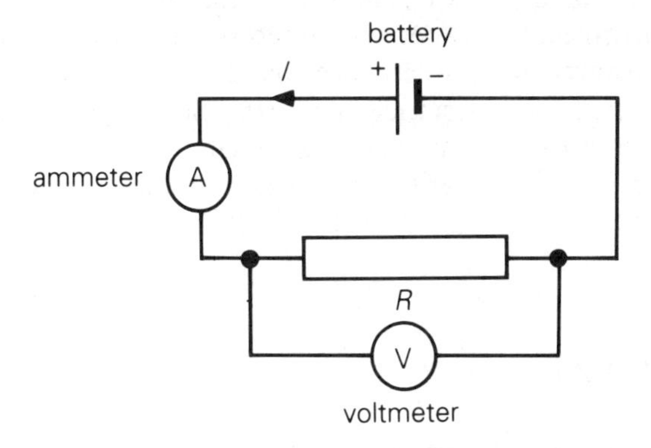

Figure 4.5 Ammeter and voltmeter.

The current starts at the positive terminal, passes through the resistance and flows back to the negative terminal.

> The current is the same everywhere in the circuit.

The current does not start off large before it gets to the resistance and then become small as a result of passing through the resistance.

The symbol used for resistance is the standard one in use throughout the world. However, there is an alternative symbol that you will find, mainly in older text books. This is shown in Figure 4.4.

Electrical units

The unit of electric current is the **ampere (A)**. The instrument used for measuring electric current is called the **ammeter**.

The unit of e.m.f. is the volt (V). There is another electrical quantity measured in volts and that is **potential difference** (p.d.). Both e.m.f. and p.d. are often referred to simply as **voltage**. The e.m.f. is the voltage of the electrical power supply (in this case the battery). The p.d. is the voltage across the components in the circuit. The resistance in Figure 4.4 has a p.d. across its ends. The resistance is connected directly to the battery terminals, so that the terminals also have a p.d. between them. When the battery is not connected to a circuit, the p.d. across the terminals has the same value as the e.m.f. With the battery connected to a circuit and supplying a current, the p.d. is a little less than the e.m.f. However, in the simple problems set in this book it will be assumed that the terminal p.d. has the same value as the e.m.f. Voltage is measured by means of a **voltmeter**. Figure 4.5 shows the way in which an ammeter and a voltmeter are connected in a circuit.

Note that the voltmeter is connected *across* the resistance in order to measure the voltage *across* it. The ammeter is connected *in* the circuit so that the current through the resistance is measured. The ammeter can either be connected between the positive terminal and the battery or between the negative terminal and the battery. The same current will be measured in each case.

Resistance

Resistance has been mentioned up till now as part of a circuit but what exactly is resistance?

$$\text{Resistance} = \frac{\text{voltage}}{\text{current}}$$

or

$$R = \frac{V}{I}$$

The unit of resistance is the ohm (Ω).

Resistance is measured on an instrument called an **ohmmeter**. Often ohmmeters are part of a **multimeter** which can measure current, potential difference and resistance. You can select which you want to measure by means of a switch.

For very high resistance measurements a special **insulation resistance tester/continuity tester** is best.

EXAMPLE 4.1

Referring to the circuit shown in Figure 4.5:

i) if the e.m.f. of the battery is 2 V and the current is 0.5 A, determine the value of the resistance of the circuit.
ii) The battery is replaced by one of e.m.f. 4 V and the resistance is increased. The new current is found to be 0.5 mA. What is the new value of the resistance?

Solution

i) $R = \frac{2}{0.5} = 4\,\Omega$.

ii) $R = \frac{4}{0.5 \times 10^{-3}} = 8 \times 10^{3} = 8\,\text{k}\Omega$.

EXAMPLE 4.2

If the circuit resistance is 12 Ω and the current is 0.25 A, what is the e.m.f. of the battery?

Solution

$V = I \times R$, this is the definition-of-resistance formula, transposed with V as the subject.

$V = 0.25 \times 12 = 4\,\text{V}$.

EXAMPLE 4.3

If the e.m.f. of the battery is 6 V and the circuit resistance is 12 Ω, what is the size of the current?

Solution

$I = \frac{V}{R}$, again this is the resistance formula, transposed with I as the subject.

$I = \frac{6}{12} = 0.5\,\text{A}$.

Ohm's law

Many materials have the property that, if a p.d. is applied across them and then, say, doubled, the current also doubles. The current is said to be proportional to the applied p.d.

> Ohm's law states that the current through a conductor is directly proportional to the p.d. across it, provided the temperature and other external conditions remain constant.

Metallic conductors obey **Ohm's law** and they are said to be **ohmic**. Resistors are ohmic, and because of this they have the resistance value written on them. It is only worthwhile doing this if the resistance remains constant as the p.d. and current vary. In fact 'resistance is constant' (as p.d. and current vary) is the easiest way to remember Ohm's law.

EXAMPLE 4.4

The diagram shows a circuit suitable for verifying Ohm's law. A student adjusts the variable resistor, takes a number of readings of p.d. and current and tabulates them as shown. The temperature of the resistance is found to remain constant. The student then draws a graph of V (y-axis) against I (x-axis). Examine the graph and state whether or not the resistance obeys Ohm's law. Give a reason for your answer. From the graph find the resistance.

V (V)	1	2	3	4	5	6	7	8	9
I (A)	0.10	0.20	0.31	0.40	0.51	0.59	0.70	0.81	0.89

Solution

The graph is a straight line through the origin. This means that Ohm's law is obeyed. The best way to find the resistance is from the gradient of the graph.

$$\text{Gradient} = \frac{\text{change in } y\text{-value}}{\text{change in } x\text{-value}} = \frac{9(\text{V})}{0.9(\text{A})} = 10\,\Omega.$$

In order to get the most accurate answer when measuring the gradient take the largest possible changes in values of y and x.

Some components do not obey Ohm's law. One example is the **diode**. The circuit symbol for the diode is shown in Figure 4.6.

When the anode (A) is made positive and the cathode (K) negative, the diode allows current to pass. This is said to be the forward direction for the diode and the diode is forward-biased. When the anode is negative, and the cathode positive no current passes. This is the reverse direction and the diode is reverse-biased. Diodes do not have a particular resistance value. Their resistance varies as the p.d. varies. Diodes are said to be **non-ohmic**.

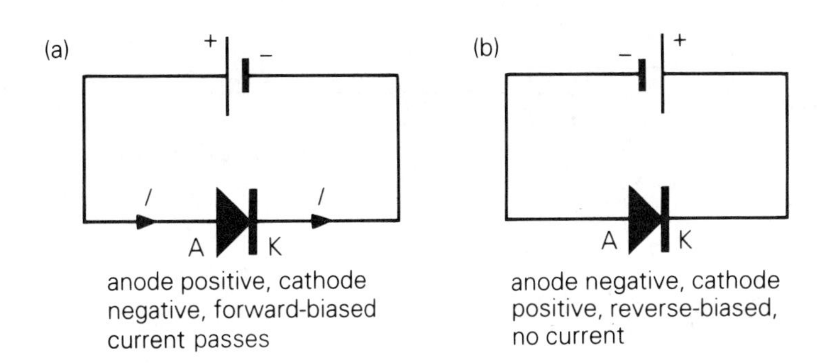

Figure 4.6 The diode: (a) forward-biased; (b) reverse-biased.

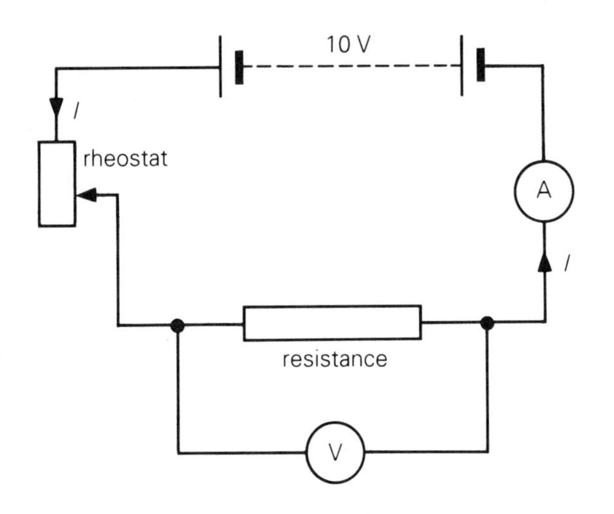

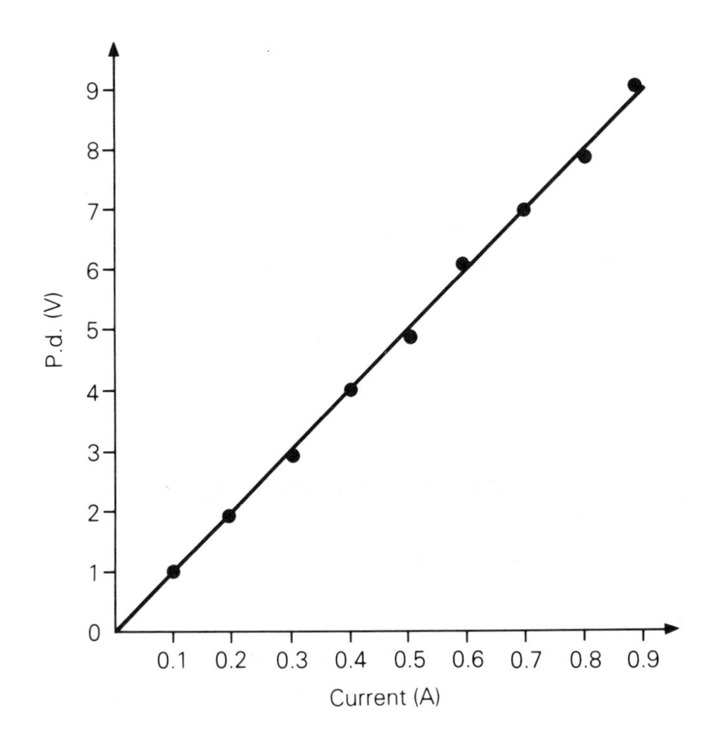

Electrical power

All power is rate at which work is done or rate at which energy is used (see Chapter 3). Electrical power, in watts, can be calculated from the current and the potential difference by using the formula:

$P = VI$

EXAMPLE 4.5

The compressor of a refrigerator takes a current of 5 A with a voltage of 250 V. Calculate the power rating of the compressor.

Solution

$P = 250 \times 5$

$= 1250$ W or 1.25 kW.

Alternating current and voltage

The current from a battery flows from positive to negative terminals, through the circuit that is connected to it. Such a current is called **direct current (d.c.)**. The battery voltage that produces direct current is called **direct voltage**. The electrical power that can be obtained from even large batteries is fairly small, so that domestic refrigerators and freezers cannot be driven by batteries. However, there are small, solid state, Peltier effect refrigerators, suitable for picnics, which can be run from car batteries (see Chapter 7).

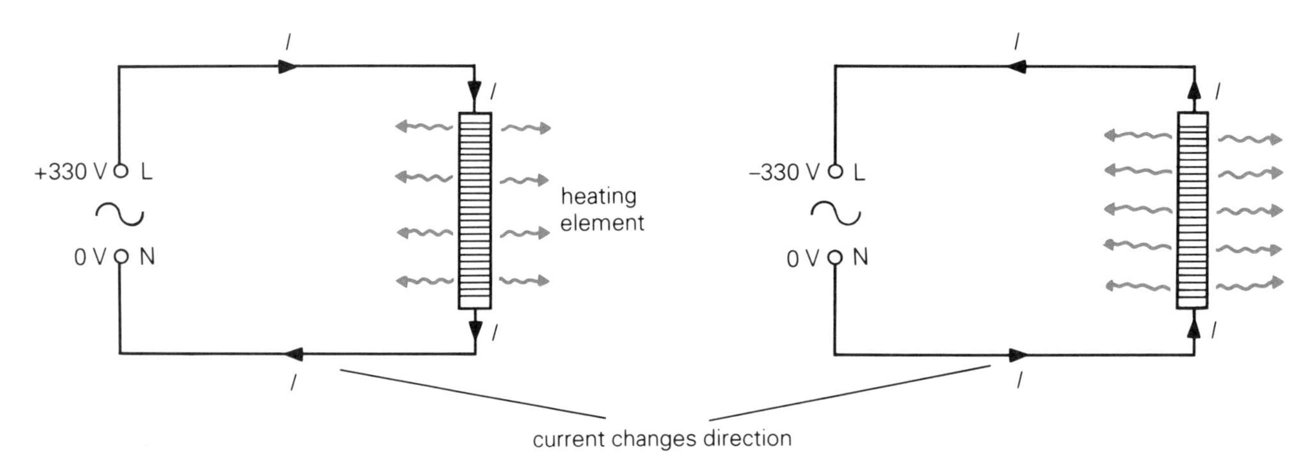

Figure 4.7 A simple circuit shown at different times.

Appliances, such as refrigerators and freezers, can only be powered by using electricity from the electrical mains (although in remote areas without electrical mains, petrol-driven internal combustion engines may have to be used). Mains supplies have socket outlets which are normally fixed to walls and the appliance is plugged into the socket. The current that comes from the mains repeatedly changes direction. Such a current is called **alternating current (a.c.)** and the voltage that produces it is **alternating voltage**. Alternating voltage is important because mains supplies are alternating or a.c. supplies. Figure 4.7 shows a simple circuit operated from an a.c. supply.

One side of the supply is called **live** and the other is **neutral**. The voltage of the neutral always stays the same at 0 V. The live repeatedly changes from about + 330 V to −330 V (UK values for household supplies). When the live is + 330 V, the current flows from live to neutral. When the live is −330 V, the neutral voltage is greater than the live and the current flows from neutral to live. The time taken for the voltage to change from + 330 V to −330 V and back to + 330 V is 1/50 s.

This time is called the **period** (T). The period is the time for one cycle of alternating voltage or current. A cycle of alternating voltage is shown in Figure 4.8. The curve for alternating current is the same shape.

The number of cycles produced every second by the supply is called the **frequency**. Frequency (f) is measured in **hertz (Hz)**. The standard household frequency in the UK is 50 Hz. Frequency and period are related by the formula:

$$f = \frac{1}{T}$$

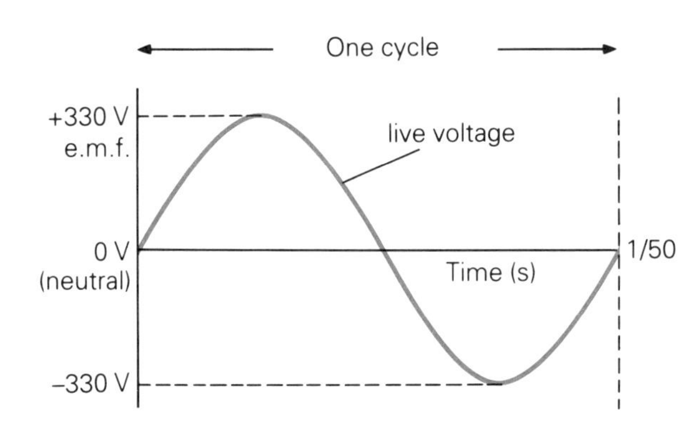

Figure 4.8 A cycle of alternating voltage.

Alternating voltage and current are changing the whole time so that it is not easy to give a value to voltage and current. However, there is a kind of 'average' value known as **root mean square (r.m.s.)** which is quoted by electricity companies:

r.m.s. value = 0.71 × peak value
so that r.m.s. voltage = 0.71 × 330 = just over 230 V.

Again this applies to the UK.

Other components

All of the components and devices described in this chapter can be seen on circuits used in refrigeration and air conditioning. There are a number of other components used, too, and a brief description of each follows. The circuit symbols are shown in Figure 4.9.

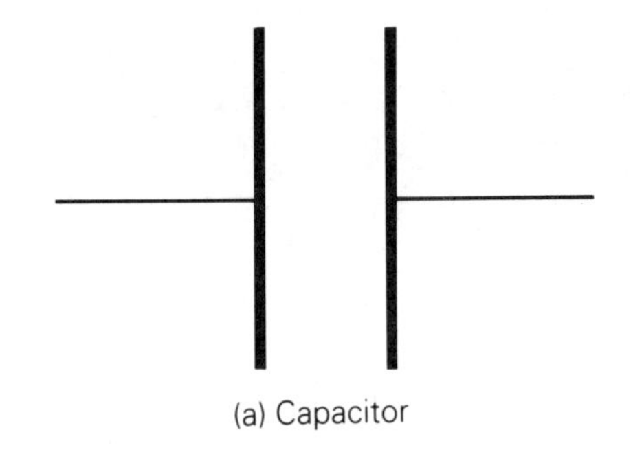
(a) Capacitor

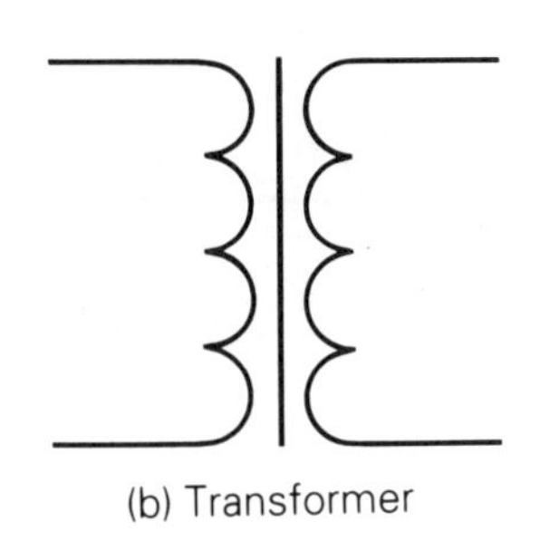
(b) Transformer

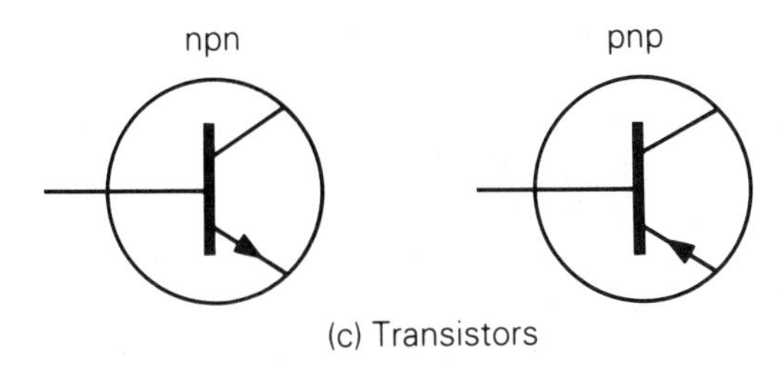

(c) Transistors

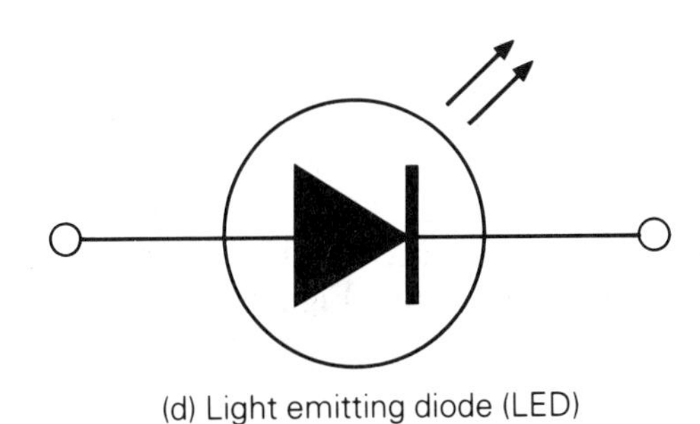
(d) Light emitting diode (LED)

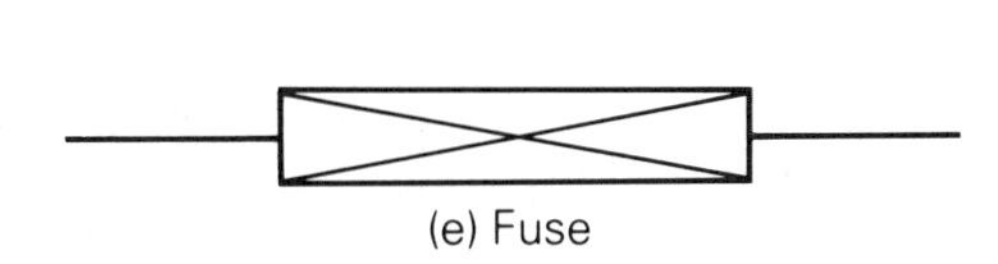
(e) Fuse

Figure 4.9 Circuit symbols.

The **capacitor** (Figure 4.9(a)) is a component which stores electric charge; that is, electrons. It has a number of uses in electrical circuits.

Transformers (Figure 4.9(b)) convert a.c. voltages to another value, either higher or lower, depending on the type of transformer.

Transistors (Figure 4.9(c)) are used in amplifiers to increase current and in computers as very fast switches so that they can count very quickly.

Light emitting diodes (LEDs) (Figure 4.9(d)) are diodes which emit light when a current passes through them. They are often used as indicator lamps in electronic equipment.

Fuses (Figure 4.9(e)) are safety devices used with electrical equipment (see Chapter 2).

Resistor colour coding

Carbon resistors, the most common type in nearly all electrical and electronic circuits, are colour coded to give their resistance value. They have coloured bands painted on them and these bands correspond to numbers:

Colour	Number	Colour	Number
Black	0	Green	5
Brown	1	Blue	6
Red	2	Violet	7
Orange	3	Grey	8
Yellow	4	White	9

Figure 4.10 shows the bands and their significance. The first band indicates the first digit, the second band the second digit and the third band the number of zeros after the first and second figures. The fourth band indicates the tolerance and it is usually gold 5% or silver 10%. No band is 20%.

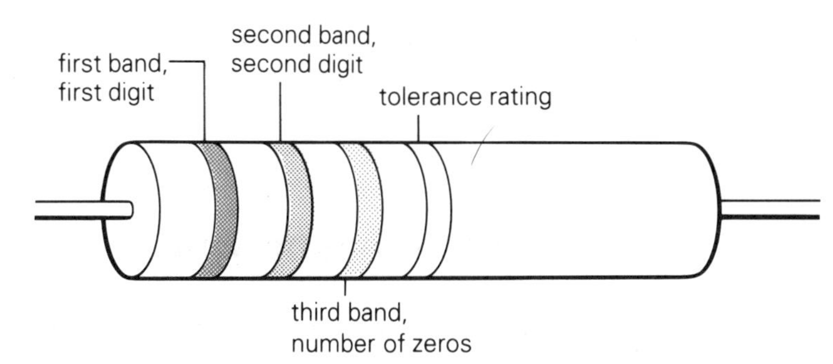

Figure 4.10 Resistor coding bands.

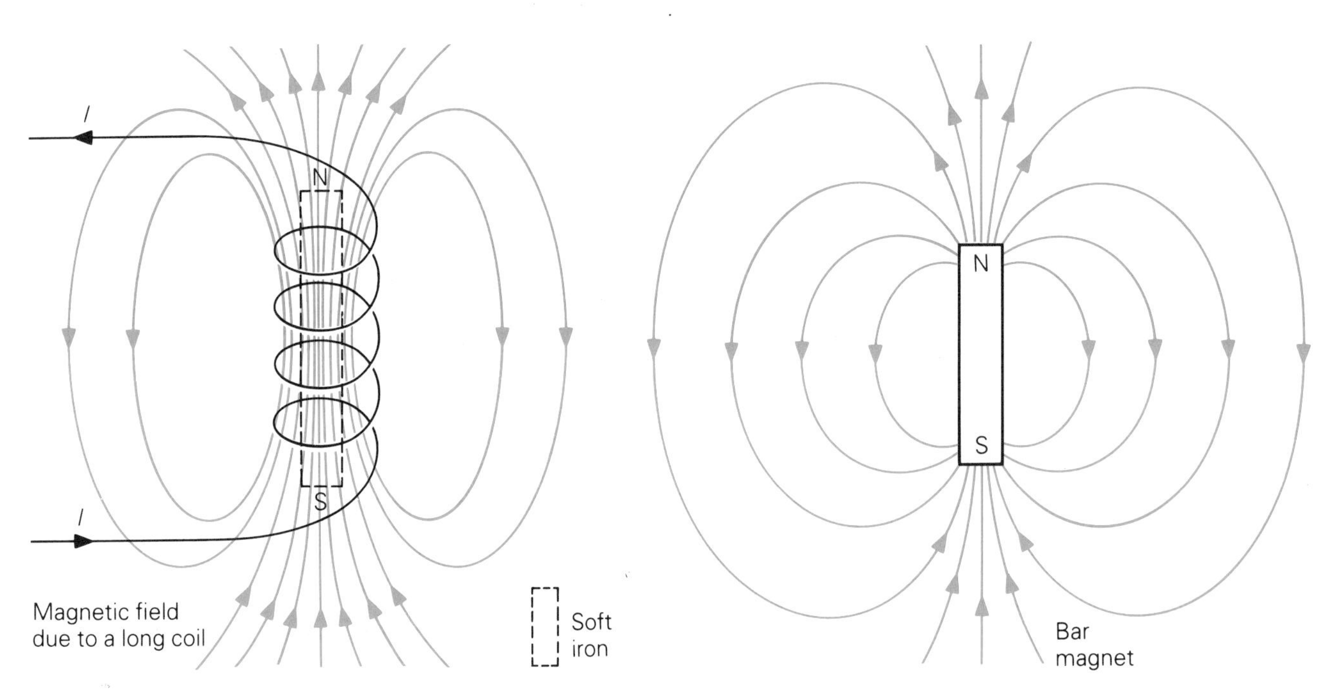

Figure 4.11 Magnetic fields.

EXAMPLE 4.5

The first band on a resistor is yellow, the second band is violet, the third is brown and the fourth silver.

i) State the value of the resistance and the tolerance.
ii) What are the maximum and minimum values the resistor can have?

Solution

i) Yellow = 4; violet = 7; brown = 1, therefore there is one zero. Resistance = 470 Ω. Silver indicates a tolerance of 10%.
ii) 10% of $470\,\Omega = \frac{10}{100} \times 470 = 47\,\Omega$.

Maximum = 470 Ω + 47 Ω = 517 Ω.
Minimum = 470 Ω − 47 Ω = 423 Ω.
The actual value of the resistance can lie anywhere between 423 Ω and 517 Ω.

Electromagnetism

When a current flows along a wire, a magnetic field can be detected around the wire. If the wire is made into a long coil then the magnetic field is the same shape as that caused by a permanent bar magnet (see Figure 4.11). The ends of a bar magnet are called the poles and one is the north (N) and the other is south (S) pole. The lines of magnetic force or flux that make up the magnetic field are reckoned to go from N to S. If the N poles of two neighbouring bar magnets are placed near one another, a force of repulsion occurs. Two S poles also repel each other. A N and a S pole brought together attract one another.

When a bar of soft iron is placed in the coil then the magnetic field is made stronger. Such a device is called an **electromagnet** and it is only magnetic when a current passes through the coil.

A **relay** is a type of switch which employs an electromagnet to attract a soft iron armature and so control another circuit. Figure 4.12 shows a relay. Relays are used in some refrigeration circuits.

Electric motors

Compressors are types of pumps which circulate refrigerant, the working fluid, through a refrigeration system. They are almost always driven by electric motors. We have already seen that whenever two magnetic fields are brought close together some sort of force results.

If a magnetic field caused by an electromagnet is

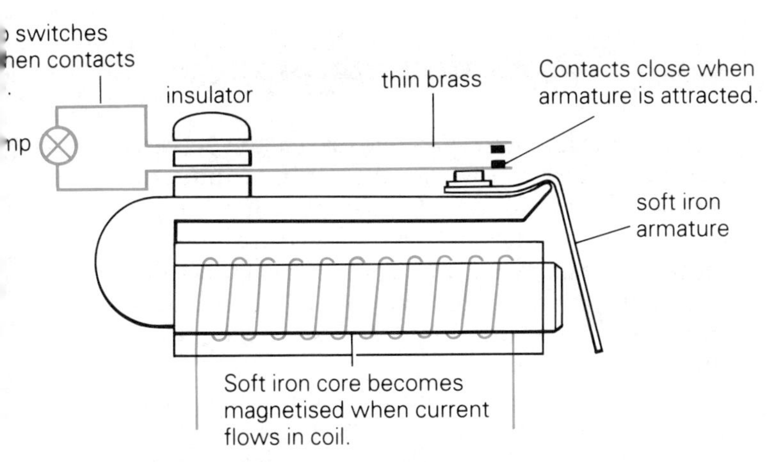

Figure 4.12 A relay.

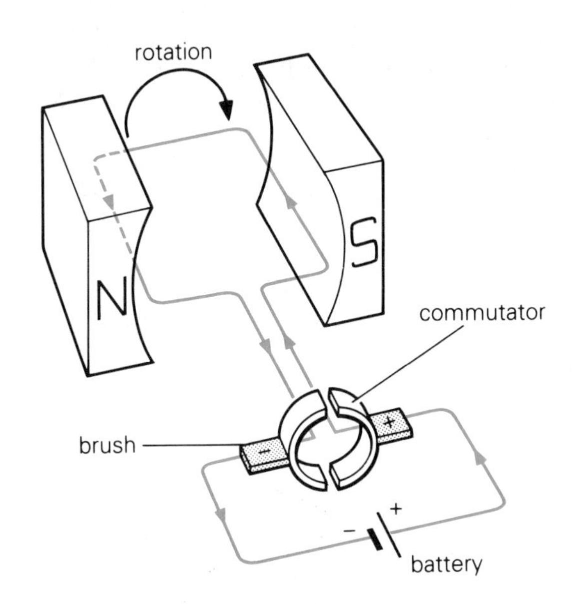

Figure 4.13 A basic electric motor.

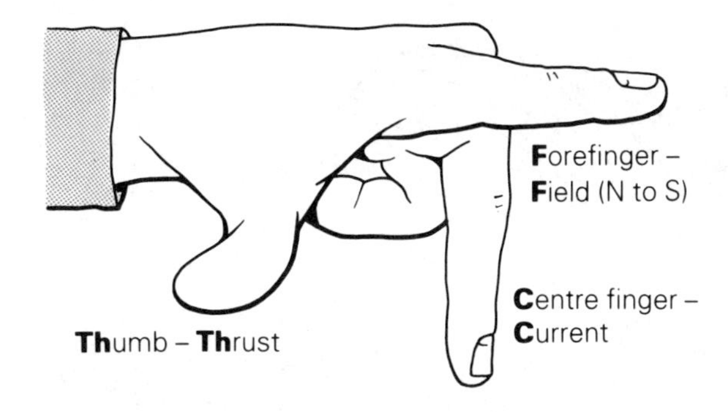

Figure 4.14 Fleming's left hand rule.

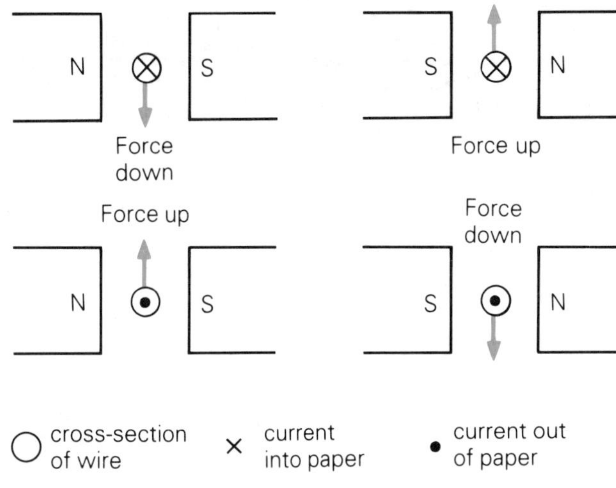

Figure 4.15 Directions of forces with Fleming's left hand rule.

brought close to that caused by a permanent magnet, forces always occur. These can be attractive or repulsive forces if the electromagnet is wound like the one shown in Figure 4.11. However, the most basic form of **electric motor** has a flat coil positioned between the poles of a permanent magnet, as shown in Figure 4.13.

For simplicity a coil with just one turn is shown in Figure 4.13, but in reality the coil will have many turns. The two magnetic fields come together in such a way that the force acting on one side of the coil is at right angles to the permanent magnetic field. The coil has two sides and one force acts upwards, the other downwards. As a result the coil rotates. This effect is the **motor effect**. The leads from the battery have to be connected to the rotating coil and this is done by means of a split brass ring known as a **commutator**. One part of the split ring is connected to one side of the coil and the other part is connected to the other side. Carbon **brushes**, connected by leads to the battery, make contact with the commutator as it rotates with the coil.

The direction of the force on each side of the coil can be determined by using **Fleming's Left Hand Rule**. Hold your left hand as shown in Figure 4.14. The **f**orefinger is pointed along the direction of the magnetic **f**ield, which is from N to S. The **c**entre finger is pointed in the direction of the **c**urrent, which flows from positive to negative. Once the forefinger and the centre finger are correctly pointed the **th**umb gives the direction of **th**rust or force on the wire.

Figure 4.15 shows the directions of forces produced with different magnetic field and current directions. The cross indicates current flowing into the paper, while the dot represents current flowing out of the paper.

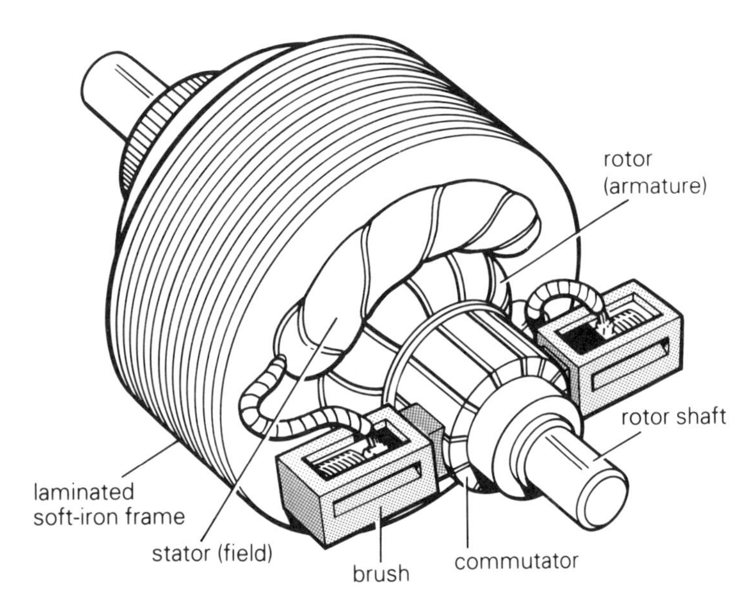

Figure 4.16 The universal motor.

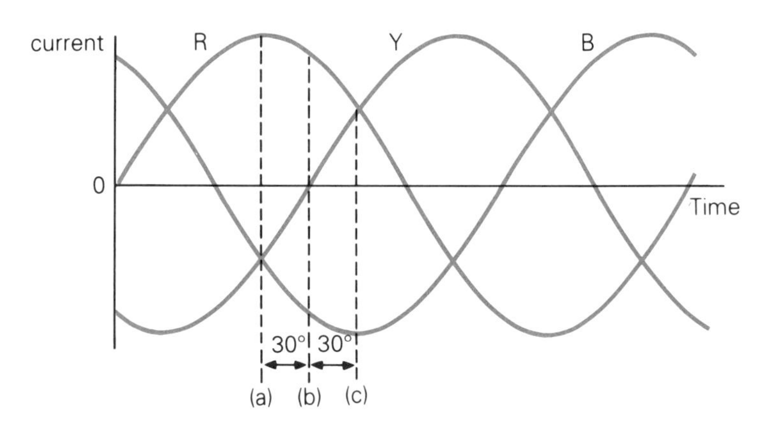

Figure 4.17 Three-phase alternating current.

A more practical electric motor consists of a number of coils wound on to a soft iron **rotor** or **armature**. The commutator is divided into a number of sections, two for every coil on the rotor. A rotor shaft runs through the centre of the motor and it is this shaft that rotates as the coils rotate. This is the shaft that connects either directly or indirectly to the fan, pump or compressor shaft. Instead of a permanent magnet, **field** or **stator** coils wound on to a soft iron frame are used. The current from the supply magnetises these coils as well as the rotor coils. This type of motor is called a **universal motor** and it can operate on either a.c. or d.c. (see Figure 4.16).

Although universal motors are sometimes used in refrigeration or air-conditioning systems, it is the **induction motor** which is more generally used.

Induction motors

Large compressors are often driven by powerful electric motors known as **three-phase induction motors. Three-phase alternating e.m.f.** is generated in power stations which then distribute it, by means of cables, to the consumer. Three-phase alternating current from the supply is fed into the stator of the motor. Figure 4.17 shows a graph of three-phase current.

Phase R reaches its peak a short time before phase Y, which in turn reaches its peak a shortly before phase B. These differences in times are used to generate a rotating magnetic field around the stator.

Note: R means red, Y means yellow and B means blue. These are the identifying colours of the leads for the three phases. The domestic consumer will not have all three phases supplied. Each house will have only a single phase and typically neighbouring houses will have R, then Y, then B alternately. Only large buildings such as factories and offices have three-phase a.c. available, so that three-phase induction motors are normally used in larger compressors for industrial refrigeration and air conditioning.

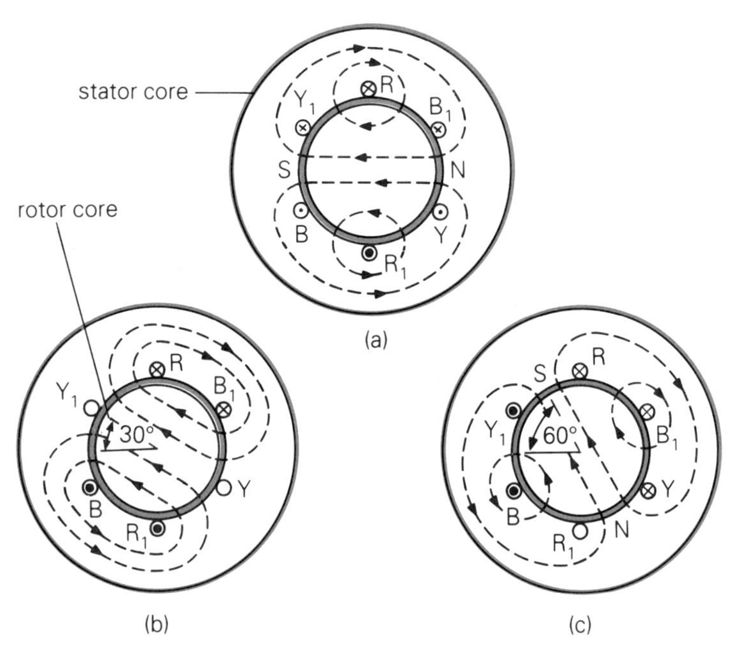

Figure 4.18 Induction motor, producing a rotating magnetic field: (a), (b) and (c) correspond to positions (a), (b) and (c) in Figure 4.17.

In order to generate a rotating magnetic field, three coils are wound on to the soft iron stator core, as shown in Figure 4.18.

For simplicity, single-turn coils are shown, although in reality, coils of many turns would have to be used. Each coil is connected to a different phase: R is the start of the 'red' coil and R_1 the finish, Y is the start of the 'yellow' coil and Y_1 the finish, B is the start of the 'blue' coil and B_1 the finish. When the current in the 'red' coil is a maximum in one direction, the currents in the other two coils are less then a maximum and in the opposite direction. The currents flow in the coils in the directions shown and the magnetic field shape is indicated in Figure 4.18(a). This corresponds to position (a) in Figure 4.17.

A short time later the current in the 'yellow' coil is zero, the current in the 'red' has decreased and the current in the 'blue' has increased in the opposite direction (position (b) in Figure 4.17). The currents flow in the directions shown and the magnetic field is indicated in Figure 4.18(b). Note that it has rotated through an angle of 30° from its position in (a). Later still, the current in the 'red' and 'yellow' phases are equal and the 'blue' phase is a maximum with the current in the opposite direction (position (c) in Figures 4.17 and 4.18). The magnetic field has rotated away from (b) and continued to move away from (a). A rotating magnetic field has been produced.

The rotor consists of a series of parallel aluminium rotor bars connected to end rings as shown in Figure 4.19. This type of rotor is called a **squirrel cage**.

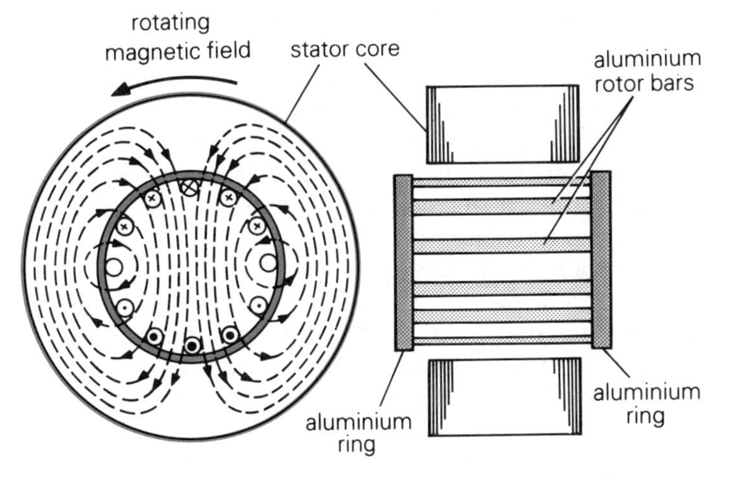

Figure 4.19 A squirrel-cage motor.

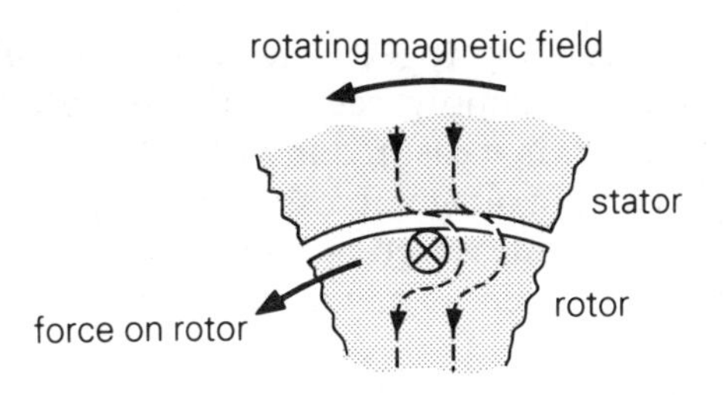

Figure 4.20 Force on the rotor.

The rotating magnetic field cuts across the aluminium bars. When a magnetic field cuts across an electrical conductor an e.m.f. is generated or induced. This process is called **electromagnetic induction** and that is where the name induction motor comes from. Because aluminium is a conductor of electricity the e.m.f. causes a current in the aluminium bars. Figure 4.20 shows the direction of current in an aluminium bar and the rotation of the magnetic flux. Using Fleming's Left Hand Rule, it can be seen that the bar and hence the whole rotor will be pushed in the direction of the magnetic field.

The squirrel-cage induction motor has no electrical connections made to the rotor. In this it differs from the universal motor. There is another type of induction motor in which connections are made to the rotor by means of a device called a **slip ring**. This is better than the squirrel-cage type in that it exerts a greater turning force when it first start up but it is also more expensive and less robust.

There are also single-phase induction motors for use on the ordinary domestic electricity supply. Single-phase motors are suitable for driving smaller compressors in, say, household refrigerators and freezers. To help them achieve their maximum turning force as soon as possible after starting up, refrigerator motors are equipped with **start windings**. The advantage of induction motors over universal motors is that induction motors can be relied upon to run at constant speed whereas universal motors vary in their speed.

CHECK YOUR UNDERSTANDING

- An atom consists of a positively charged nucleus and negatively charged electrons which orbit the nucleus. The total positive charge is equal to the total negative charge.
- An ion is a charged atom.

- Atoms can join together to form molecules.
- E.m.f. of a supply causes current to flow in a circuit. E.m.f. is measured in volts (V).
- P.d. is the voltage across the components in a circuit. P.d. is measured in volts (V).
- Electric current is measured in amperes (A).
- Resistance in ohms(Ω) $= \dfrac{\text{voltage in volts}}{\text{current in amperes}}$.
- E.m.f. and p.d. are measured using a voltmeter, current is measured with an ammeter and resistance is measured with an ohmmeter.
- Ohm's law states that I is directly proportional to V, if the temperature is constant.
- Some components, such as resistors, obey Ohm's law and are said to be ohmic. Others, such as diodes, are non-ohmic.
- Alternating current (a.c.) is caused by alternating voltage which is a voltage that repeatedly changes direction.
- Direct current (d.c.) is caused by direct voltage which does not change direction.
- The time for a cycle of a.c. is the period (T) and $T = 1/f$ where f is the frequency in cycles per second or hertz (Hz).
- When an electric current is passed along the coils of an electromagnet a magnetic field is generated around the electromagnet.
- When a current flows in a conductor which is perpendicular to a magnetic field and, as a result, a force occurs at right angles to both of them, this effect is called the motor effect.
- One type of electric motor is the universal motor which has a stationary stator, together with rotating coils, a commutator and brushes.
- Another type of electric motor is the induction motor in which a rotating magnetic field is produced at the stator and a rotor follows the rotating field.
- There are many components which are important in electrical circuits used with refrigeration systems. These include resistors, diodes, capacitors, transformers, transistors and light emitting diodes (LEDs).
- The values of carbon resistors are indicated by a colour code and a working knowledge of this code is useful in understanding many electrical circuits.

REVISION EXERCISES AND QUESTIONS

1 State the relationship between voltage, current and resistance, giving the units of each.

In problems (2), (3) and (4) refer to the circuit shown in Figure 4.5.

2 i) If the e.m.f. of the battery is 3 V and the current is 0.3 A, determine the value of the resistance of the circuit.
ii) The battery is replaced by one of e.m.f. 6 V and the resistance is increased. The new current is found to be 0.3 mA. What is the new value of the resistance?

3 If the circuit resistance is 18 Ω and the current is 0.5 A, what is the e.m.f. of the battery?

4 If the e.m.f. of the battery is 12 V and the circuit resistance is 6 Ω, what is the size of the current?

5 In a circuit suitable for verifying Ohm's law, a student adjusts the variable resistor, takes a number of readings of p.d. and current and tabulates them.

However, instead of using a resistance the student uses a diode. The temperature of the diode is found to remain constant. He then draws a graph of V against I. With the diode forward-biased he obtains a curve and with reverse-bias he cannot obtain a current no matter how large a p.d. he uses. State whether or not the diode obeys Ohm's law, giving reasons.

6 The period for one cycle of a.c. is 1/100 s (0.01 s) and the peak value of current is 3 A. Find the frequency of the a.c. and the r.m.s. value of the current.

7 Explain the purpose of the following components:
i) the capacitor, and
ii) the transistor.

8 The first band on a resistor is blue, the second band is grey, the third is red and the fourth gold.
i) State the value of the resistance and the tolerance.
ii) What are the maximum and minimum values the resistor can have?

9 Explain the meaning of the term *motor effect*.

10 By reference to the motor effect, explain why a current-carrying coil, placed in a magnet field, begins to rotate.

11 Explain the meaning of the term *electromagnetic induction*.

12 By reference to electromagnetic induction, explain why the conductors in the rotor of an induction motor have a current flowing in them.

13 Explain the meaning of the term *three-phase* a.c.

5

Liquids and vapours

Introduction

In order to understand refigeration well it is necessary to have a working knowledge of the behaviour of liquids and vapours. This is because the refrigerator working fluid, the refrigerant, repeatedly changes **phase** from liquid to vapour and from vapour back to liquid. Air conditioners alter the amount of moisture in the air so that it is necessary to be familiar with the evaporation and condensation of water. In a compressor (see Chapter 10) the refrigerant vapour is compressed and as a result its volume decreases. A knowledge of the way in which pressure and volume change is needed. **Boyle's law** shows one way in which pressure and volume are related.

Boyle's law

> Boyle's law states that the volume of a given mass of gas is inversely proportional to the pressure applied to the gas, provided that the temperature remains constant.

Inversely proportional means that if the pressure is doubled the volume is halved and if the pressure is halved the volume is doubled (see Figure 5.1). A fourfold increase in pressure means the volume goes down to a quarter of its original value and so on.

If, for example, the volume of mass of gas is 4 m^3 at a pressure of 100 kPa, then if the pressure is increased to 200 kPa the volume goes down to 2 m^3. Conversely, if the pressure is decreased to 50 kPa, then the volume goes up to 8 m^3. Atmospheric gases such as oxygen and nitrogen obey Boyle's law very well. Refrigerant vapour obeys it much less well but it does serve to illustrate the fact that as the volume increases the pressure decreases and vice versa. It should also be noted that in a compressor, the change in pressure occurs so quickly that there is a change in temperature. This type of change is said to be **adiabatic**, whereas Boyle's law changes are **isothermal** with no temperature change.

Isothermal and adiabatic changes

If a volume of gas in a container is subjected to a slow increase in pressure, such that any heat generated has time to leave the system and the temperature is kept constant, then the change is said to be isothermal. As we saw above, Boyle's law applies to isothermal changes.

If the change is so rapid that heat cannot flow either in or out of the container, then the change is

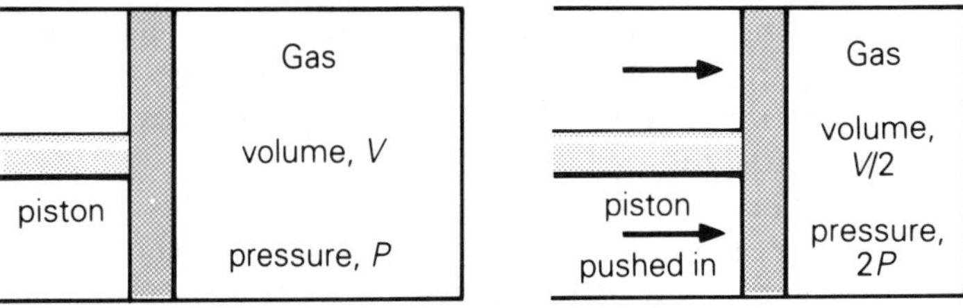

Figure 5.1 Boyle's law.

adiabatic and the temperature alters. With an adiabatic compression there is always an increase in temperature. For an adiabatic expansion there is a decrease in temperature. There is more than one form of adiabatic change. One form occurs with no change of enthalpy, another with no change of entropy (see below and also Chapter 6).

EXAMPLE 5.1

The volume of a mass of gas is 6 m^3 and the pressure is 80 kPa. If the pressure is now increased to 160 kPa, without change of temperature, what is the new volume?

Solution
The pressure doubles from 80 kPa to 160 kPa so the volume is halved. The volume therefore decreases from 6 m^3 to 3 m^3.

Saturated vapours and liquids

The temperature at which a liquid changes into a vapour or a vapour changes into a liquid is called the **saturation temperature**.

The vapour which is above the surface of the liquid is called a **saturated vapour**. Molecules from the liquid are passing through the surface and entering the vapour the whole time, while molecules from the vapour re-enter the liquid. The liquid is called a **saturated liquid**.

The saturation temperature depends upon the atmospheric pressure or at least upon the pressure above the surface of the liquid. At standard pressure (see Chapter 3) the saturation temperature for water is 100°C. Water boils at this temperature, vaporisation occurs throughout the body of the liquid and bubbles of steam are formed. These rise to the surface causing agitation and it is this agitation that indicates to an observer that the water is boiling. The same principle applies to other liquids, too.

The term **vaporisation**, as used in this chapter, refers to the boiling process and not to the type of evaporation, mentioned in Chapter 3, where molecules leave the liquid surface at all temperatures and the higher the temperature, the greater is the rate of evaporation.

> The saturation temperature is equal to the boiling point of a liquid.

As the atmospheric pressure changes, so will the saturation temperature. For example, at the top of a high mountain the air pressure is low and so water will boil at a temperature a lot lower than 100°C. Inside a pressure cooker the pressure will be high and so the boiling point will increase to a value much greater than 100°C. Of course the pressure inside the cooker is no longer that of the atmosphere. It is the pressure above the surface of the liquid which is important and this can either be that of the atmosphere or some other pressure. The pressures inside the boilers of large modern power stations produce saturation temperatures of several hundred degrees Celsius.

Superheated vapour

A vapour heated to a temperature above saturation temperature is said to be **superheated**. The temperature can only be raised by the addition of heat energy known as **superheat**. Superheating can only occur once a liquid has been completely vaporised or the vapour is removed completely from the presence of the liquid.

Subcooled liquids

A liquid at any temperature below its saturation temperature is called a **subcooled liquid**.

Critical temperature

A vapour can be condensed, to form a liquid, by cooling it. This happens all the time to the water in the atmosphere. When temperatures are high during the day all of the atmospheric water is in the form of a vapour. Of course, this only applies on a dry day, not when it is raining. However, at night the temperatures fall and some of the water vapour in the air condenses to form a liquid known as dew.

A vapour can also be condensed by increasing

the pressure without changing the temperature. We saw in Chapter 3 that the molecules in a liquid are closer together than those in a vapour. When a vapour is compressed its volume goes down and some of the molecules will be pushed together sufficiently to form a liquid. As the pressure is further increased more and more vapour will condense into the liquid phase.

The temperature of a vapour can be raised to a point at which it cannot be liquefied (or saturated) by pressure alone. The temperature at which this occurs is the **critical temperature**. The principal gases that make up the air: nitrogen and oxygen, are well above their critical temperatures, which are much less than −100°C. Liquid oxygen and liquid nitrogen can only be produced at very low temperatures. The critical temperature is sometimes used to distinguish between gases and vapours. Thus, dry air (mainly nitrogen and oxygen) is said to be a gas (or a permanent gas), whereas the water in the atmosphere is said to be a vapour.

Enthalpy

The **enthalpy** of a body is the total amount of energy supplied to it, relative to an energy taken as the zero point of enthalpy. Enthalpy is defined by the formula:

$$H = U + pV$$

where H is the enthalpy in joules (J), U is the **internal energy**, also in joules, p is the pressure in pascals and V is the volume in m^3.

Enthalpy is sometimes known as 'total heat'.

The **specific enthalpy** is the total enthalpy divided by the mass of the body or total enthalpy per unit mass:

$$h = \frac{H}{m}$$

where h is the specific enthalpy and m is the mass. Specific enthalpy is measured in joules per kilogramme (J/kg).

The internal energy (U) of a body depends upon the potential and kinetic energies of its molecules:

$$U = P.E. + K.E.$$

P.E. is the potential energy of attraction between the molecules. The forces of (chemical) attraction are electrical in nature, so the potential energy is electrical. In a liquid (or solid) potential energy makes up a significant part of the internal energy. This is because the molecules in a liquid are close to one another and the attraction between them is large. In a gas or vapour, however, the potential energy is relatively much smaller because the molecules are further apart. Even so the amount of potential energy varies. In a vapour near to its saturation temperature the potential energy is quite large. This is true for water vapour in the atmosphere which often changes into a liquid as air pressure and temperature vary. With the so-called permanent gases, nitrogen and oxygen, the potential energy factor is very small at ordinary temperatures (about, say, 300K or 27°C). Internal energy is approximately equal to the kinetic energy of the molecules that make up the gas.

Entropy

As we saw in Chapter 3, heat flows from a hot body to a colder one. The **entropy** of a body depends on two factors, heat flow (or transfer) into the body and absolute temperature in kelvin:

$$\text{change of entropy} = \frac{\text{heat transferred}}{\text{absolute temperature}}$$

Entropy is measured in joules per kelvin (J/K). **Specific entropy** is the entropy per unit mass and it is measured in joules per kilogramme kelvin (J/kg K).

A simple refrigerator

Most refrigerators work on the **vapour-compression** cycle. Such refrigerators start with a hollow pipe wrapped around a freezing compartment. This hollow pipe is known as the **evaporator** coil. The fluid used in a refrigerator is known as the **refrigerant**. Most refrigerants would be in the vapour state at atmospheric pressure and at room temperature because they boil at temperatures below zero on the Celsius scale. However, in some of the high pressure parts of a refrigerator the refrigerant is a liquid.

In theory a simple system could be set up where the refrigerant is allowed to boil in the evaporator

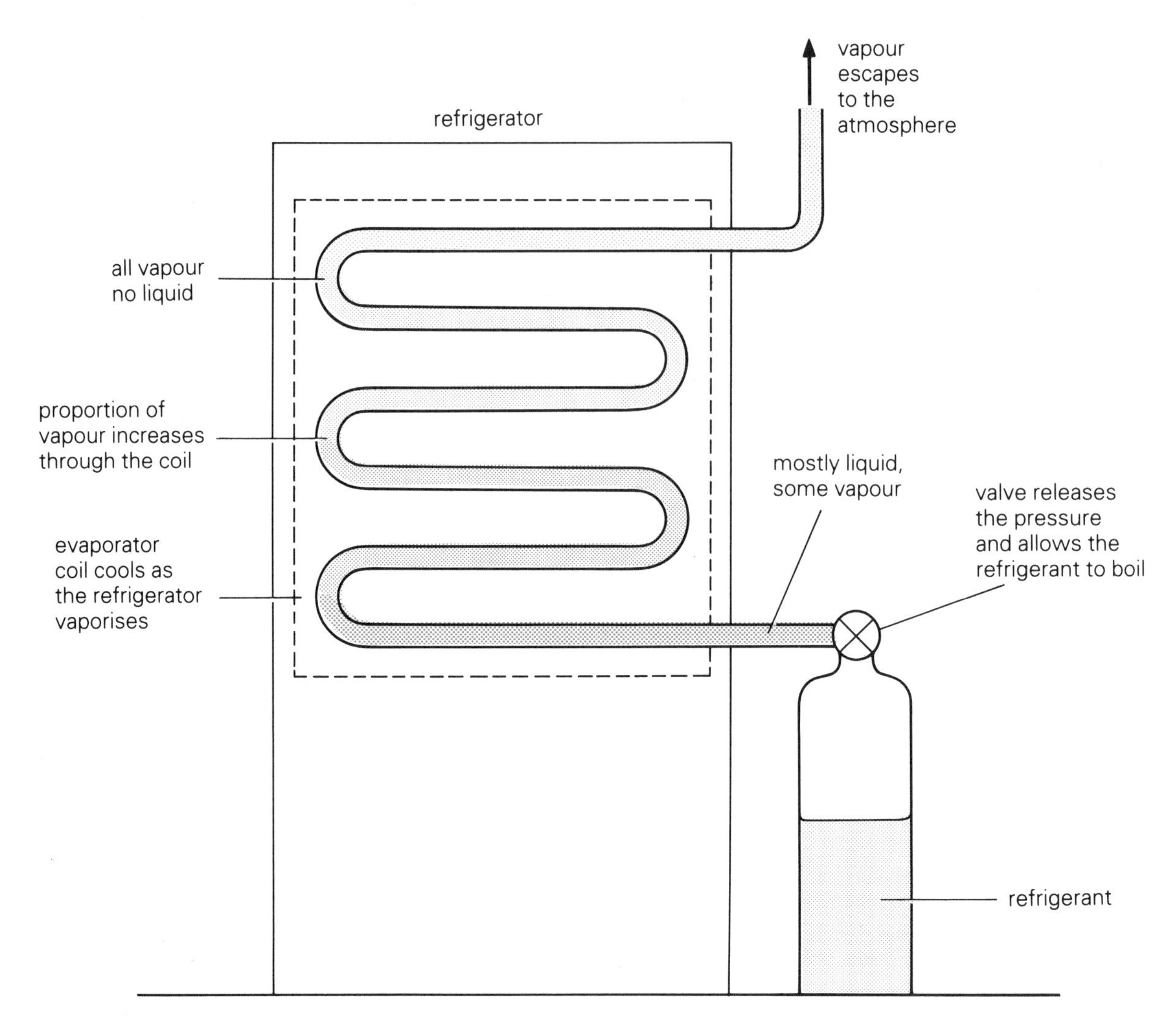

Figure 5.2 A simple system with escaping refrigerant.

coil and escape into the atmosphere (see Figure 5.2).

A liquid needs (latent) heat in order to keep boiling and in this case the only place that the heat can come from is the space surrounding the evaporator. As a result, the temperature around the evaporator drops.

This system has two disadvantages: the expense involved in loss of refrigerant and the pollution produced in the atmosphere. To overcome these problems other devices are required in the refrigerator so that the refrigerant may be recycled and passed through the evaporator many times. Figure 5.3 shows a basic refrigerator in which the important parts are labelled.

The refrigerator system consists of two parts: the low pressure section or **low side**, and the high pressure section or **high side**. The low side of the system contains the evaporator and the **suction**

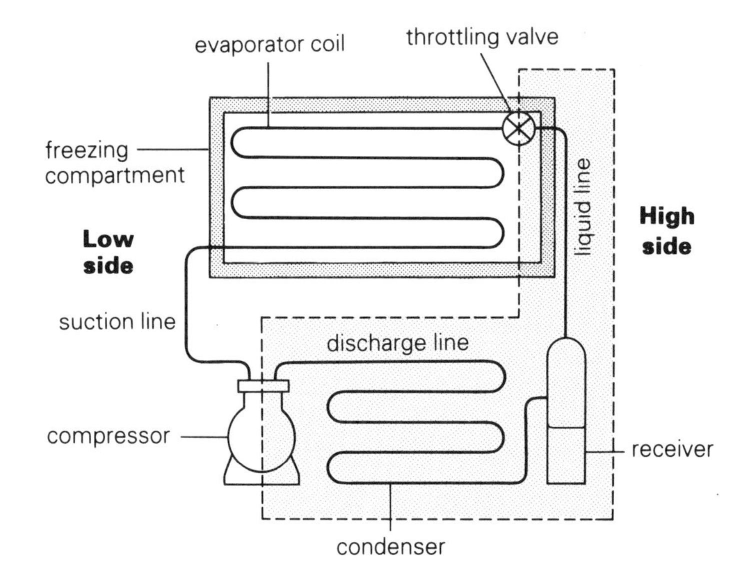

Figure 5.3 A simple refrigerator.

line. The high side consists of the **discharge line**, the **condenser**, the **receiver** and the **liquid line**. The pressure changes from high to low in the **throttling valve** and from low to high in the **compressor**.

As the refrigerant passes through the system it changes phase twice, starting with evaporation in the evaporator, going on to condensation in the condenser and eventually evaporating again. This makes up the vapour-compression cycle in which the condensation is achieved by compression. Figure 5.4 shows a refrigeration system with the refrigerant in different states in the various parts of the cycle. The values of temperature are fairly typical values for a domestic refrigerator and the corresponding pressures come from the **Mollier diagram** and Thermodynamic Tables (see Chapter 6) for ICI refrigerant KLEA 134a (R134a).

In Figure 5.4 high pressure, subcooled, liquid refrigerant flows from the receiver and passes through the throttling valve (1). Here the pressure is reduced and the refrigerant passes into the evaporator (2) and becomes a mixture of liquid and vapour. Suppose that we want a temperature of −10°C in the evaporator. Looking at the refrigerant table for R134a or at the Mollier diagram in Chapter 6, −10°C corresponds to a pressure of 2.0 bar G (all pressures in the system are gauge pressures). If the pressure in the evaporator is 2.0 bar, then the refrigerant will boil at −10°C. (The use of the Mollier diagram and Tables is explained more fully in Chapter 6.) The latent heat to cause the change of phase must come from somewhere. In the example on latent heat of vaporisation, shown in Chapter 3, it came from a Bunsen burner. Here it comes from the refrigerated space around the coil (the freezing compartment in a domestic refrigerator). As the heat flows into the coil, the temperature of the space surrounding it reduces.

Inside the evaporator a liquid is evaporating and therefore the vapour is saturated (3). The compressor pumps the vapour from the evaporator, through the suction line. This process causes the vapour to separate from its liquid, heat flows from the surrounding air into the suction line and superheating occurs. The temperature of the superheated vapour rises considerably by the time it gets to the compressor (4) and a likely value is about 8°C. However, the pressure does not change, and it is approximately the same as the vapour pressure inside the evaporator.

The compressor compresses the superheated

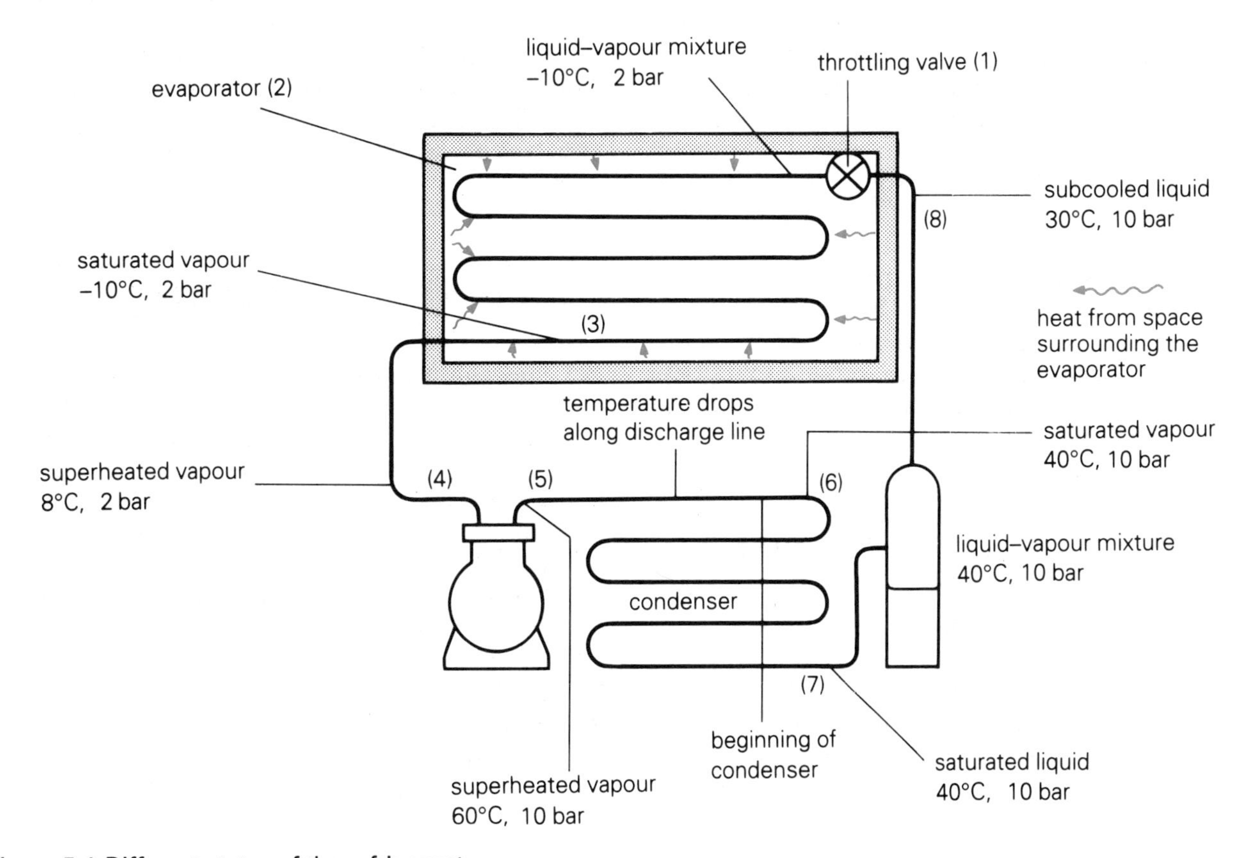

Figure 5.4 Different states of the refrigerant.

vapour very quickly, so this is an adiabatic compression and there is a temperature rise. This is because, with the high speed of compression, there is no time for heat to flow from the compressor to the air outside. Because of the rise in temperature and therefore of internal energy and because of the increase in pressure there is an increase in enthalpy. The superheated vapour with its higher temperature and pressure now enters the discharge line (5). A likely temperature at this point is about 60°C at a pressure of, say, 10 bar.

As the vapour passes along the discharge line it loses heat to the atmosphere and the temperature drops. This is because the 60°C at (5) is well above atmospheric temperature. It also continues to lose temperature in the upper part of the condenser until it reaches its saturation or condensing temperature (6). The vapour now starts to condense and so becomes a saturated vapour. From the Mollier diagram the condensing temperature at a pressure of 10 bar is 40°C. By the time the refrigerant passes through the condenser (7) it is a saturated liquid at the same temperature and pressure. The refrigerant gives out its latent heat as it is condensed and heat flows through the walls of the condenser into the surrounding atmosphere. Heat leaves the condenser at the same rate as heat is taken in at the evaporator and compressor. The condenser, which is normally at the back of a domestic refrigerator, feels hot to the touch.

The saturated liquid now enters the receiver, where there is enough space for a small amount of evaporation to take place. From the receiver the refrigerant passes along the liquid line where, because of its high temperature, it loses heat to the surrounding air. Thus the refrigerant cools to a temperature of, say, 30°C at 10 bar (1). The cycle of changes in the condition of the refrigerant is now complete. Because the pressure in the liquid line is about constant, the liquid is subcooled by the time it gets to the throttling valve.

CHECK YOUR UNDERSTANDING

- The temperature at which a liquid changes into a vapour or a vapour changes into a liquid is called the saturation temperature.
- Vapour above the surface of its liquid is called saturated vapour. The liquid is a saturated liquid.
- The saturation temperature is equal to the boiling point of a liquid.
- A vapour heated above saturation temperature is said to be superheated.
- A liquid cooled below saturation temperature is said to be subcooled.
- Critical temperature is the temperature above which a vapour cannot be liquefied by pressure alone.
- Enthalpy, $H = U + pV$, where U is the internal energy, p is the pressure and V is the volume.
- Change of entropy = heat transferred/absolute temperature.
- If the pressure and the volume of a gas or vapour change in such a way that the temperature remains constant, then the change is isothermal.
- If the pressure and the volume of a gas or vapour change in such a way that the temperature alters, then the change is adiabatic.
- A refrigerator working on the vapour-compression cycle (see Chapter 6) consists of a compressor, a condenser, a receiver, a throttling valve and an evaporator.
- Liquid refrigerant expands and boils in the evaporator, having passed through the throttling valve. Latent heat is taken in and the temperature drops.
- Low pressure superheated vapour is pumped into the compressor and high pressure superheated vapour comes out and enters the condenser.
- In the condenser the vapour is condensed into a liquid, latent heat is given out and the temperature rises. The liquid enters the receiver and from there it passes back to the throttling valve in a subcooled state.

REVISION EXERCISES AND QUESTIONS

1. The volume of a mass of gas is $5\,m^3$ and the pressure is 60 kPa. If the pressure is now decreased to 30 kPa, what is the new volume, assuming that Boyle's law is obeyed?
2. What is meant by *saturation temperature*?
3. Explain the terms *saturated vapour* and *saturated liquid*.
4. Explain the terms *superheated vapour* and *subcooled liquid*.
5. What is meant by the term *critical temperature*?
6. In terms of molecular potential and kinetic energy, explain the meaning of *enthalpy*.
7. What is a *vapour-compression cycle* as applied to refrigeration?

6

The vapour-compression cycle

Introduction

We saw in Chapter 5 that the refrigerant undergoes changes of phase, temperature and pressure as it passes through the refrigeration system. Exact information about these changes can be taken from Thermodynamic Tables for refrigerants and one of these is shown in Chapter 14. Another table is used in this chapter. However, the study is made simpler by the use of graphical representations known as **cycle diagrams**.

There are two types of cycle diagrams:

1 the **pressure–enthalpy diagram**; and
2 the **temperature–entropy diagram**.

The pressure–enthalpy diagram or Mollier diagram is the most used and it will be used here to explain the vapour-compression cycle.

The Mollier diagram

Figure 6.1 shows a complete Mollier diagram for R134a (KLEA 134a). KLEA 134a is a trade name used by ICI.

Figure 6.2 shows a simplified version with most of the lines missed off. It shows that the Mollier diagram is divided into three regions. On the left-hand side is the **subcooled region** in which the refrigerant is in the form of a subcooled liquid. On the right-hand side in the **superheated region**, the refrigerant is a superheated vapour. The central section of the chart, an area of change between the liquid and vapour phases, is sometimes known as the **mixture region**. The curved line which separates the subcooled region and the phase-change region is the **saturated liquid line**. The part of the mixture region near the saturated liquid line represents a mixture which is predominantly liquid, while the part near the saturated vapour line represents a mixture which is nearly all vapour. *Constant quality lines* give the precise percentages of liquid and vapour in the mixture.

The change from liquid to vapour takes place from left to right and the change from vapour to liquid takes place from right to left. This is indicated by arrows on the diagram.

Other important lines on the chart are shown in Figure 6.3.

The *equal temperature lines* in the mixture area are parallel to the *equal pressure lines*. This is because at the same pressure the temperature of the saturated liquid and the saturated vapour are the same (the liquid is at the saturation temperature).

In Chapter 5 it was stated that enthalpy is defined in relation to a fixed reference point. This reference point is chosen for convenience when scientists actually make measurements on enthalpy. 0°C is chosen as the reference temperature and the specific enthalpy at this temperature is taken as 100 kJ/kg. For the entropy scale, the reference point is taken as 1 kJ/kg K for refrigerant at 0°C. In theory, all enthalpies and entropies could be measured from absolute zero but this creates enormous practical difficulties.

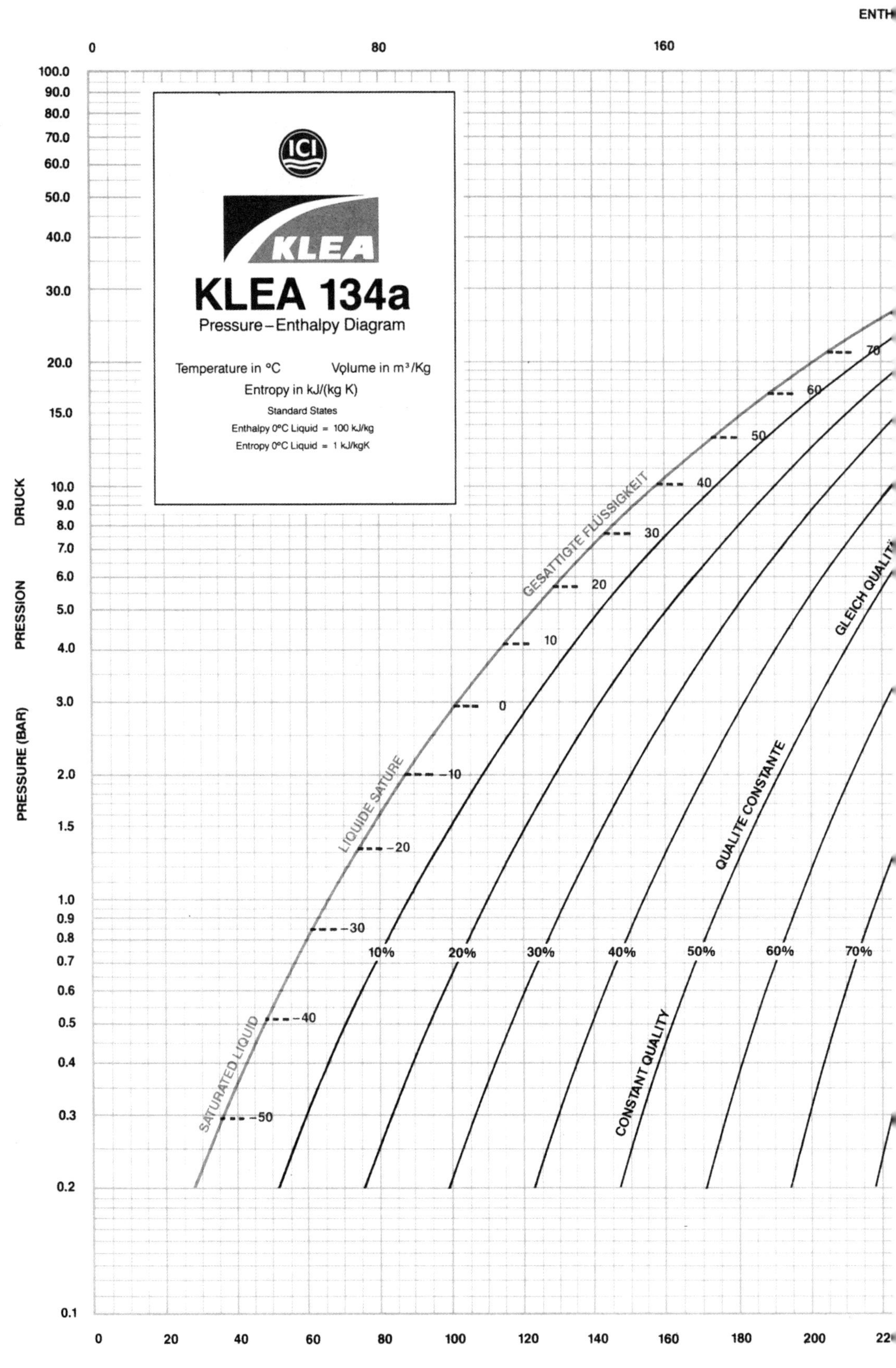

Figure 6.1 Mollier diagram for R134a. (Reproduced with permission of ICI Klea. 'Klea' is a trademark of ICI Chemicals and Polymers Ltd. © ICI Chemicals and Polymers Limited 1994.)

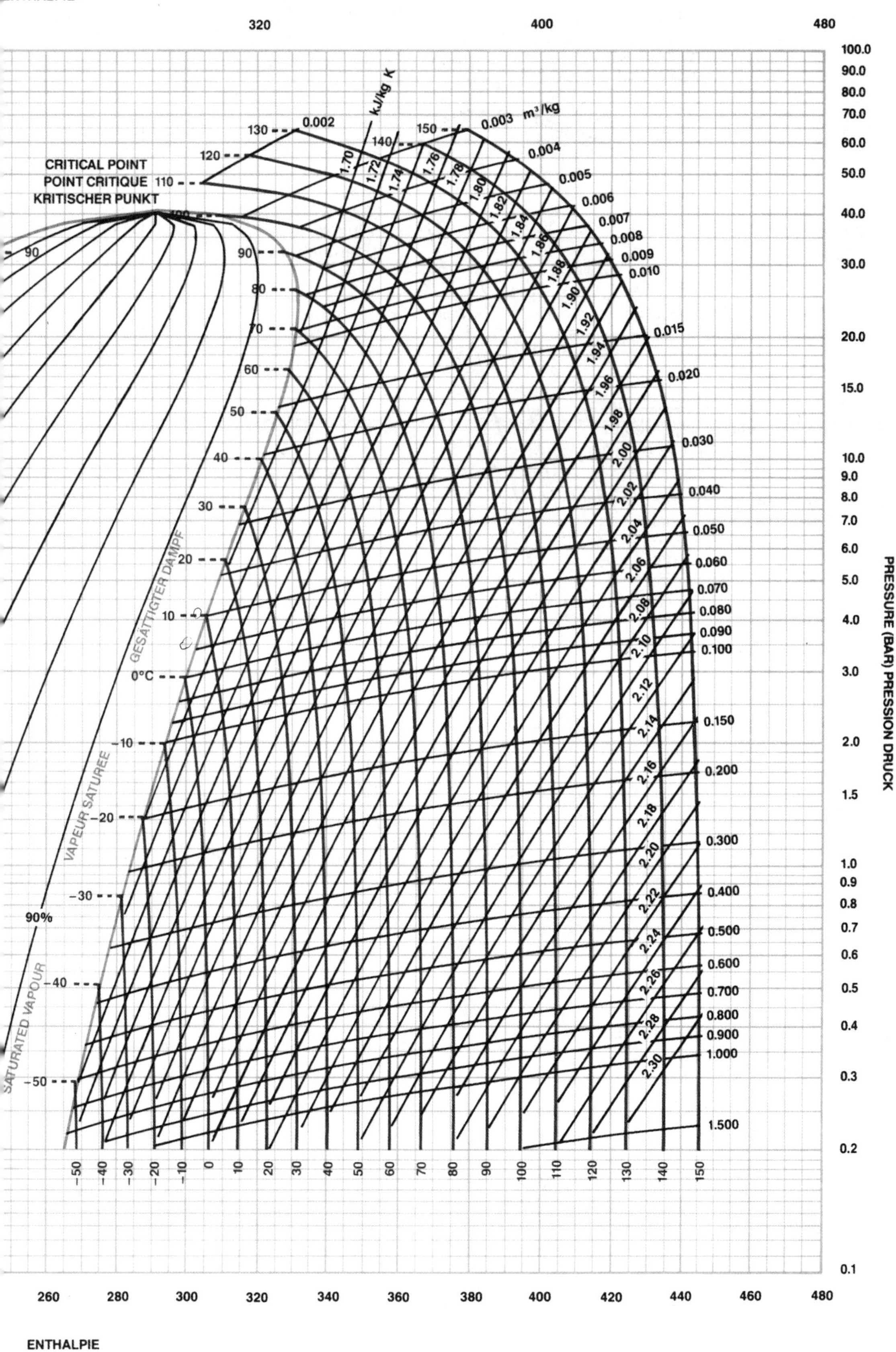
ENTHALPIE
320
400
480
CRITICAL POINT
POINT CRITIQUE
KRITISCHER PUNKT
kJ/kg K
0.002
0.003 m³/kg
PRESSURE (BAR) PRESSION DRUCK
SATURATED VAPOUR
VAPEUR SATUREE
GESÄTTIGTER DAMPF
90%
0°C
260
280
300
320
340
360
380
400
420
440
460
480
ENTHALPIE
CP/34409/31087/6Ed/53/394

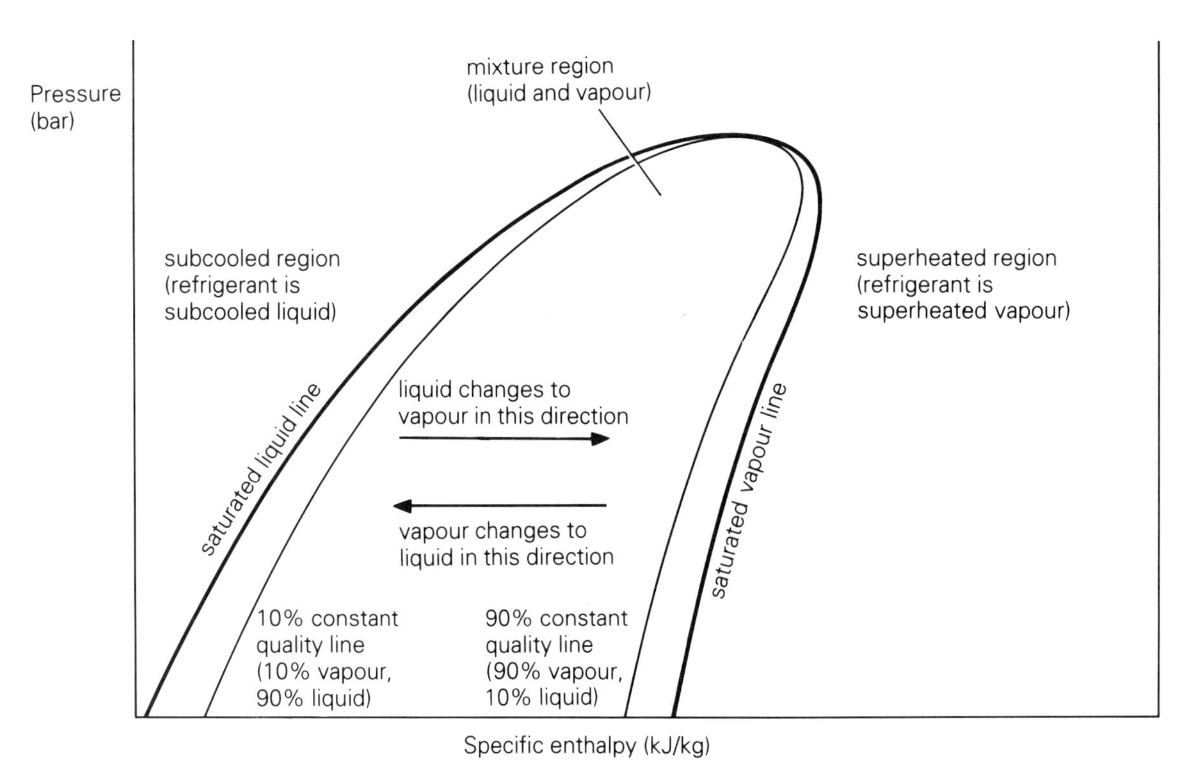

Figure 6.2 The regions of a Mollier diagram.

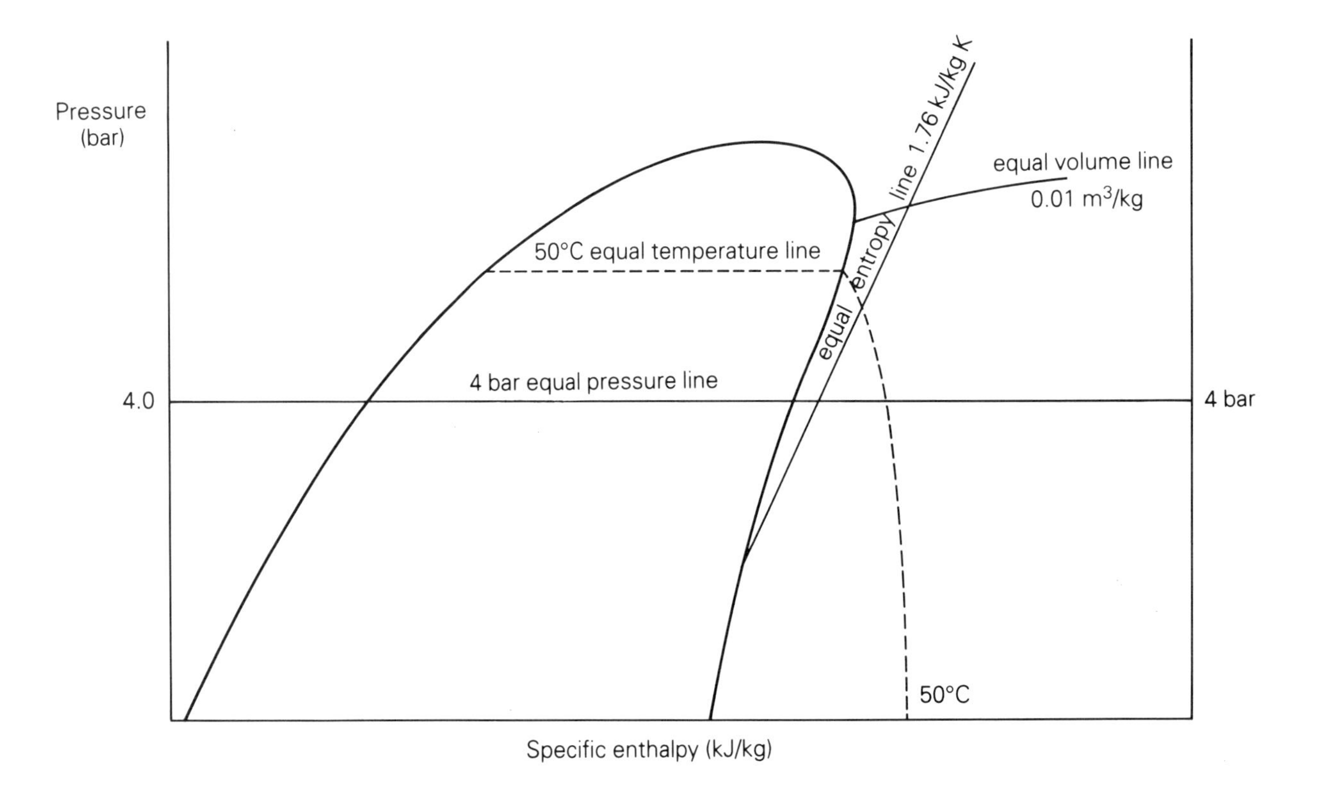

Figure 6.3 Important lines on a Mollier diagram.

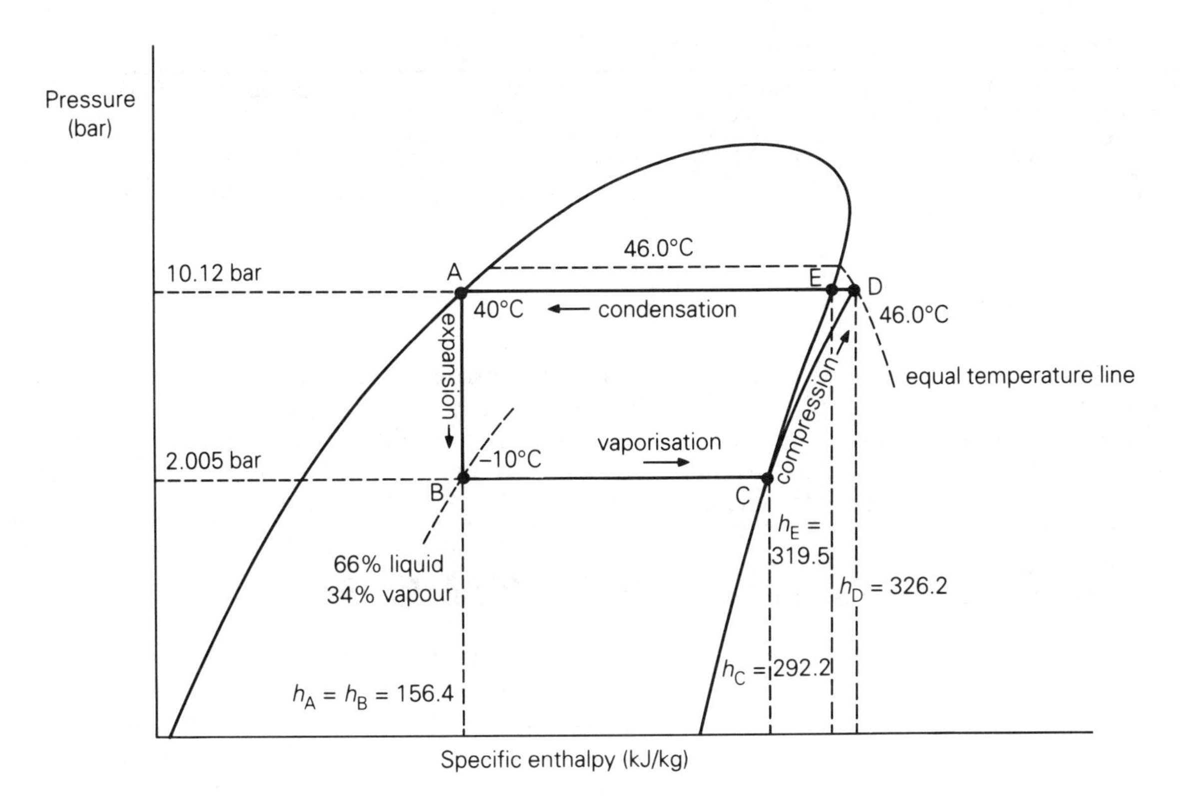

Figure 6.4 A complete vapour-compression cycle.

The simple vapour-compression cycle and the Mollier diagram

The assumption will be made that the vaporising temperature in the evaporator is −10°C and the condensing temperature in the condenser is 40°C. These are the same values as those chosen in Chapter 5 to illustrate typical values of temperature and pressure. The points A, B, C, D and E shown on the simplified Mollier diagram in Figure 6.4 represent a complete cycle of events and these points are also indicated on the refrigerator flow diagram in Figure 6.5.

It is possible to get values from Mollier diagrams which are as accurate as is needed for many purposes. If very accurate figures are required it is necessary to consult refrigerant Thermodynamic Tables. Part of the R134a Table is included at the end of this chapter, as Table 6.1. At 40°C, in the condenser (point A) the refrigerant is a saturated liquid at a pressure of 10.12 bar, enthalpy $h = 156.4$ kJ/kg, specific volume $(v) = 0.872$ L/kg.

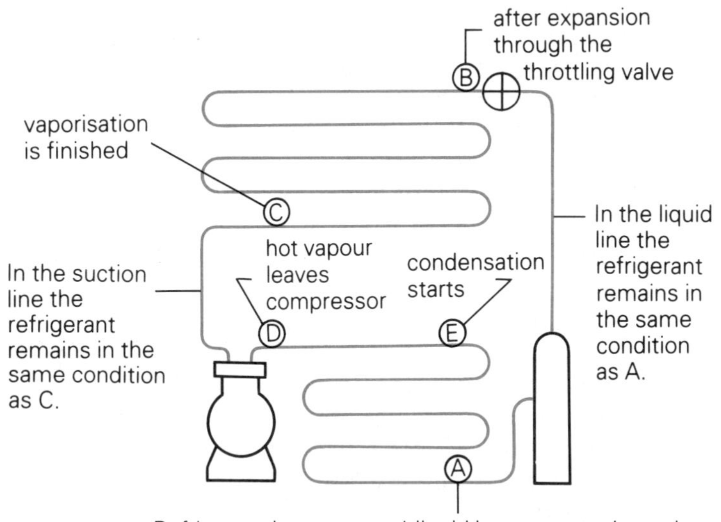

Figure 6.5 Flow diagram for a simple cycle.

($1\ m^3 = 10^3$ L or 1000 L) and specific entropy $(S) = 1.19$ kJ/kg K. These numbers are taken to a maximum of four significant figures and the appropriate line in the table is reproduced below.

HFC 134a Saturation properties (SI units)

Temp. (K)	Absolute pressure (bar)	Volume (L/kg) Liquid	Volume (m³/kg) Vapour	Density (kg/L) Liquid	Density (kg/m³) Vapour	Enthalpy (kJ/kg) Liquid	Enthalpy (kJ/kg) Latent	Enthalpy (kJ/kg) Vapour	Entropy (kJ/kg K) Liquid	Entropy (kJ/kg K) Vapour	Temp. (°C)
313.15	**10.1219**	**0.87178**	0.020083	1.1471	49.792	**156.370**	162.829	319.198	**1.19038**	1.71035	**40**

Note that 40°C is shown as 313.15K. This is because, to 5 significant figures, 0°C is 273.15K (in Chapter 3 the value was given to 3 significant figures). 313.15 − 273.15 = 40°C. For reference the temperature in degrees Celsius is given at the end of the line.

The refrigerant is in the state of a saturated liquid so that point A must lie along the saturated liquid line.

The expansion process

After leaving the condenser the refrigerant flows through the liquid line to the throttling valve. In reality there is a drop in temperature when this happens (see Figure 5.4) but in the simple cycle the temperature is assumed to remain constant. When the liquid passes through the valve it expands very rapidly into the evaporator and vaporises. The temperature drops to −10°C. This type of expansion, which occurs very rapidly, is adiabatic and is sometimes called throttling or **wiredrawing**. With an adiabatic expansion of this kind there is no change of enthalpy but as with all adiabatic expansions there is a drop in temperature. Therefore, the point B is directly below A at a temperature of −10°C. At point B the refrigerant is mainly liquid with some vapour, lying between the 30% and 40% constant quality lines at about 34% vapour, 66% liquid. From Table 6.1, a temperature of −10°C. gives a pressure of 2.005 bar, with h unchanged at 156.4 kJ/kg.

Specific entropy and specific volume are of no interest at point B and in any case, because the refrigerant is a liquid–vapour mixture, the values cannot be found from the *Saturation Properties* part of Table 6.1.

The vaporising process

From B to C the refrigerant vaporises in the evaporator by absorbing heat from the refrigerated space. This heat is transferred by conduction through the metal surface of the evaporator. The heat vaporises all the remaining liquid (66% of the refrigerant) and because it acts as latent heat the temperature remains constant. The pressure is constant throughout the evaporator so that point C is on the same horizontal line as B and lies on the saturated vapour curve. From Table 6.1, with p still equal to 2.005 bar and T still −10°C, h increases to 292.2 kJ/kg, $v = 99.54$ L/kg, $S = 1.732$ kJ/kg. The heat absorbed by the refrigerant from the refrigerated space is given by the change of enthalpy:

$$q_e = h_c - h_b,$$

where q_e is the heat absorbed or **refrigerating effect** in kilojoules per kilogramme.

In this case $q_e = 292.2 - 156.4 = 135.84$ kJ/kg.

The compression process

In reality, as the refrigerant flows along the suction line to the compressor, superheating will occur, as heat flows through the walls of the pipe from the

HFC 134a Saturation properties (SI units)

Temp. (K)	Absolute pressure (bar)	Volume (L/kg) Liquid	Volume (m³/kg) Vapour	Density (kg/L) Liquid	Density (kg/m³) Vapour	Enthalpy (kJ/kg) Liquid	Enthalpy (kJ/kg) Latent	Enthalpy (kJ/kg) Vapour	Entropy (kJ/kg K) Liquid	Entropy (kJ/kg K) Vapour	Temp. (°C)
263.15	**2.00512**	0.75355	0.099541	1.3271	10.046	86.637	205.563	292.200	0.95042	1.73159	**−10**

surrounding atmosphere and increases the temperature. However, in the simple cycle it is assumed that the temperature remains constant and also that there is no change in pressure between the output of the evaporator and the input of the compressor. In the compressor there is a rapid compression which brings the refrigerant to condition D. Again the process is adiabatic but this time it takes place without a change of entropy, so that point D can be located where the line of constant entropy meets the 10.12 bar pressure line. This is in the superheated region and so the *Superheated Vapour* section of Table 6.1 is needed. Because there is no change of entropy, S is still 1.732 kJ/kg K. For a pressure of 10.12 bar, the saturation temperature is 40°C. The table does not give exactly these but for 10.0 bar the saturation temperature is 39.55°C. This is as close as is needed. For example, the fourth line shows an entropy of 1.7333, which to 3 significant figures (1.73) is the same as 1.732. The temperature of the vapour is 319.15K or 46°C, enthalpy $h_D = 326.2$ kJ/kg and $v = 21.26$ L/kg.

Temp. (K)	Absolute pressure (bar)					
	9.8			10.0		
	Satn. temp. = 311.95K 38.80°C			Satn. temp. = 312.70K 39.55°C		
	V	H	S	V	H	S
315.15	0.021247	322.245	1.72217	0.020697	321.761	1.71930
317.15	0.021531	324.458	1.72917	0.020980	323.992	1.72636
319.15	0.021810	326.652	1.73606	**0.021258**	326.204	**1.73331**

The compressor exerts a force on the molecules that make up the refrigerant and moves them through a certain distance during the compression process. It therefore does work on them. By the Law of Conservation of Energy, this is equal to the change in enthalpy that occurs during compression:

$$q_w = h_d - h_c$$

where q_w is the work done during compression per kilogramme of refrigerant, h_c is the specific enthalpy at C and h_d is the specific enthalpy at D. Using the values obtained at the two points:

$$q_w = 326.2 - 292.2 = 34.0 \text{ kJ/kg}$$

The superheated refrigerant now flows along the discharge line, losing some heat through the line.

The condensing process

The refrigerant flows from the discharge line into the upper part of the condenser, losing more heat as it does so, until the temperature drops to 40°C, without change of pressure. Most of the temperature drop of 6°C occurs in the condenser. The cycle is now at point E on the saturated vapour line and so condensation begins. The properties of the saturated vapour, either from the table or the chart are: $p = 10.12$ bar (no change), $T = 40$°C, $h = 319.5$ kJ/kg, $S = 1.712$ kJ/kg and $v = 20.41$ L/kg.

Temp. (K)	Absolute pressure (bar)					
	9.8			10.0		
	Satn. temp. = 311.95K 38.80°C			Satn. temp. = 312.70K 39.55°C		
	V	H	S	V	H	S
SAT N	0.020778	318.660	1.71073	0.020342	318.997	1.71049
313.15	0.020956	320.014	1.71506	**0.020408**	**319.509**	**1.71213**

The heat removed partly in the discharge line but mainly in the top of the condenser, $q_{c1} = h_d - h_e = 326.2 - 319.5 = 6.7$ kJ per kilogramme of refrigerant.

From E to A the process of condensation occurs in the main part of the condenser. This takes place at constant pressure and the total amount of heat given out per kilogramme (q_{c2}) is equal to the change in enthalpy.

$$q_{c2} = h_e - h_a$$
$$= 319.5 - 156.4 = 163.1 \text{ kJ/kg}$$

where h_D is the specific enthalpy of the superheated vapour. The total heat given out by the whole of the condenser is:

$$q_{c1} + q_{c2} = 6.7 + 163.1 = 169.8 \text{ kJ/kg}$$

This is called q_c and $q_c = q_{c1} + q_{c2}$. q_c can also be calculated by direct subtraction

$$h_d - h_a = 326.2 - 156.4 = 169.8 \text{ kJ/kg}$$

The refrigerant has now gone through a complete cycle and the refrigerant is in the same state as it was at the beginning.

At two points during the cycle the refrigerant absorbs energy. These are:

1 in the evaporator, where it takes on heat from the refrigerated space; and
2 in the compressor where heat is taken in as a result of the mechanical work done by the compressor.

Therefore, the total amount of heat taken in during the cycle is the sum of (1) and (2); that is, $q_e + q_w$.

Heat is given out in the condenser (q_c) and

because, by the Law of Conservation of Energy the heat given out is the same as the heat taken in, then:

$$q_c = q_e + q_w$$

where:
$q_e = 135.83$ kJ/kg (see *The vaporising process*),
$q_w = 34.0$ kJ/kg (see *The compression process*),
$q_e + q_w = 169.8$ kJ/kg (this is the same as the value, q_c obtained from the DA part of the cycle, above).

Refrigerating rate

Suppose that m is the mass flow rate of refrigerant through the system in kg/s.

If Q_e, the rate of at which heat is taken in from the refrigerated space or **refrigerating rate**, is set at 1 kW, then:

$$Q_e = mq_e$$

and then the value of m is given by:

$$m = \frac{1}{135.83} = 0.00736 \text{ kg/s}$$

If Q_c is the total heat leaving the condenser every second, then using the same mass flow rate:

$$Q_c = mq_c = 0.00736 \times 169.8 = 1.25 \text{ kW}$$

If Q_w is the total work of compression per second, done in the compressor:

$$Q_w = mq_w = 0.00903 \times 34.0 = 0.307 \text{ kW}$$

Q_w is the power necessary to produce a refrigerating rate of 1 kW. This is a theoretical value and it does not take into account power losses in the compressor. Real power required of the compressor is much greater than this.

Coefficient of performance

Coefficient of performance (C.O.P.) is a measure of the efficiency of the refrigerating cycle:

C.O.P. = heat energy absorbed from *the refrigerated space*

or

C.O.P. = heat energy equivalent of the energy supplied to the compressor

For the simple cycle

$$\text{C.O.P.} = \frac{\text{refrigerating effect}}{\text{heat of compression}} = \frac{q_e}{q_w} = \frac{135.8}{34.0} = 4.0$$

The values chosen for evaporator and condenser temperature can be altered and this has an effect on the coefficient of performance or efficiency of the cycle. First let us look at what happens when the evaporator temperature is changed.

Change of evaporator temperature and cycle efficiency

1 The vaporising temperature is changed to −5°C and the cycle is shown as A, B', C', D', E, in Figure 6.6.
From Table 6.1:
$q_e = 295.2 - 156.4 = 138.8$ kJ/kg
$q_w = 326.2 - 295.2 = 31.0$ kJ/kg
$q_c = 326.2 - 156.4 = 169.8$ kJ/kg
$$C.O.P. = \frac{132.82}{31.0} = 4.5$$

2 The vaporising (evaporator) temperature is changed to −15°C and the cycle is shown as A, B'', C'', D'', E in Figure 6.6.
From Table 6.1
$q_e = 289.2 - 156.4 = 132.8$ kJ/kg
$q_w = 326.2 - 289.2 = 37.0$ kJ/kg
$q_c = 326.2 - 156.4 = 169.8$ kJ/kg
$$C.O.P. = \frac{132.8}{37.0} = 3.6$$
where q_e is the refrigerating effect and this is greater for the 'high temperature' cycle: approximately 138.2 kJ/kg, as opposed to 132.8 kJ/kg.

Looking at the three values obtained for C.O.P., which is a measure of efficiency, it can be seen that the greater the evaporator temperature, the greater is the C.O.P.

The mass flow rate of the refrigerant through the system depends on the refrigerating effect and this is lowest at the −5°C evaporator temperature and

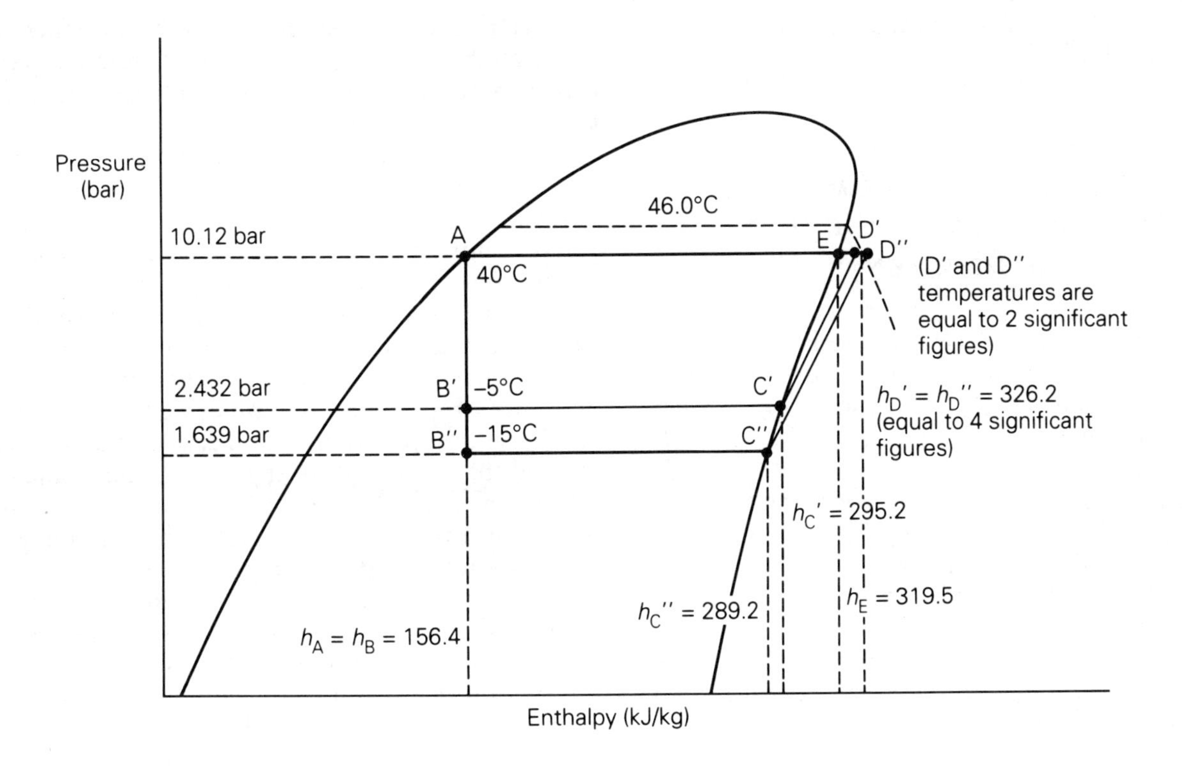

Figure 6.6 Change of evaporator temperature.

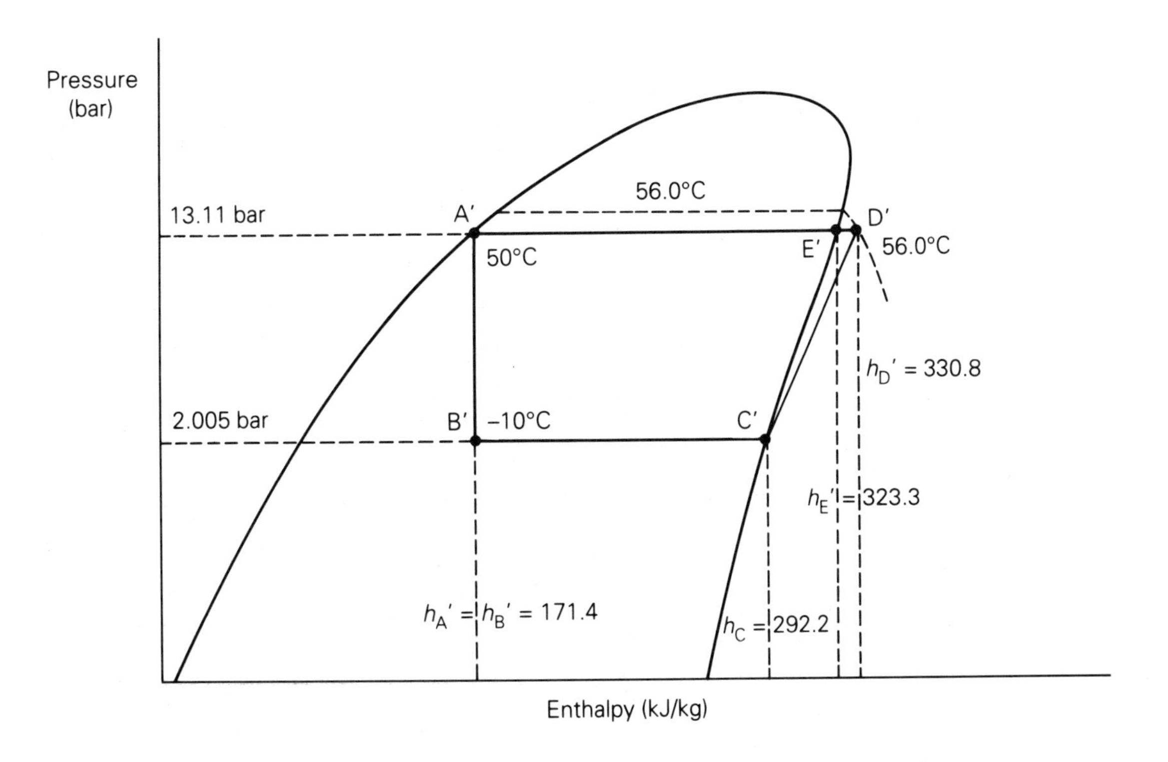

Figure 6.7 Change of condenser temperature.

highest at −15°C. The volume flow rate is also highest at −15°C.

Change of condenser temperature and cycle efficiency

Suppose the condenser temperature is increased to 50°C, while the evaporator temperature remains at the original value of −10°C. This situation is shown in Figure 6.7 and the cycle is labelled A', B',C', D', E'.

From Table 6.1:

$q_e = 292.2 - 171.4 = 120.8$ kJ/kg

$q_w = 330.8 - 292.2 = 38.6$ kJ/kg

$q_c = 330.8 - 171.4 = 159.4$ kJ/kg

$C.O.P. = 3.1$

Note that the refrigerating effect is reduced from 135.8 to 120.8 kJ/kg and the corresponding mass flow rate of refrigerant must therefore be greater. So the volume flow rate must increase and the power used by the compressor goes up. The coefficient of performance decreases.

A refrigeration system should be designed to work at the highest possible evaporator temperature and the lowest possible condenser temperature.

A real refrigerating cycle departs from the simple one described in this chapter in a number of ways. Some of these ways have been described in the text. For example, the refrigerant travelling along the suction line from the evaporator to the compressor superheats in a real cycle. Refrigerant travelling from the condenser to the evaporator along the liquid line subcools. Another departure is that of pressure drop along the pipes, evaporator and condenser, caused by friction between the refrigerant and the inner walls of the system and inside the refrigerant itself. In the simple cycle it is assumed that the pressure only changes at the beginning of the evaporator and in the compressor. In a real refrigerator, pressure falls as the refrigerant flows through the evaporator and through the condenser. It also falls in the liquid line, the discharge line and the suction line. Even in the compressor the pressure drops to a lower value than its theoretical one owing to friction. A more detailed treatment of real refrigerating cycles is beyond the scope of this book.

Table 6.1 HFC 134a Saturation properties (SI units)

Temp. (K)	Absolute pressure (bar)	Volume (L/kg)	Volume (m^3/kg)	Density (kg/L)	Density (kg/m^3)	Enthalpy (kJ/kg)			Entropy (kJ/kg K)		Temp. (°C)
		Liquid	Vapour	Liquid	Vapour	Liquid	Latent	Vapour	Liquid	Vapour	
263.15	2.00512	0.75355	0.099541	1.3271	10.046	86.637	205.563	292.200	0.95042	1.73159	−10
264.15	2.08541	0.75535	0.095884	1.3239	10.429	87.962	204.838	292.800	0.95543	1.73089	−9
265.15	2.16817	0.75716	0.092389	1.3207	10.824	89.290	204.109	293.399	0.96042	1.73021	−8
266.15	2.25344	0.75899	0.089047	1.3175	11.230	90.620	203.376	293.996	0.96540	1.72954	−7
267.15	2.34129	0.76084	0.085850	1.3143	11.648	91.952	202.639	294.591	0.97038	1.72890	−6
268.15	2.43175	0.76270	0.082790	1.3111	12.079	93.287	201.898	295.185	0.97534	1.72827	−5
269.15	2.52488	0.76458	0.079862	1.3079	12.522	94.625	201.152	295.777	0.98029	1.72765	−4
270.15	2.62074	0.76648	0.077058	1.3047	12.977	95.965	200.403	296.368	0.98523	1.72705	−3
271.15	2.71937	0.76839	0.074372	1.3014	13.446	97.307	199.649	296.956	0.99016	1.72647	−2
272.15	2.82083	0.77033	0.071798	1.2981	13.928	98.652	198.891	297.543	0.99509	1.72590	−1
273.15	2.92517	0.77228	0.069331	1.2949	14.423	100.000	198.128	298.128	1.00000	1.72535	0
274.15	3.03244	0.77425	0.066966	1.2916	14.933	101.350	197.361	298.711	1.00490	1.72481	1
275.15	3.14271	0.77624	0.064697	1.2883	15.457	102.703	196.589	299.293	1.00980	1.72428	2
276.15	3.25602	0.77826	0.062520	1.2849	15.995	104.059	195.813	299.872	1.01468	1.72377	3
277.15	3.37242	0.78029	0.060430	1.2816	16.548	105.417	195.032	300.449	1.01956	1.72327	4
278.15	3.49198	0.78234	0.058424	1.2782	17.116	106.778	194.246	301.024	1.02443	1.72278	5
279.15	3.61474	0.78442	0.056498	1.2748	17.700	108.142	193.455	301.596	1.02929	1.72230	6
280.15	3.74077	0.78651	0.054647	1.2714	18.299	109.508	192.659	302.167	1.03414	1.72184	7
281.15	3.87013	0.78863	0.052868	1.2680	18.915	110.877	191.858	302.735	1.03898	1.72138	8
282.15	4.00286	0.79077	0.051158	1.2646	19.547	112.249	191.051	303.301	1.04382	1.72094	9

Table 6.1 (continued) **HFC 134a saturation properties (SI units)**

Temp. (K)	Absolute pressure (bar)	Volume (L/kg)	Volume (m^3/kg)	Density (kg/L)	Density (kg/m^3)	Enthalpy (kJ/kg)			Entropy (kJ/kg K)		Temp. (°C)
		Liquid	Vapour	Liquid	Vapour	Liquid	Latent	Vapour	Liquid	Vapour	
283.15	4.13902	0.79293	0.049514	1.2611	20.196	113.624	190.239	303.864	1.04864	1.72051	10
284.15	4.27868	0.79512	0.047933	1.2577	20.863	115.002	189.422	304.424	1.05346	1.72009	11
285.15	4.42188	0.79733	0.046411	1.2542	21.547	116.383	188.600	304.983	1.05827	1.71968	12
286.15	4.56870	0.79956	0.044947	1.2507	22.248	117.766	187.772	305.538	1.06307	1.71927	13
287.15	4.71918	0.80182	0.043537	1.2472	22.969	119.153	186.938	306.091	1.06787	1.71888	14
288.15	4.87339	0.80411	0.042180	1.2436	23.708	120.543	186.098	306.641	1.07266	1.71849	15
289.15	5.03138	0.80642	0.040872	1.2400	24.467	121.935	185.252	307.188	1.07744	1.71812	16
290.15	5.19322	0.80876	0.039612	1.2365	25.245	123.331	184.401	307.732	1.08221	1.71775	17
291.15	5.35897	0.81113	0.038398	1.2329	26.043	124.730	183.543	308.272	1.08698	1.71738	18
292.15	5.52868	0.81352	0.037227	1.2292	26.862	126.132	182.679	308.810	1.09174	1.71703	19
293.15	5.70243	0.81595	0.036099	1.2256	27.702	127.537	181.808	309.345	1.09649	1.71668	20
294.15	5.88026	0.81840	0.035010	1.2219	28.563	128.945	180.931	309.876	1.10124	1.71633	21
295.15	6.06224	0.82088	0.033959	1.2182	29.447	130.356	180.048	310.404	1.10598	1.71600	22
296.15	6.24844	0.82340	0.032946	1.2145	30.353	131.771	179.157	310.928	1.11071	1.71566	23
297.15	6.43892	0.82594	0.031967	1.2107	31.282	133.189	178.260	311.449	1.11544	1.71534	24
298.15	6.63374	0.82852	0.031022	1.2070	32.235	134.611	177.356	311.966	1.12016	1.71501	25
299.15	6.83297	0.83113	0.030110	1.2032	33.212	136.035	176.444	312.479	1.12487	1.71469	26
300.15	7.03666	0.83378	0.029228	1.1994	34.214	137.464	175.525	312.989	1.12958	1.71437	27
301.15	7.24489	0.83646	0.028376	1.1955	35.241	138.896	174.598	313.494	1.13429	1.71406	28
302.15	7.45773	0.83918	0.027553	1.1916	36.294	140.331	173.664	313.995	1.13899	1.71375	29
303.15	7.67523	0.84194	0.026757	1.1877	37.373	141.770	172.722	314.492	1.14368	1.71344	30
304.15	7.89746	0.84473	0.025987	1.1838	38.480	143.212	171.772	314.985	1.14837	1.71313	31
305.15	8.12449	0.84756	0.025243	1.1799	39.615	144.659	170.814	315.473	1.15305	1.71283	32
306.15	8.35640	0.85043	0.024523	1.1759	40.779	146.109	169.847	315.956	1.15773	1.71252	33
307.15	8.59324	0.85335	0.023826	1.1719	41.972	147.563	168.872	316.435	1.16241	1.71221	34
308.15	8.83509	0.85631	0.023151	1.1678	43.195	149.020	167.888	316.908	1.16708	1.71191	35
309.15	9.08202	0.85931	0.022498	1.1637	44.449	150.482	166.895	317.377	1.17175	1.71160	36
310.15	9.33409	0.86236	0.021865	1.1596	45.735	151.948	165.893	317.841	1.17641	1.71129	37
311.15	9.59139	0.86545	0.021252	1.1555	47.054	153.418	164.881	318.299	1.18107	1.71098	38
312.15	9.85397	0.86859	0.020659	1.1513	48.406	154.892	163.860	318.751	1.18573	1.71067	39
313.15	10.1219	0.87178	0.020083	1.1471	49.792	156.370	162.829	319.198	1.19038	1.71035	40
314.15	10.3953	0.87503	0.019526	1.1428	51.214	157.852	161.787	319.639	1.19503	1.71003	41
315.15	10.6742	0.87832	0.018985	1.1385	52.673	159.339	160.735	320.074	1.19968	1.70971	42
316.15	10.9587	0.88168	0.018461	1.1342	54.168	160.831	159.672	320.503	1.20433	1.70938	43
317.15	11.2488	0.88508	0.017952	1.1298	55.703	162.327	158.598	320.926	1.20897	1.70904	44
318.15	11.5447	0.88855	0.017459	1.1254	57.277	163.828	157.513	321.341	1.21361	1.70870	45
319.15	11.8464	0.89208	0.016980	1.1210	58.892	165.334	156.416	321.750	1.21825	1.70836	46
320.15	12.1540	0.89567	0.016516	1.1165	60.549	166.845	155.307	322.152	1.22290	1.70800	47
321.15	12.4676	0.89932	0.016064	1.1119	62.249	168.361	154.186	322.547	1.22754	1.70764	48
322.15	12.7872	0.90305	0.015626	1.1074	63.995	169.882	153.052	322.934	1.23217	1.70727	49
323.15	13.1130	0.90684	0.015201	1.1027	65.786	171.409	151.904	323.313	1.23681	1.70689	50
324.15	13.4450	0.91070	0.014787	1.0981	67.626	172.941	150.744	323.684	1.24146	1.70650	51
325.15	13.7832	0.91464	0.014385	1.0933	69.514	174.478	149.569	324.047	1.24610	1.70610	52
326.15	14.1279	0.91866	0.013995	1.0885	71.454	176.022	148.379	324.401	1.25074	1.70568	53
327.15	14.4791	0.92277	0.013615	1.0837	73.447	177.572	147.175	424.747	1.25539	1.70525	54
328.15	14.8368	0.92695	0.013246	1.0788	75.494	179.128	145.955	325.083	1.26003	1.70481	55
329.15	15.2012	0.93123	0.012887	1.0739	77.598	180.690	144.719	325.409	1.26468	1.70436	56
330.15	15.5724	0.93560	0.012538	1.0688	79.761	182.259	143.466	325.725	1.26934	1.70389	57
331.15	15.9504	0.94006	0.012198	1.0638	81.984	183.835	142.196	326.032	1.27400	1.70340	58
332.15	16.3353	0.94463	0.011867	1.0586	84.271	185.419	140.908	326.327	1.27866	1.70289	59

Table 6.1 (continued) HFC 134a Properties of superheated vapour (SI units)

Temp. (K)	Absolute pressure (bar)												Temp. (°C)
	9.8			10.0			10.5			11.0			
	Satn. temp. = 311.95K 38.80°C			Satn. temp. = 312.70K 39.55°C			Satn. temp. = 314.53K 41.38°C			Satn. temp. = 316.29K 43.14°C			
	V	H	S	V	H	S	V	H	S	V	H	S	
SAT N	0.020778	318.660	1.71073	0.020342	318.997	1.71049	0.019320	319.804	1.70991	0.018387	320.564	1.70933	
313.15	0.020956	320.014	1.71506	0.020408	319.509	1.71213							40
315.15	0.021247	322.245	1.72217	0.020697	321.761	1.71930	0.019408	320.519	1.71218				42
317.15	0.021531	324.458	1.72917	0.020980	323.992	1.72636	0.019689	322.799	1.71939	0.018506	321.560	1.71248	44
319.15	0.021810	326.652	1.73606	0.021258	326.204	1.73331	0.019963	325.055	1.72648	0.018778	323.867	1.71973	46
321.15	0.022084	328.831	1.74287	0.021530	328.398	1.74016	0.020232	327.292	1.73347	0.019045	326.149	1.72685	48
323.15	0.022353	330.996	1.74959	0.021797	330.578	1.74693	0.020496	329.510	1.74036	0.019305	328.410	1.73387	50
325.15	0.022618	333.148	1.75623	0.022060	332.743	1.75361	0.020754	331.712	1.74715	0.019561	330.651	1.74079	52
327.15	0.022879	335.289	1.76279	0.022319	334.897	1.76021	0.021008	333.900	1.75385	0.019811	332.875	1.74760	54
329.15	0.023136	337.419	1.76928	0.022574	337.040	1.76674	0.021258	336.074	1.76048	0.020057	335.083	1.75433	56
331.15	0.023390	339.541	1.77571	0.022825	339.172	1.77320	0.021504	338.236	1.76703	0.020299	337.277	1.76098	58
333.15	0.023640	341.654	1.78207	0.023073	341.296	1.77960	0.021747	340.388	1.77351	0.020537	339.458	1.76755	60
335.15	0.023888	343.760	1.78838	0.023318	343.413	1.78593	0.021986	342.531	1.77992	0.020772	341.629	1.77404	62
337.15	0.024132	345.860	1.79462	0.023560	345.522	1.79221	0.022222	344.665	1.78627	0.021003	343.789	1.78047	64
339.15	0.024374	347.954	1.80082	0.023799	347.625	1.79843	0.022456	346.791	1.79256	0.021231	345.940	1.78683	66
341.15	0.024613	350.043	1.80696	0.024035	349.723	1.80459	0.022686	348.911	1.79879	0.021456	348.083	1.79313	68
343.15	0.024850	352.128	1.81305	0.024269	351.816	1.81071	0.022914	351.025	1.80497	0.021678	350.219	1.79937	70
345.15	0.025084	354.209	1.81910	0.024501	353.905	1.81678	0.023139	353.134	1.81110	0.021898	352.349	1.80556	72
347.15	0.025316	356.287	1.82510	0.024731	355.990	1.82280	0.023362	355.238	1.81717	0.022116	354.473	1.81170	74
349.15	0.025547	358.363	1.83106	0.024958	358.072	1.82878	0.023583	357.338	1.82321	0.022331	356.592	1.81779	76
351.15	0.025775	360.436	1.83698	0.025183	360.152	1.83472	0.023802	359.435	1.82920	0.022544	358.707	1.82382	78
353.15	0.026001	362.507	1.84287	0.025407	362.230	1.84062	0.024019	361.529	1.83514	0.022755	360.818	1.82982	80
355.15	0.026226	364.577	1.84871	0.025629	364.306	1.84649	0.024234	363.621	1.84105	0.022964	362.926	1.83577	82
357.15	0.026449	366.646	1.85452	0.025849	366.381	1.85231	0.024447	365.710	1.84692	0.023171	365.031	1.84168	84
359.15	0.026671	368.715	1.86029	0.026068	368.454	1.85810	0.024659	367.799	1.85275	0.023377	367.134	1.84755	86
361.15	0.026891	370.783	1.86604	0.026285	370.528	1.86386	0.024869	369.886	1.85854	0.023581	369.235	1.85339	88
363.15	0.027109	372.851	1.87175	0.026500	372.601	1.86958	0.025078	371.972	1.86430	0.023783	371.335	1.85919	90
365.15	0.027326	374.919	1.87743	0.026714	374.674	1.87528	0.025285	374.058	1.87003	0.023984	373.434	1.86495	92
367.15	0.027542	376.988	1.88308	0.026927	376.748	1.88094	0.025490	376.143	1.87573	0.024183	375.532	1.87068	94
369.15	0.027757	379.058	1.88870	0.027139	378.822	1.88658	0.025695	378.229	1.88139	0.024381	377.630	1.87638	96
371.15	0.027970	381.129	1.89429	0.027349	380.897	1.89218	0.025898	380.316	1.88703	0.024578	379.728	1.88205	98
373.15	0.028183	383.201	1.89986	0.027558	382.974	1.89776	0.026100	382.403	1.89264	0.024773	381.826	1.88768	100
375.15	0.028394	385.274	1.90541	0.027766	385.052	1.90331	0.026301	384.491	1.89822	0.024968	383.924	1.89329	102
377.15	0.028604	387.350	1.91092	0.027973	387.131	1.90884	0.026501	386.580	1.90377	0.025161	386.024	1.89887	104
379.15	0.028813	389.427	1.91642	0.028179	389.212	1.91435	0.026699	388.670	1.90930	0.025353	388.124	1.90443	106
381.15	0.029022	391.507	1.92189	0.028384	391.295	1.91982	0.026897	390.763	1.91480	0.025544	390.226	1.90996	108

CHECK YOUR UNDERSTANDING

- The most used diagram for the vapour-compression cycle is the pressure–enthalpy diagram or Mollier diagram.
- The temperature–entropy diagram is sometimes used.
- On the left-hand side of the Mollier diagram is the subcooled (liquid) region, in the middle is the mixture region (of liquid and vapour) and on the right-hand side is the superheated region.
- Refrigeration rate and coefficient of performance were found for a number of cycles with different evaporator and condenser temperatures.
- At point A of the cycle (condenser output) the refrigerant is a saturated liquid.
- Point B (evaporator input) is directly below A and the refigerant is mainly liquid with some vapour. Between A and B there is a temperature drop.
- Between B and C (evaporator output) the refigerant vaporises completely.
- Between C and D (compressor output) there is a rapid (adiabatic) compression in the compressor, there is a temperature rise and the vapour becomes superheated at D.
- Between D and E (condenser input) the refrigerant drops in temperature but the pressure remains the same.
- From E to A condensation occurs in the condenser.
- The points A, B, C, D and E represent a simplified cycle.
- Refrigerating rate is the rate at which heat is taken in from the refrigerated space.

Table 6.1 (continued) **HFC 134a Properties of superheated vapour (SI units)**

Temp. (K)	Absolute pressure (bar)												Temp. (°C)
	11.5			12.0			12.5			13.0			
	Satn. temp. = 318.00K 44.85°C			Satn. temp. = 319.65K 46.50°C			Satn. temp. = 321.25K 48.10°C			Satn. temp. = 322.81K 49.66°C			
	V	H	S	V	H	S	V	H	S	V	H	S	
SAT N	0.017532	321.280	1.70876	0.016745	321.953	1.70818	0.016019	322.587	1.70760	0.015346	323.183	1.70702	
319.15	0.017688	322.634	1.71301										46
321.15	0.017953	324.966	1.72029	0.016943	323.739	1.71376							48
323.15	0.018211	327.273	1.72745	0.017201	326.097	1.72107	0.016264	324.876	1.71471	0.015390	323.607	1.70833	50
325.15	0.018464	329.557	1.73450	0.017453	328.427	1.72826	0.016515	327.258	1.72206	0.015642	326.045	1.71586	52
327.15	0.018712	331.820	1.74144	0.017699	330.733	1.73533	0.016760	329.610	1.72927	0.015887	328.449	1.72323	54
329.15	0.018955	334.064	1.74828	0.017939	333.017	1.74229	0.016999	331.937	1.73636	0.016125	330.823	1.73046	56
331.15	0.019194	336.293	1.75503	0.018175	335.282	1.74915	0.017233	334.242	1.74334	0.016358	333.171	1.73757	58
333.15	0.019428	338.506	1.76169	0.018407	337.529	1.75592	0.017462	336.526	1.75022	0.016586	335.495	1.74457	60
335.15	0.019658	340.706	1.76827	0.018634	339.761	1.76260	0.017687	338.792	1.75700	0.016809	337.797	1.75146	62
337.15	0.019886	342.894	1.77478	0.018858	341.979	1.76920	0.017908	341.041	1.76369	0.017027	340.080	1.75825	64
339.15	0.020109	345.071	1.78122	0.019078	344.184	1.77572	0.018125	343.276	1.77030	0.017242	342.347	1.76495	66
341.15	0.020330	347.239	1.78760	0.019294	346.378	1.78217	0.018338	345.498	1.77683	0.017452	344.598	1.77157	68
343.15	0.020548	349.399	1.79391	0.019508	348.562	1.78855	0.018549	347.708	1.78329	0.017660	346.836	1.77811	70
345.15	0.020763	351.550	1.80016	0.019719	350.736	1.79487	0.018756	349.907	1.78968	0.017864	349.061	1.78458	72
347.15	0.020975	353.695	1.80636	0.019927	352.903	1.80113	0.018960	352.097	1.79601	0.018065	351.275	1.79097	74
349.15	0.021185	355.834	1.81250	0.020133	355.063	1.80733	0.019162	354.278	1.80227	0.018263	353.479	1.79730	76
351.15	0.021393	357.967	1.81859	0.020336	357.216	1.81348	0.019361	356.452	1.80848	0.018459	355.674	1.80357	78
353.15	0.021599	360.096	1.82464	0.020537	359.363	1.81958	0.019558	358.619	1.81463	0.018652	357.862	1.80979	80
355.15	0.021803	362.221	1.83064	0.020736	361.506	1.82563	0.019753	360.780	1.82074	0.018843	360.042	1.81594	82
357.15	0.022004	364.343	1.83659	0.020933	363.644	1.83163	0.019945	362.935	1.82679	0.019032	362.216	1.82205	84
359.15	0.022204	366.461	1.84251	0.021128	365.778	1.83759	0.020136	365.086	1.83279	0.019219	364.385	1.82810	86
361.15	0.022403	368.577	1.84838	0.021321	367.910	1.84351	0.020325	367.233	1.83876	0.019404	366.548	1.83411	88
363.15	0.022599	370.691	1.85422	0.021513	370.038	1.84939	0.020512	369.377	1.84467	0.019587	368.707	1.84007	90
365.15	0.022794	372.803	1.86002	0.021703	372.164	1.85523	0.020697	371.518	1.85055	0.019768	370.863	1.84599	92
367.15	0.022988	374.914	1.86579	0.021891	374.288	1.86103	0.020881	373.656	1.85639	0.019948	373.015	1.85187	94
369.15	0.023180	377.024	1.87152	0.022079	376.411	1.86679	0.021064	375.792	1.86219	0.020126	375.165	1.85771	96
371.15	0.023371	379.134	1.87722	0.022264	378.533	1.87253	0.021245	377.926	1.86796	0.020302	377.312	1.86351	98
373.15	0.023561	381.243	1.88289	0.022449	380.654	1.87823	0.021424	380.059	1.87369	0.020478	379.458	1.86928	100
375.15	0.023749	383.352	1.88852	0.022632	382.775	1.88389	0.021602	382.192	1.87939	0.020651	381.602	1.87501	102
377.15	0.023937	385.462	1.89413	0.022814	384.896	1.88953	0.021780	384.323	1.88506	0.020824	383.746	1.88070	104
379.15	0.024123	387.573	1.89971	0.022995	387.016	1.89514	0.021955	386.455	1.89070	0.020995	385.888	1.88637	106
381.15	0.024308	389.684	1.90527	0.023174	389.138	1.90072	0.022130	388.587	1.89630	0.021166	388.030	1.89201	108

- $\text{C.O.P} = \dfrac{\text{refrigerating effect}}{\text{heat of compression}}$.
- A refrigeration system should be designed to work at the highest possible evaporator temperature and the lowest possible condenser temperature.

REVISION EXERCISES AND QUESTIONS

1 For the following condenser temperatures find the pressure and the specific enthalpy, at the saturated liquid stage, from the Thermodynamic Tables for R134a. Take 0°C as 273.15K.
   i) 45°C,
   ii) 35°C,
   iii) 42°C.

2 For the following evaporator temperatures find the pressure and the specific enthalpy, at the saturated liquid stage, from the Thermodynamic Tables for R134a. Take 0°C as 273.15K.
   i) 5°C,
   ii) 0°C,
   iii) −3°C,
   iv) −8°C.

3 Explain the term *refrigerating effect* as applied to a refrigerating cycle.

4 What is meant by the *coefficient of performance* of a refrigerating cycle?

5 Distinguish between the adiabatic change that occurs at the throttling valve and that which occurs at the compressor.

7 Other forms of refrigeration

Introduction

Other forms of refrigeration include the simple air cycle, the absorption cycle and thermoelectric refrigeration.

The simple air cycle

Probably the most straightforward form of refrigeration is the **simple air cycle** in which air is compressed by using a compressor. In this respect it is similar to the vapour compression cycle, where a compressor is also used. The compressed air is then passed through a small hole and allowed to expand into the refrigerated space, causing a gain in potential energy of the molecules and hence a loss in kinetic energy. The loss in kinetic energy means a drop in temperature and the refrigerated space cools. The process is essentially the same as that which occurs when refrigerant enters the evaporator in the vapour-compression cycle, except there is no change of phase.

A form of air cycle is used in order to air condition aircraft. Air from outside the aircraft is compressed in the engine and this compression causes a rise in temperature. Cooling is then produced by the forward motion of the aircraft. Air, moving very fast in relation to the fuselage, flows into a tube and from there into a **heat exchanger**, where it cools the compressed air. This fast moving air used for cooling is called ram air. The compressed air then passes into a compressor where it is compressed still more and again it is cooled using ram air. Further cooling by expansion, ready for air conditioning, is produced by a rotating machine called an **expansion turbine**. Some of the water is removed and the conditioned air is passed into the cabin of the aircraft. Exhaust air which has passed through the cabin is released back into the atmosphere.

The absorption cycle

Another refrigeration cycle is the **absorption cycle**. This differs from the vapour-compression cycle in that it has no compressor. Figure 7.1 shows an absorption system.

The compressor is replaced by an **absorber** and **generator**. The refrigerant is often ammonia, dissolved in a liquid known as the **absorbent** which is often water. Liquid ammonia from the condenser passes through a valve, expands into the evaporator, and becomes a vapour. This evaporation causes a drop in temperature and heat from the surrounding space flows in. The surrounding space is cooled.

The pressure of the ammonia vapour in the evaporator is greater than that of the combined ammonia vapour and water vapour above the liquid in the absorber. Ammonia vapour therefore flows to the absorber and dissolves in the water. In effect the ammonia is sucked into the absorber. As the ammonia condenses, latent heat is released and the temperature rises. Absorbers often have cooling fins in order to lose heat.

Water, from the absorber, containing dissolved ammonia is pumped to the generator. The pump

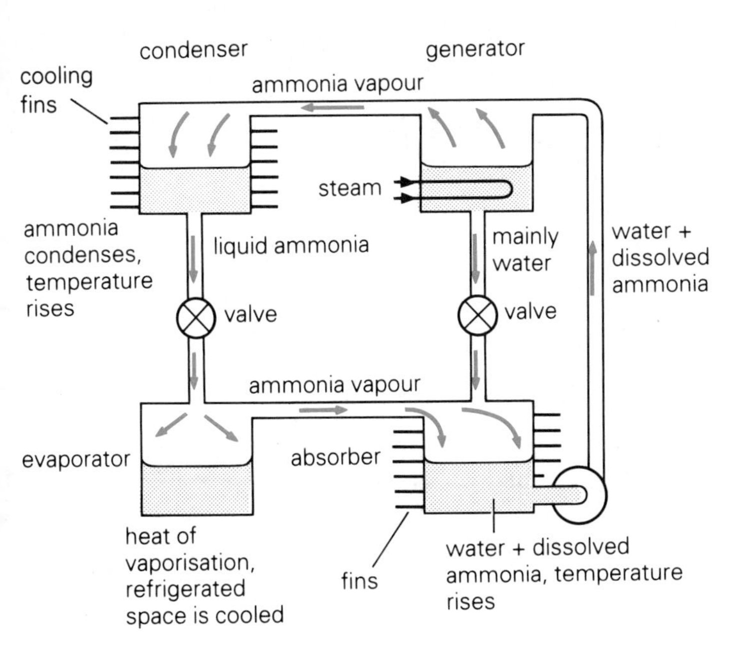

Figure 7.1 An absorption system.

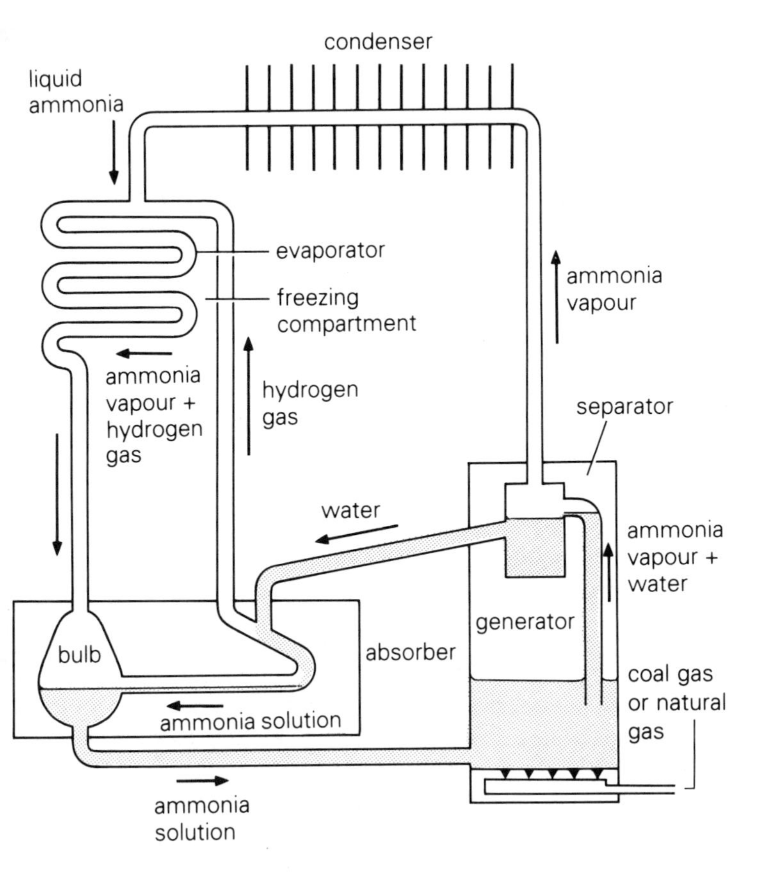

Figure 7.2 A gas refrigerator.

needed to do this is fairly small and requires little electrical power. The generator is heated, sometimes by using steam, sometimes with a naked flame. The heat releases the dissolved ammonia which passes on to the condenser and the cycle is completed. The absorbent left behind, mainly water but with some ammonia still dissolved in it, returns to the absorber through a valve which reduces the pressure.

Comparing absorption refrigeration to the vapour-compression type, the absorber is equivalent to the input of the compressor (from the evaporator) and the generator compares to the discharge side. Absorption refrigeration can be economical in situations where a cheap supply of spare steam is available. This happens in some industrial plants.

Domestic absorption refigerators are often used where there is no electricity supply, such as in caravans and on camp sites. The flame needed to heat the generator comes from liquefied petroleum gas. There is no pump and hydrogen gas is used to keep the ammonia refrigerant circulating through the system. Figure 7.2 shows a small absorption refrigerator.

The hydrogen is contained in the evaporator and it mixes with the ammonia vapour. The mixture falls into the absorber bulb where the ammonia dissolves in the water. The hydrogen is unaffected by the water and it circulates back to the evaporator.

Air conditioning systems sometimes use lithium bromide absorption. Here the absorbent is lithium bromide and the refrigerant is water. Because of this the evaporator temperature must not go below 0°C, otherwise the refrigerant will freeze.

Thermoelectric refrigeration

If two junctions are made up using two different metals and one of the junctions is heated, then an e.m.f. is generated, a current flows and the device can be used as a thermometer. This type of thermometer is a **thermocouple** thermometer. A thermocouple thermometer is shown in Figure 7.3.

Instead of heating one of the junctions, a d.c. supply (an e.m.f.) can be connected to the thermocouple so that a current flows through it. When this happens, one of the junctions is warmed and the other cooled. This effect is called the **Peltier effect**. If the e.m.f. is reversed, then the effect reverses

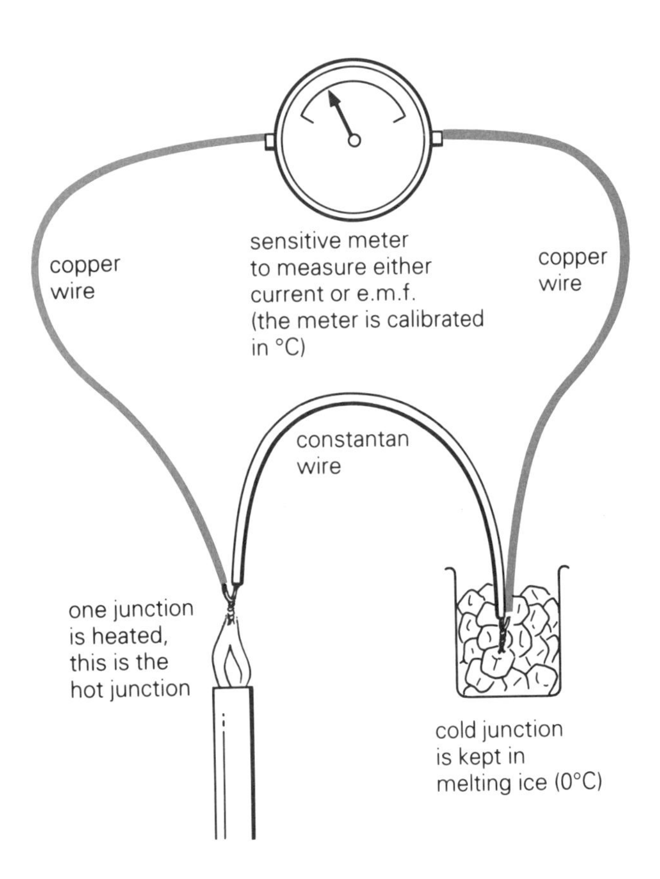

Figure 7.3 A thermocouple thermometer.

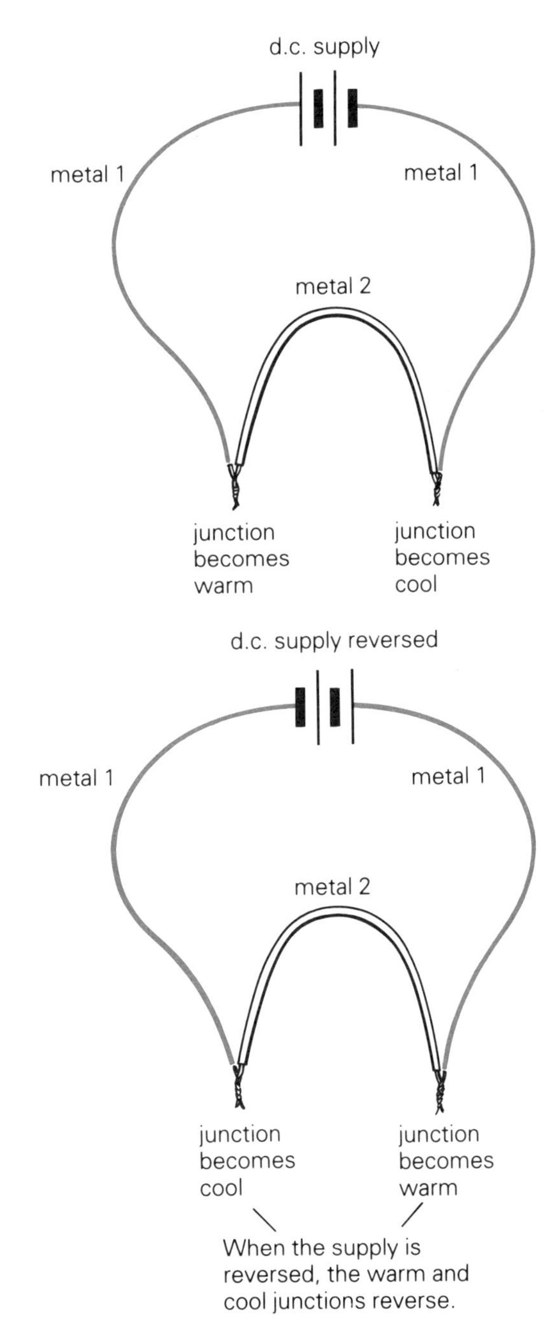

Figure 7.4 The Peltier effect.

itself and the junction that was warmed is now cooled. The former cool junction is warmed (see Figure 7.4).

One of the junctions is always warmed and the other is always cooled, but which loses and which gains heat depends on the direction of the current from the supply.

Today it is possible to make refrigerators using the Peltier effect. Instead of using metals to make the junctions, materials called **semiconductors** are used. Semiconductors are materials that do not conduct electricity as well as metals but conduct much better than insulators, such as glass or rubber. Semiconductors come in between metals and insulators in their ability to conduct electricity. The most commonly used semiconductor is silicon and circuits called 'silicon chips' are used to make computers. Refrigeration produced by the Peltier effect is called **thermoelectric refrigeration.**

Bismuth telluride is the semiconductor used in modern Peltier or thermoelectric refrigerators. The bismuth telluride is doped (chemicals are added) to make up two types of material, **n-type and p-type.** n-type has more free or conduction electrons than has pure bismuth telluride and p-type has more positive charge carriers. Charge carriers are small charged particles that move to make up electric currents. Electrons are negative charge carriers. Thermocouple junctions are made by joining p- and n-type semiconductor. Thermoelectric (TE) modules consist of a number of thermocouples (see Figure 7.5).

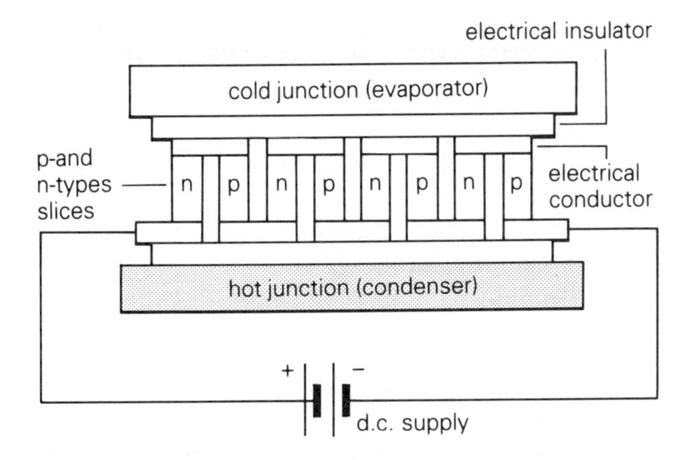

Figure 7.5 A thermoelectric module.

A module is a solid state device, usually a few millimetres across and consisting of semiconductor and other materials (see Figure 7.6).

The number of thermocouples in a module varies from about three to over a hundred, depending on the amount of refrigeration needed.

In a domestic refrigerator, the cold junction would be used to extract heat from the freezing compartment (like the evaporator) and the hot junction used to reject heat (like the condenser). This can be done, but TE refrigerators are more expensive than refrigerant types. TE refrigerators must use a d.c. supply but most domestic power supplies are a.c. Circuits which convert a.c. to d.c. have to be included and this adds to the expense.

However, TE refrigerators do have some advantages. For example, maintenance is easier as there are no moving parts. Damaged modules can simply be removed and new ones soldered in. Since there is no refrigerant, there is no possibility of damage to the earth's ozone layer (see Chapter 14) and it may be that one day TE refrigeration is the only type allowed. Of course, with mass production, Peltier refrigerators will become a lot cheaper. Small TE refrigerators, working from car batteries, are manufactured for use as picnic cool boxes. TE modules are used for cooling where something less than a refrigerator is needed. For example, modules are placed in some vending machines to keep a low temperature. Some television cameras have them. They are used by the armed forces in places where other cooling devices might be damaged.

CHECK YOUR UNDERSTANDING

- The simple air cycle is utilised in air-conditioning systems for aircraft. Compressed air passes through a small hole, expands and cools.
- In the absorption system, the compressor is replaced by an absorber and generator. The

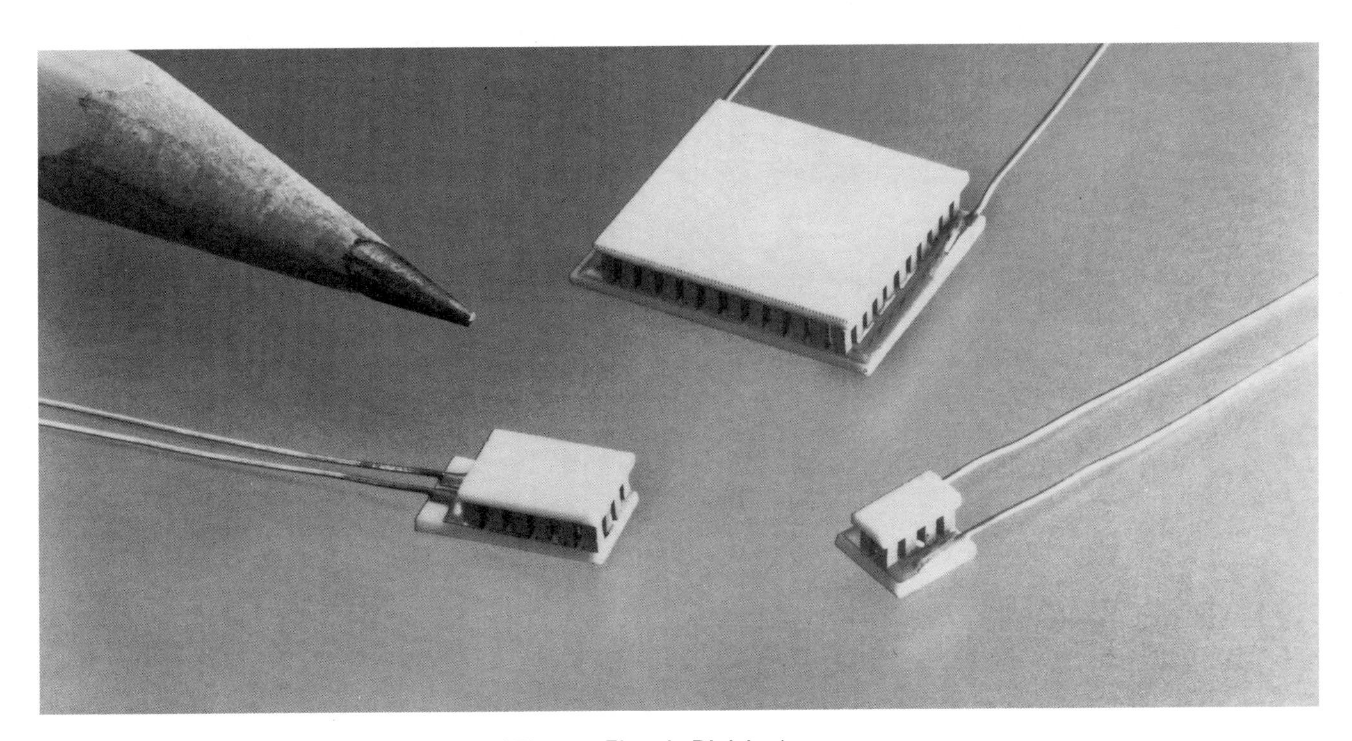

Figure 7.6 The small modules (courtesy of Thermo Electric Division).

absorber is equivalent to the input of the compressor and the generator compares to the discharge side.

- The refrigerant is often ammonia, dissolved in a liquid called the absorbent, which is often water.
- Liquid ammonia evaporates in the evaporator and cools the surrounding space.
- In domestic absorption refrigerators, a gas flame is used to heat the generator. Hydrogen gas keeps the ammonia circulating.
- Air-conditioning systems sometimes use lithium bromide absorbent, with water as a refrigerant.
- If you pass a current through a thermocouple made of two different metals, then one junction will become hot and the other cold. This is the Peltier effect.
- Modern thermoelectric effect (TE) modules use a semiconductor called bismuth telluride and not metals.
- Bismuth telluride is doped to make up n- and p-type material, so that two junctions can be formed. The cold junction is equivalent to the evaporator and the hot junction corresponds to the condenser. One advantage is that TE refrigerators cannot damage the ozone layer. They are, however, more expensive.

REVISION EXERCISES AND QUESTIONS

1. Explain the term *ram* air.
2. What is the function of the *expansion turbine*?
3. What is meant by a *thermocouple*?
4. Explain the *Peltier effect.*
5. Distinguish between *p- and n-type semiconductors.*
6. TE modules have a hot and a cold junction. What is the equivalent of these in vapour-compression refrigeration?
7. List one advantage and one disadvantage of TE refrigeration.
8. What two parts in an absorption system perform the same function as the compressor in the vapour-compression system?
9. Explain why an absorption refrigerator can operate in circumstances where there is no electrical supply.
10. Name two refrigerants which can be used in absorption systems.
11. What part of an absorption refrigerator is heated and what function does the heating perform?

8 Psychrometry

Introduction

Psychrometry is the study of air and its water vapour content for use in air conditioning. In air-conditioning plants, the temperature and water vapour content are changed to suit the requirements of the customer. For example, in domestic air conditioners the amount of moisture in the air is important because it determines how comfortable people feel.

When people sweat, water and salt appear on the surface of the skin. The rate at which the water evaporates depends upon air temperature, the speed at which the air moves and humidity. If the air temperature is high, then sweat will evaporate quickly. At the same time, however, more sweat will be produced because of the high temperature. When evaporation takes place, cooling occurs and the body feels more comfortable. Sweating is the body's way of keeping a steady temperature.

As we saw in Chapter 3, evaporation is the movement of molecules through the surface of a liquid to make up a vapour. If the air is very still, nearly as many molecules will return to the skin as leave it. The sweat stays on the skin and little cooling takes place. Cooling is improved in moving air because the molecules in the water vapour above the skin are blown away. New molecules then take their place from the sweat and cooling by evaporation is promoted.

In **humid** air, where the water vapour content is high, as many molecules move back to the skin as leave it. Domestic air conditioners aim to prevent this happening by controlling the speed of the air and the humidity. They also prevent very low humidity from occurring. Figure 8.1 shows cooling caused by evaporation.

Dry air is a mixture of gases, including nitrogen which takes up about 78% of the total volume. Oxygen takes up about 21% and the other 1% is taken up by gases such as carbon dioxide, helium, neon, argon, krypton and xenon. In heavily industrialised areas there are frequently impurities such as hydrogen sulphide and sulphur dioxide. Oxygen, nitrogen and the other gases of dry air are all in a highly superheated state. For example, the saturation temperature of oxygen is about −183°C and

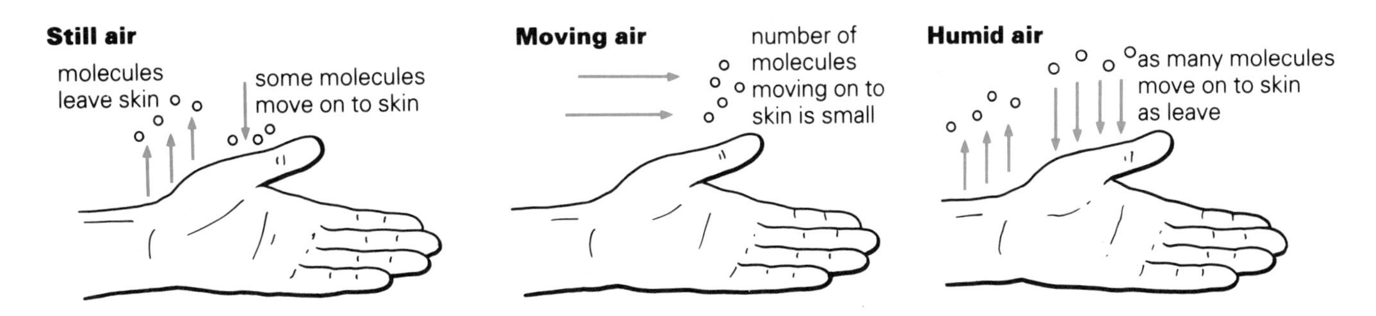

Figure 8.1 Cooling caused by evaporation.

for nitrogen −195°C. This means that dry air is also in a superheated condition.

However, atmospheric air is never dry as it contains water vapour. This vapour is in a superheated state but it can be cooled to a saturated vapour and then condensed to form a liquid. It is possible for water vapour to be in a superheated state and yet be at ordinary atmospheric temperatures well below the normal boiling point of water. This is because the water vapour and the dry air both exert separate pressures, according to a law known as **Dalton's law of partial pressures**.

> Dalton's law of partial pressures states that in a mixture of gases or vapours
> - each one exerts a partial pressure equal to that it would exert if it occupied the space alone, and
> - the total pressure is equal to the sum of the partial pressures.

If the atmospheric temperature is above the saturation temperature for the partial pressure exerted by the water vapour then the water vapour will be superheated. When the air temperature cools to the saturation temperature, then the water vapour becomes saturated. The temperature at which this occurs is called the **dew point** (D.P.) of the air. The dew point is the saturation temperature corresponding to the partial pressure of the water vapour.

EXAMPLE 8.1

The air temperature is 20°C. and the partial pressure of the water vapour is 0.0107 bar. From the Water Properties Table (Table 8.1), determine the dew point of the air.

Solution

Temp. (°C)	Saturation vapour pressure 10^5 Pa (bar)
0	0.006108
2	0.007055
4	0.008129
6	0.009345
8	**0.010720**

The saturation temperature for a pressure of 0.0107 bar is 8°C.

Absolute humidity

> The **absolute humidity** is the mass of water vapour per unit volume of air.

The water vapour takes up the same volume as the air so the absolute humidity is the vapour density of the moisture in the air. This is the reciprocal of the specific volume, which can be found from Table 8.1. Specific volume of the vapour at 8°C = 121 m^3/kg, therefore the absolute humidity = 1/121 kg/m^3 = 0.0083 kg/m^3.

Table 8.1 Water properties

Temp. (°C)	Saturation vapour pressure 10^5 Pa (bar)	Specific volume (m^3/kg)	
		Liquid	Vapour
0	0.006108	0.0010002	206.3
2	0.007055	0.0010001	179.9
4	0.008129	0.0010000	157.3
6	0.009345	0.0010000	137.8
8	0.010720	0.0010001	121.0
10	0.012270	0.0010003	106.4
12	0.014014	0.0010004	93.84
14	0.015973	0.0010007	82.90
16	0.018168	0.0010010	73.38
18	0.02062	0.0010013	65.09
20	0.02337	0.0010017	57.84
22	0.02642	0.0010022	51.49
24	0.02982	0.0010026	45.93
26	0.03360	0.0010032	41.03
28	0.03778	0.0010037	36.73
30	0.04241	0.0010043	32.93
32	0.04753	0.0010049	29.57
34	0.05318	0.0010056	26.60
36	0.05940	0.0010063	23.97
38	0.06624	0.0010070	21.63
40	0.07375	0.0010078	19.55
42	0.08198	0.0010086	17.69
44	0.09100	0.0010094	16.04
46	0.10086	0.0010103	14.56
48	0.11162	0.0010112	13.23
50	0.12335	0.0010121	12.05
52	0.13613	0.0010131	10.98
54	0.15002	0.0010140	10.02
56	0.16511	0.0010150	9.159
58	0.18147	0.0010161	8.381

Table 8.1 (continued) Water properties

Temp. (°C)	Saturation vapour pressure 10^5 Pa (bar)	Specific volume (m^3/kg)	
		Liquid	Vapour
60	0.19920	0.0010171	7.679
62	0.2184	0.0010182	7.044
64	0.2391	0.0010193	6.469
66	0.2615	0.0010205	5.948
68	0.2856	0.0010217	5.475
70	0.3116	0.0010228	5.046
72	0.3396	0.0010241	4.656
74	0.3696	0.0010253	4.300
76	0.4019	0.0010266	3.976
78	0.4365	0.0010279	3.680
80	0.4736	0.0010292	3.409
82	0.5133	0.0010305	3.162
84	0.5557	0.0010319	2.935

Specific humidity

Specific humidity, sometimes called the moisture content of air, is the mass of water vapour per unit mass of dry air.

Specific humidity is measured in kg/kg or g/kg. According to some authorities the mass of water vapour is measured relative to a unit mass of moist air.

Relative humidity

Relative humidity is the type of humidity which is important in air conditioning. When people complain about the weather and say it is too humid, they really mean that the relative humidity is too high for comfort. Relative humidity is a measure of how near the moisture in the air is to saturation. Absolute humidity is important but it does not show itself through the senses in the same way.

$$\text{Relative humidity} = \frac{\text{s.v.p. at the dew point}}{\text{s.v.p at the air temperature}} \times 100$$

where s.v.p. is the saturation vapour pressure.

EXAMPLE 8.2

The air temperature at noon is found to be 24°C and the dew point is 12°C. Later in the day the temperature drops to 20°C. Find the relative humidity of the air at each temperature if the absolute humidity of the air remains constant.

Solution

Temp. (°C)	Saturation vapour pressure 10^5 Pa (bar)	Temp. (°C)	Saturation vapour pressure 10^5 Pa (bar)
0	0.006108	14	0.015973
2	0.007055	16	0.018168
4	0.008129	18	0.02062
6	0.009345	20	0.02337
8	0.010720	22	0.02642
10	0.012270	**24**	**0.02982**
12	**0.014014**		

From Table 8.1 the s.v.p. at 24°C is 0.02982 and that at 12°C is 0.014014. Therefore, the relative humidity at 24°C is given by:

$$RH = \frac{0.014014}{0.02982} \times 100 = 47\%$$

At 20°C,

$$RH = \frac{0.014014}{0.02337} \times 100 = 60\%.$$

The relative humidity is higher at the lower temperature because the moisture in the air is closer to saturation. There is no change in the absolute humidity.

Relative humidity is measured using a **hygrometer** or **psychrometer**. The type of psychrometer which is most useful when making measurements for air conditioning purposes is the *sling psychrometer*. A sling psychrometer consists of two thermometers, with the bulb of one kept dry and the bulb of the other kept wet. The wet bulb has a cloth wick wrapped around it and this is soaked in water. To measure the relative humidity, the psychrometer is take by the handle and whirled around for about a minute. A sling psychrometer is shown in Figure 8.2.

Then the **dry bulb** (DB) and **wet bulb** (WB) temperature readings are taken. The procedure is repeated several times to make sure that the wet bulb reading is the same in each case. The difference between the wet and dry bulb temperatures is

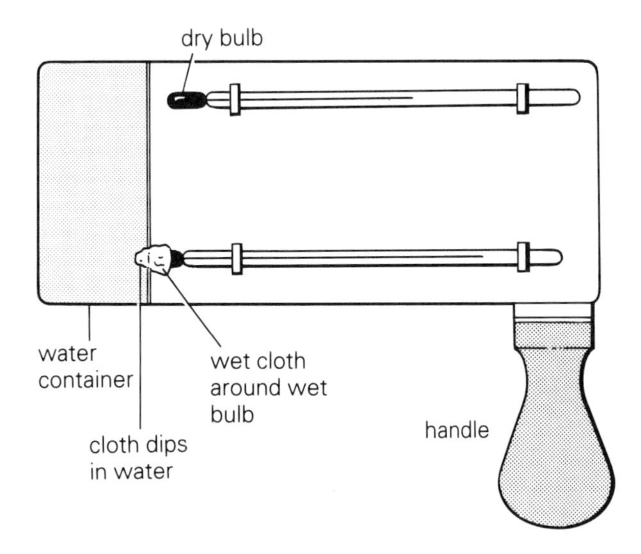

Figure 8.2 A sling psychrometer.

called the wet bulb depression, as the wet bulb reading is always lower than that of the dry bulb. A psychrometric table gives the relative humidity from the dry bulb reading and the wet bulb depression.

The specific enthalpy of the air is given by the relationship:

$$h_m = h_d + h_w$$

where h_m is the enthalpy of moist atmospheric air, h_d is the enthalpy of dry air and h_w is the enthalpy of the water vapour. The WB temperature is a measure of h_m, the enthalpy of moist atmospheric air. For any combination of DB and DP temperatures there is only one WB temperature and only one value for enthalpy.

The psychrometric chart

This is a graphical way of solving problems concerning the quality of air. A **psychrometric chart** is shown in Figure 8.3. It shows the relationship between factors such as WB temperature, DB temperature, DP temperature and relative humidity. Details on enthalpy, specific heat capacity, specific volume and specific humidity are given.

EXAMPLE 8.3

In a sample of air the temperature is measured as 25°C and the wet bulb temperature is 15°C. Using the chart, find the relative humidity, the specific enthalpy, the specific humidity, the dew point and the specific volume.

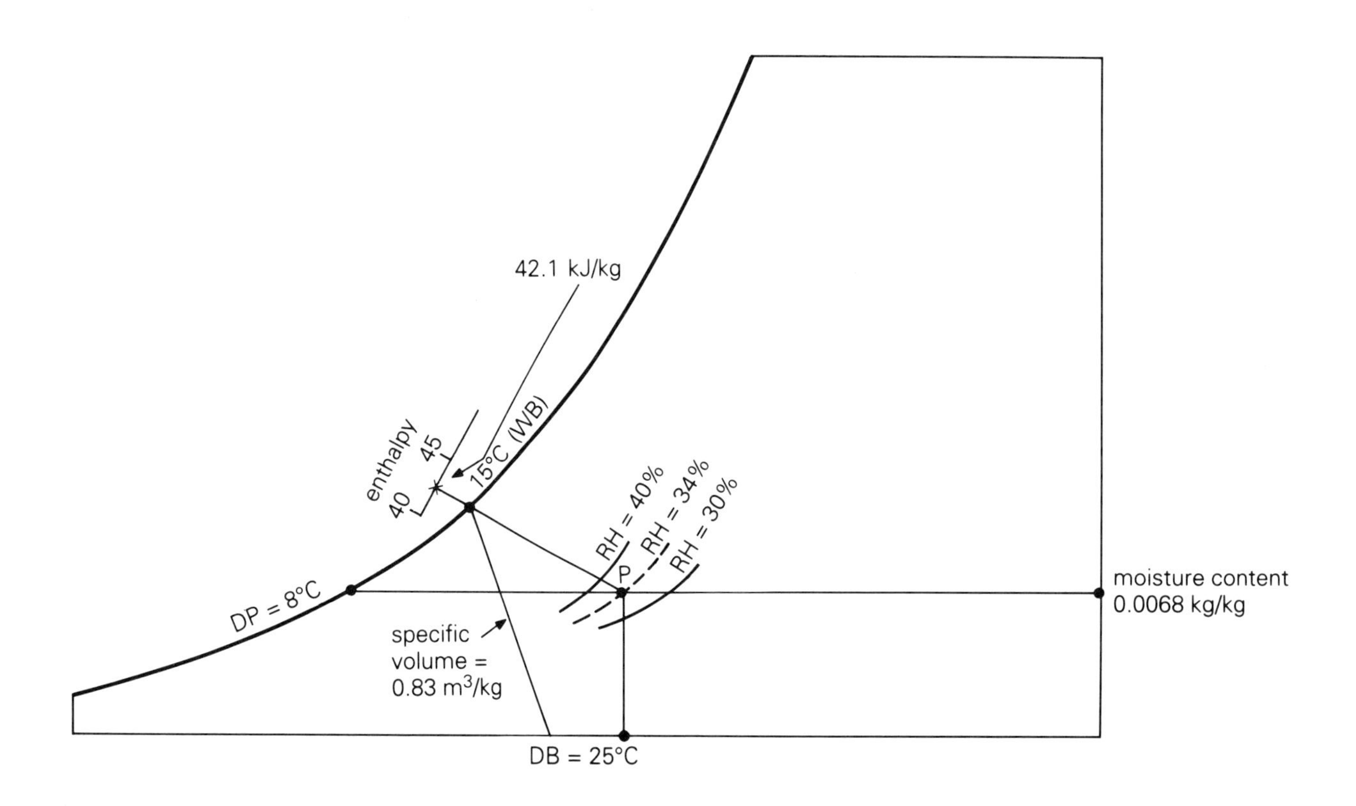

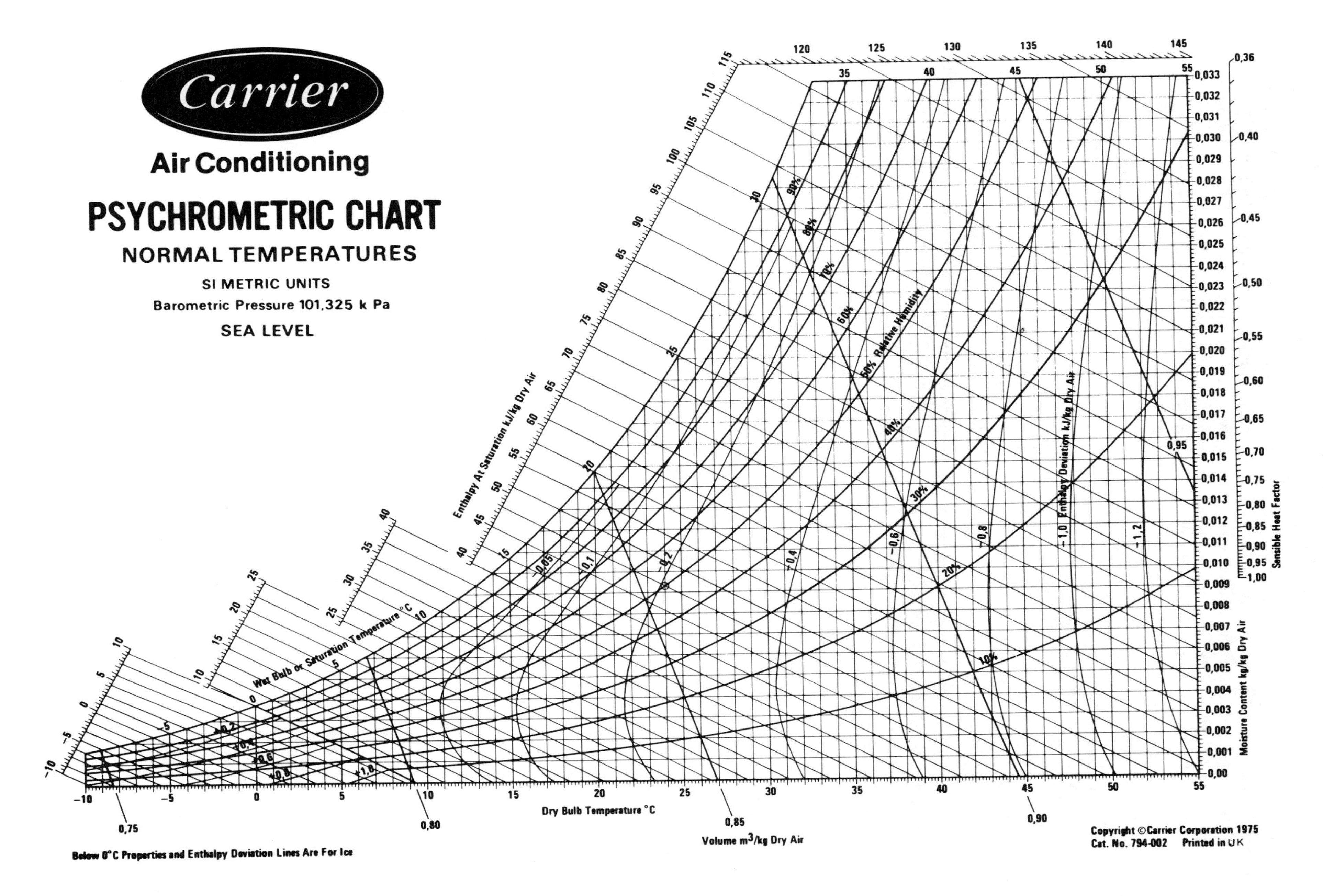

Figure 8.3 'Carrier' psychrometric chart.

Solution
The point, P, where the WB temperature and the DB temperature lines meet is shown. P lies between the 30% and 40% relative humidity lines at 34%. The specific enthalpy (close to the wet bulb temperature) is 42.1 kJ/kg. On the right-hand side of the chart is the moisture content or specific humidity 0.0068 kg/kg. DP is where the horizontal line from the specific humidity, through P meets the curved WB line. DP = 8°C. The specific volume line is the diagonal one running through WB = 15°C and parallel to the other specific volume lines. Specific volume = 0.83 m^3/kg.

Sensible heating of air

If air is heated without raising the moisture content then the enthalpy of the air increases. When the enthalpy increases the WB temperature increases.

EXAMPLE 8.4

A body of air, of WB temperature 12°C, is heated from a DB temperature of 14°C to 23°C and no moisture is added.

i) Find the DP, the moisture content and the total heat added per kilogramme of air.
ii) What is the effect on the relative humidity as the air is heated?
iii) If 200 m^3 of air is heated every minute and the density of air is 1.3 kg/m^3, calculate the heat added per minute.

Solution
The solution is shown in the diagram.
i) The original DB temperature line and the WB temperature line meet at P. The horizontal line through P gives both DP and moisture content (specific humidity). DP = 10.5°C and moisture content = 0.008 kg/kg. Specific enthalpy at WB = 12°C = 34.0 kJ/kg. The horizontal line and the 23°C line meet at P' and the diagonal line gives a specific enthalpy at that temperature of 44 kJ/kg. Total heat added = 44 − 34 = 10 kJ/kg.
ii) Relative humidity at P is 80% and it drops to 47% at P'; that is, as the temperature increases from 14°C to 23°C.
iii) The mass of air heated every minute is 1.3 × 200 = 260 kg. Heat added per kilogramme = 10 kJ, therefore heat added = 260 × 10 = 2600 kJ/min.

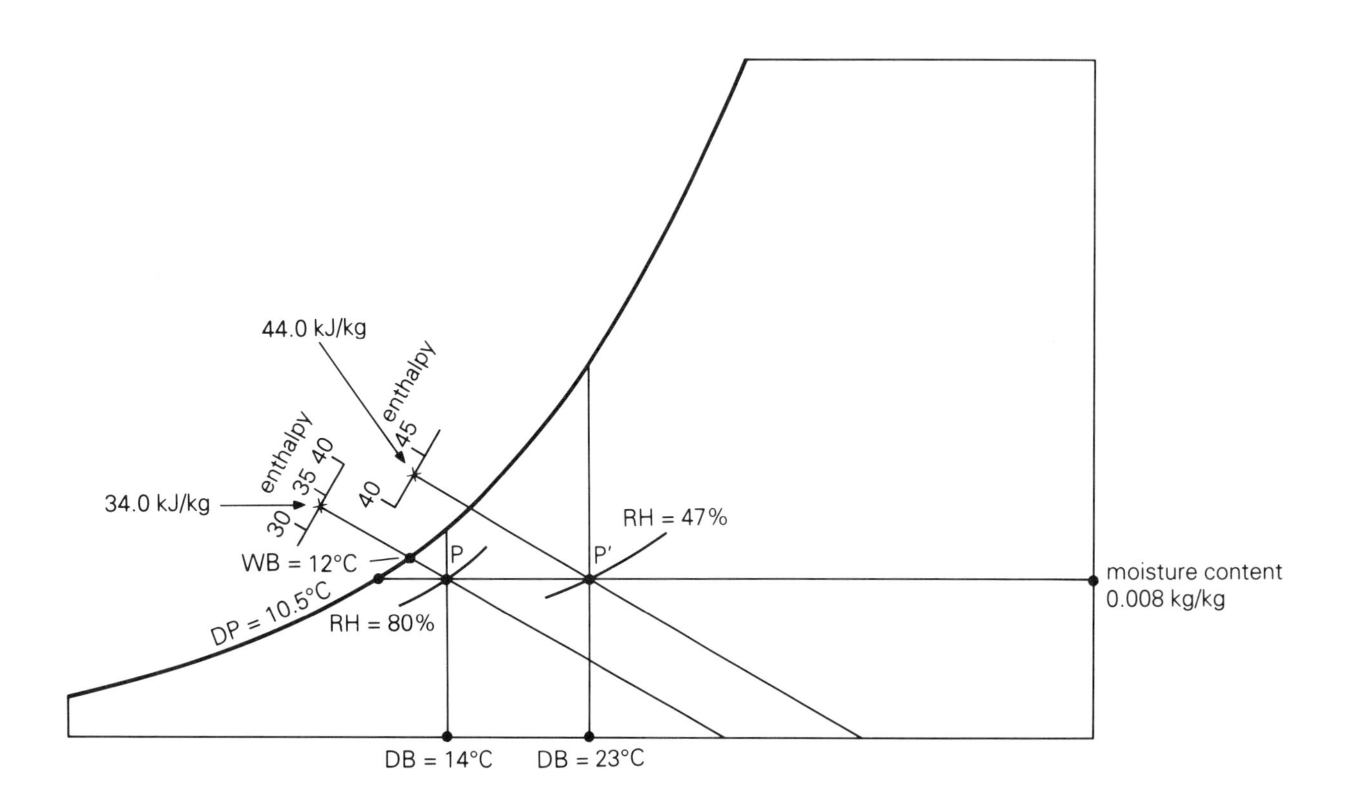

Humidification

Adding moisture to air is called **humidifying** it. This can be done with or without heating. In the example below it is done without heating.

EXAMPLE 8.5

A body of air is at a temperature of 23°C and a relative humidity of 50%. Its moisure content is increased from 0.0086 kg/kg to 0.0124 kg/kg.

i) Find the increase in WB temperature, DP and the specific enthalpy.
ii) Determine the change in relative humidity.
iii) If 200 m^3 of air is passed through the system every minute and the density of air is 1.3 kg/m^3, calculate the mass of moisture added per minute.

Solution

i) Point P represents a DB temperature of 23°C, a relative humidity of 50% and a specific humidity of 0.0086 kg/kg. The horizontal line through P gives a DP of 12°C and the diagonal line a WB temperature of 16°C with a specific enthalpy of 45 kJ/kg. Point P' gives a DP of 17.5°C and the diagonal line indicates a WB temperature of 19.2°C with a specific enthalpy of 55 kJ/kg. Thus the WB temperature increases from 16°C to 19.2°C, the DP increases from 12°C to 17.5°C and the specific enthalpy increases from 45 kJ/kg to 55 kJ/kg.
ii) The relative humidity line that passes through point P' is 70%. This means the humidity changes from 50% to 70%.
iii) The mass of air passing per minute is $200 \times 1.3 = 260$ kg. The moisture added is $0.0124 - 0.0086 = 0.0038$ kg/kg of air. Therefore the mass of moisture added per minute is $260 \times 0.0038 = 0.988$ kg.

In Example 8.4 we saw what happened when air is heated without humidification, and in Example 8.5 there was humidification without heating. Air can be both heated and humidified and problems on this can be solved using the psychrometric chart. Cooling and **dehumidification** are also necessary processes in air-conditioning systems.

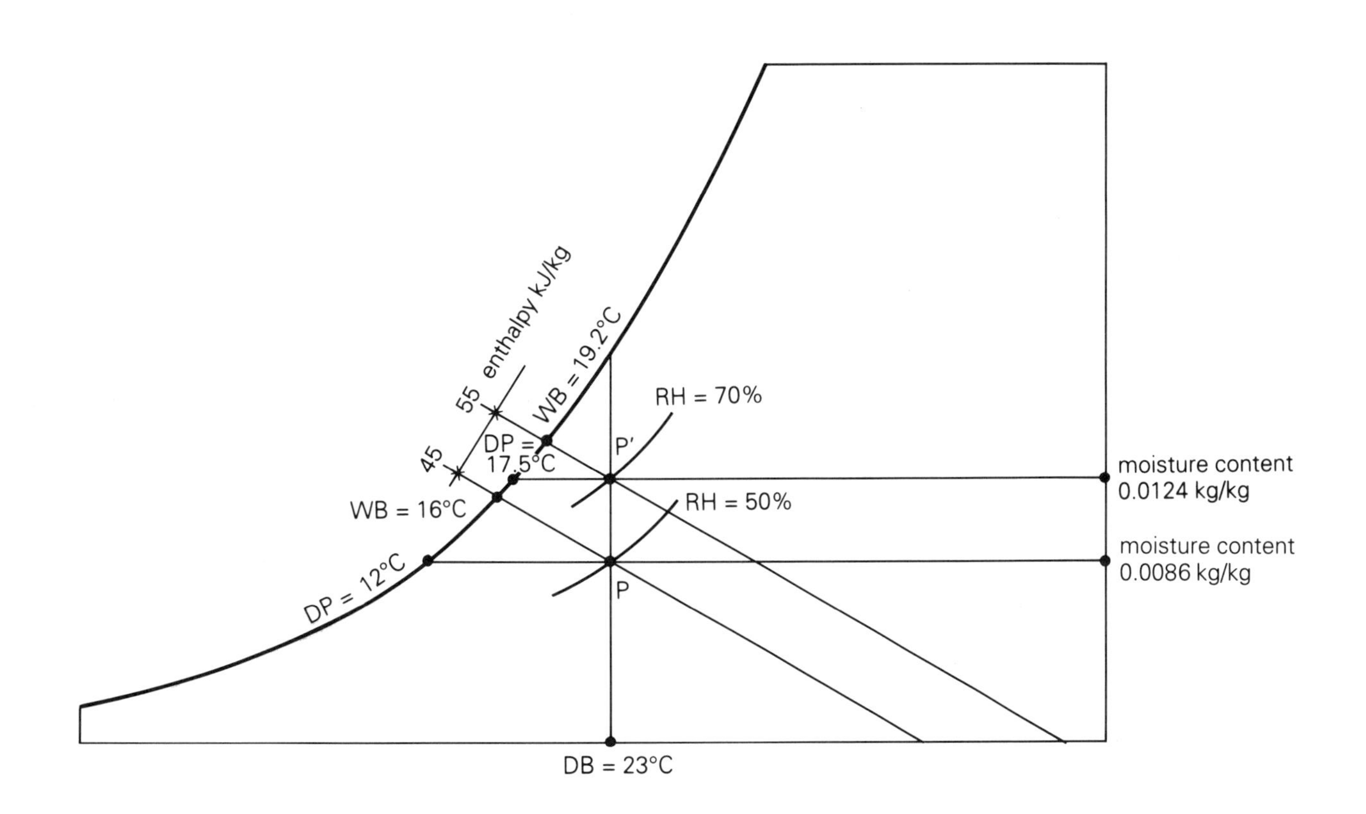

Dehumidification

EXAMPLE 8.6

Air is to be cooled and dehumidified by contact with a cooling coil in order to make the DB temperature drop from 30°C to 16°C. The WB temperature before cooling is 25°C.

i) Using the psychrometric chart, determine the final WB temperature and the changes in relative humidity, DP, moisture content and specific enthalpy.
ii) Illustrate the process by means of appropriate lines, using arrows to indicate the direction of change.

Solution

It is best to consider the change as being made up of two separate processes:

1 sensible cooling; and
2 cooling and dehumidifying.

i) Point A indicates DB temperature of 30°C and a WB temperature of 25°C. The specific enthalpy is 76.5 kJ/kg, the DP is 23.2°C and the moisture content is 0.018 kg/kg. The relative humidity is 68%. The change from point A to point B is one of sensible cooling and B represents saturation with a consequent relative humidity of 100%. The change from B to C is one of cooling and dehumidifying. The temperature at C is 16°C and this is also the WB reading and the DP, as saturation has occurred. The specific enthalpy has changed from 76.5 kJ/kg to 45 kJ/kg and the moisture content has dropped from 0.018 kg/kg to 0.0114 kJ/kg.
The line AC represents the complete process.
ii) The appropriate lines are shown on the chart.

The process described in the example above is purely theoretical as, in practice, not all of the air passing through the system actually makes contact with the cooling surface of the coil. The air which is not cooled is called bypass air and the percentage of bypass air is the coil bypass factor (coil BPF). A more practical example of cooling and dehumidification can only be studied by knowing the coil BPF. The process of cooling and dehumidification produces air close to saturation.

The mixing of different bodies of air is a common process in air-conditioning systems. The chart can be used to find the condition of the air in the mixture.

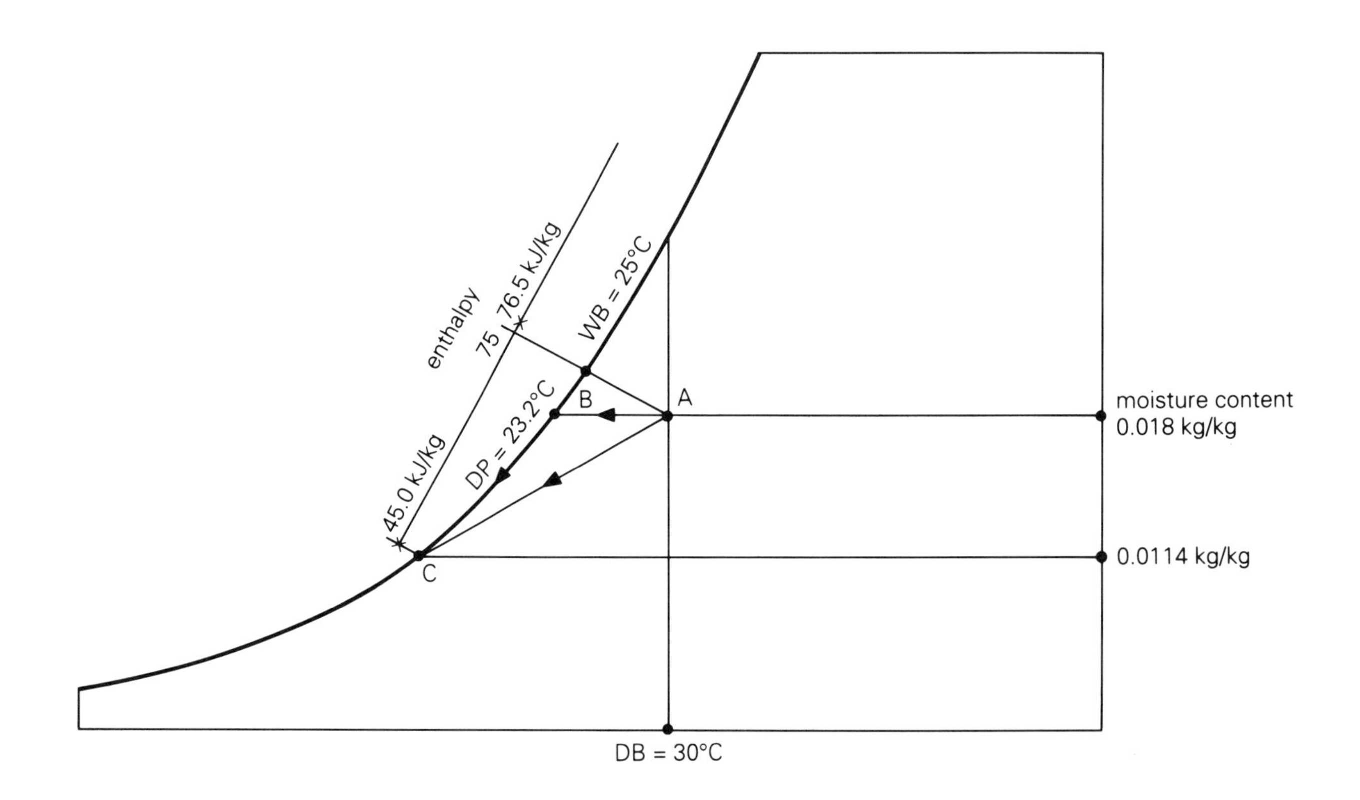

EXAMPLE 8.7

A body of fresh air of DB temperature 30°C and WB temperature 27°C is mixed with return air of DB temperature 23°C and WB temperature 18°C. (Return air is air that has been used for air conditioning and then returned to the air conditioner.) Twice the mass of return air is used, as fresh air. Find the DB and WB temperatures of the mixture, together with the relative humidity, the moisture content and the specific enthalpy.

Solution
The return air condition is indicated by point A and the fresh air condition by point B. A line is drawn between A and B and the mixture point, C, lies on the line. The position of C is calculated from the ratios of the masses:

$$T_c = \frac{(2 \times 23) + (1 \times 30)}{3} = 25.3°\text{C}$$

where T_c is the DB temperature of the mixture, 23°C is the DB temperature of the return air and 30°C is the DB temperature of the fresh air. The factors 2 and 1 are used because there is twice as much return air as fresh. The bottom line is $2 + 1 = 3$. C is located along AB from the DB temperature of the mixture.

From the chart, the WB temperature is 21.3°C, specific enthalpy is 61 kJ/kg, the moisture content is 0.0142 kg/kg and the relative humidity is 70%.

CHECK YOUR UNDERSTANDING

- Atmospheric air is never dry and it contains water vapour.
- Dalton's law of partial pressures says:
  - A) that each vapour exerts a partial pressure equal to that which it would exert if it occupied the space alone; and
  - B) that the total pressure is equal to the sum of the partial pressures.
- Dew point (DP) is the saturation temperature corresponding to the partial pressure of the water vapour.
- Absolute humidity is the mass of water vapour per unit mass of dry air.

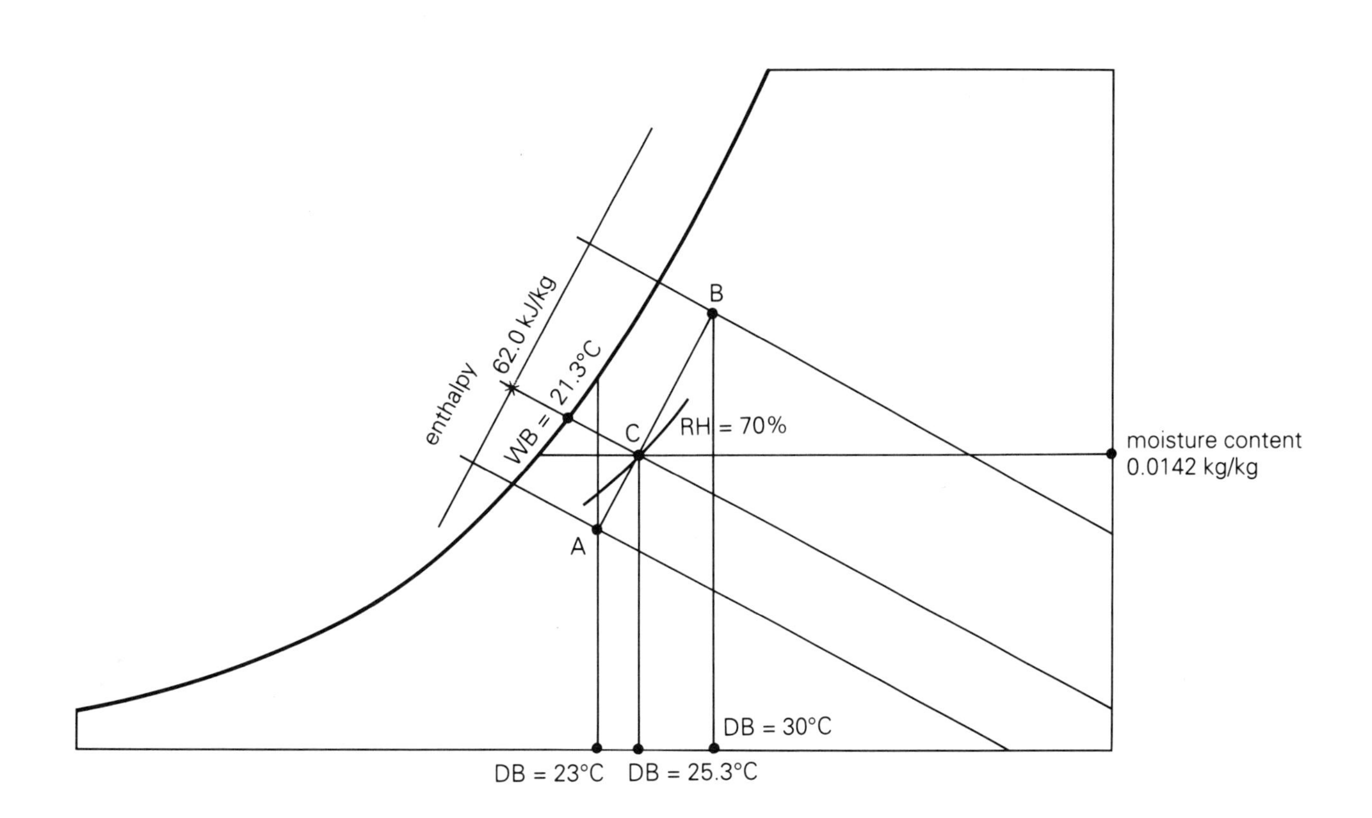

- Specific humidity is the mass of water vapour per unit volume of air.
- Relative humidity =

$$\frac{\text{s.v.p. at dew point}}{\text{s.v.p. at the air temperature}} \times 100$$

- Relative humidity is measure using a psychrometer. A sling or whirling psychrometer is the most useful. This has a wet bulb (WB) and a dry bulb (DB).
- The psychrometric chart is a graphical way of solving problems concerning the quality of air. It shows the relationship between factors such as WB temperature, DB temperature, DP temperature and relative humidity. Details on enthalpy, specific heat capacity, specific volume and specific humidity are given.
- Adding moisure to air is humidifing it.
- Removing moisure fom air is dehumidifying it.

REVISION EXERCISES AND QUESTIONS

1. The air temperature is 22°C and the partial pressure of the water vapour is 0.0123 bar. From Table 8.1 determine the dew point of the air.
2. The air temperature at noon is found to be 26°C and the dew point is 10°C. Later in the day the temperature drops to 22°C. Find the relative humidity of the air at each temperature if the absolute humidity of the air remains constant.
3. In a sample of air the DB temperature is measured as 23°C and the wet bulb temperature is 13°C. Using the chart, find the relative humidity, the specific enthalpy, the specific humidity, the dew point and the specific volume.
4. A body of air is heated from a DB temperature of 12°C to 20°C where the WB temperature is 10°C and no moisture is added.
   i) Find the DP, the moisture content and the total heat added per kilogramme of air.
   ii) What is the effect on the relative humidity as the air is heated?
   iii) If 200 m^3 of air is heated every minute and the density of air is 1.3 kg/m^3, calculate the heat added per minute.
5. A body of air is at a temperature of 25°C and a relative humidity of 50%. Its moisure content is increased from 0.010 kg/kg to 0.014 kg/kg.
   i) Find the increase in WB temperature, DP and the specific enthalpy.
   ii) Determine the change in relative humidity.
   iii) If 200 m^3 of air is passed through the system every minute and the density of air is 1.3 kg/m^3, calculate the mass of moisture added per minute.
6. Air is to be cooled and dehumidified by contact with a cooling coil in order to make the DB temperature drop from 32°C to 18°C. The WB temperature before cooling is 26°C.

   Using the psychrometric chart, determine the final WB temperature and the changes in relative humidity, DP, moisture content and specific enthalpy.
7. A body of fresh air of DB temperature 32°C and WB temperature 29°C is mixed with return air of DB temperature 24°C and WB temperature 18°C. Twice the mass of return air as fresh air is used. Find the DB and WB temperatures of the mixture, together with the relative humidity, the moisture content and the specific enthalpy.

9 Air conditioning

Introduction

Air conditioning is treating air in such a way that temperature, humidity and contamination by dust particles are adjusted to levels suitable for the purpose for which the air conditioning is intended. Air can be conditioned to provide comfort for people at home or at work or it can be conditioned for a commercial purposes to supply the best environment for machinery or technical equipment. Computer rooms, for example, work best in an atmosphere of properly-conditioned air. Of course, in many cases, as with computer rooms, the air-conditioning system may serve two purposes, that of prolonging the life of the equipment and of comfort.

In all types of air conditioning, the room or building which is air conditioned is called the **air-conditioned space**. The conditioned air supplied to the air-conditioned space is the **supply air**. Air which has passed through the air-conditioned space is called **exhaust air** and the exhaust air returned to the air-conditioning system is **return air**. Air taken in from outside the building is **outside air** or **fresh air**.

Comfort air conditioning

In **comfort air-conditioning** systems for homes, offices, shops, theatres and so on, in addition to temperature and humidity control, it is necessary to maintain the correct speed of circulation of air. This, along with controlled temperature and humidity, promotes the correct degree of evaporation from the skin, and people feel comfortable (see Chapter 8). With too little air circulation people feel sweaty, and with too much there will be a draught and they will be uncomfortable for different reasons. The movement of air should be uniform (the same everywhere in the room) and gentle, so as not to be annoying. Comfort systems must also be fitted with filters to remove dust and pollen from the atmosphere.

In any place where air conditioning is needed, heat will come in from a number of sources. This places a **cooling load** on the refrigerating equipment that operates the air-conditioning system. The cooling load is made up from the following sources:

1 heat conducted in through the walls;
2 heat radiated in through windows;
3 warm air coming in through gaps under doors or through partly open windows;
4 heat emitted from electrical equipment in the building; and
5 heat given off by people.

The refrigerating equipment will have to be sufficient to cope with heat from all these sources and still provide a comfortable environment.

In areas of a country, say in mountainous regions, where the winter is cold, air-conditioning equipment must be fitted with electrical heating elements to provide heated air for the building.

Room air conditioners

For a single room, or for a small shop, a **room air conditioner** is used. This comprises refrigerating

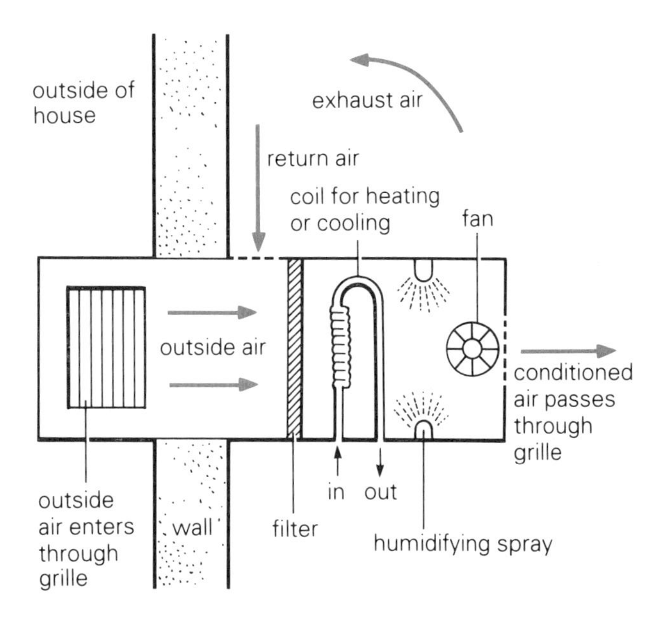

Figure 9.1 A room air conditioner.

equipment, a fan and filters all contained in a single box, with a grille at the front to allow out the conditioned or supply air. Another grille allows air that has been passed through the room, the exhaust air, back into the conditioner as return air. The return air is then filtered and added to outside air and the combined air stream is then conditioned. The psychrometry of combining air streams is explained in Chapter 8. Room air conditioners can be installed by mounting them through a wall, a window or above a door. Some are placed in positions where they have no access to outside air and so they merely recirculate the return air. A room air conditioner is shown in Figure 9.1.

The cooling coil is an evaporator which cools the air and so dehumidifies it. This can be done by reducing the temperature to below the dew point to make the water condense. In some air-conditioning systems, it is necessary to cool air without changing the moisture content. In this case the air is reduced to a temperature above dew point and although the relative humidity increases, the actual water content does not. If the air is too dry it must be humidified. This can be done by using a warm water spray to raise the temperature of the air and then increase the moisture content. Room air conditioners are fitted with **humidistats** to control the humidity of air from the unit and hence the air in the room (see Chapter 21). If the humidity is too low then the humidifying spray will be switched on. If, however, the humidity is too high then the air will be cooled and dehumidified.

Thermostats are devices which control temperature and it is these that determine the temperature of the air to be supplied to the room. Often the fan speed can be altered using a three-speed switch which controls the motor. All of the controls are mounted on the cabinet.

Units larger than room air conditioners are **split units**. These consist of a compressor, evaporator, evaporator fan, throttling valve and controls mounted in a cabinet inside the building. The condenser with its fan is mounted on an outside wall.

Central units

For large air-conditioning systems a **central air handling** unit moves the air through a series of large pipes, known as **ducts**. Outside air is taken in through a duct with an opening on the roof or on a wall. A protection grille stops large objects and small animals and birds entering the system. The air handling unit contains a number of components such as filters, heating coils, cooling coils, humidifiers and fans. The condenser, evaporator and compressor are mounted separately, with the condenser often on an outside wall or on a roof. The cooling coils work from the evaporator with secondary refrigerant being used. The cooling coils can be used for heating by pumping water over a heating element and then passing the hot water through the coil (see Figure 9.2).

Figure 9.3 shows an air-handling unit with part of the system of ducts.

The large ducts feed smaller ducts, which then distribute air to the individual rooms through outlet grilles. A control on the wall regulates the air supply for each room (Figure 9.4).

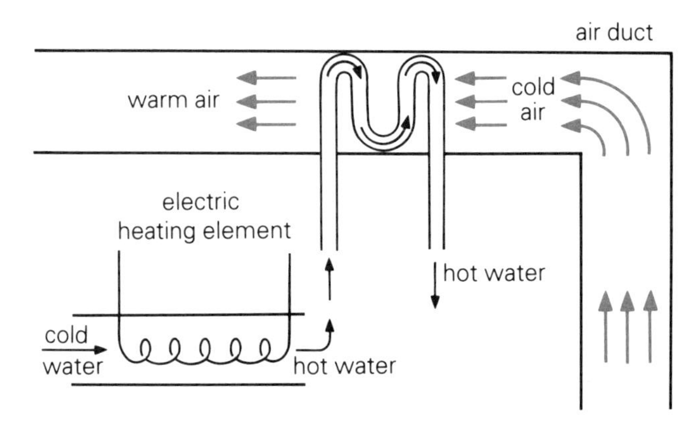

Figure 9.2 A heating coil.

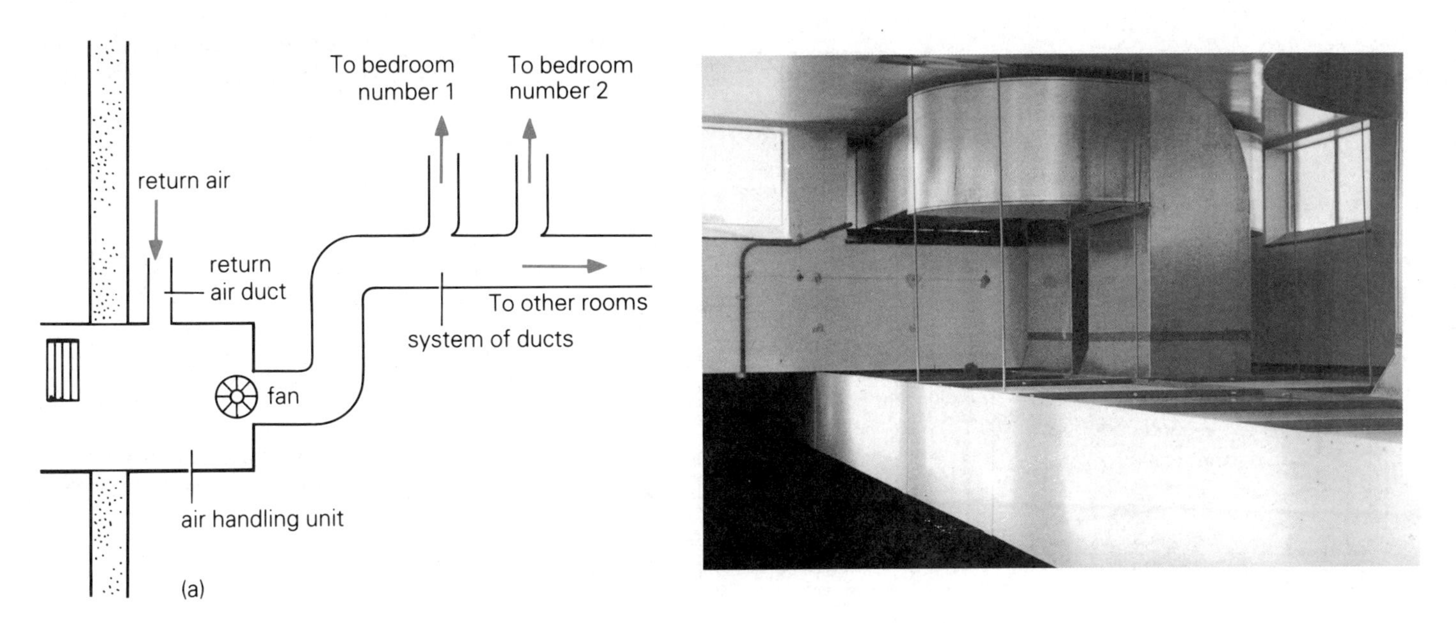

Figure 9.3 (a) Air handling unit with system of ducts, (b) part of a system of ducts (courtesy of Air Movement Technology).

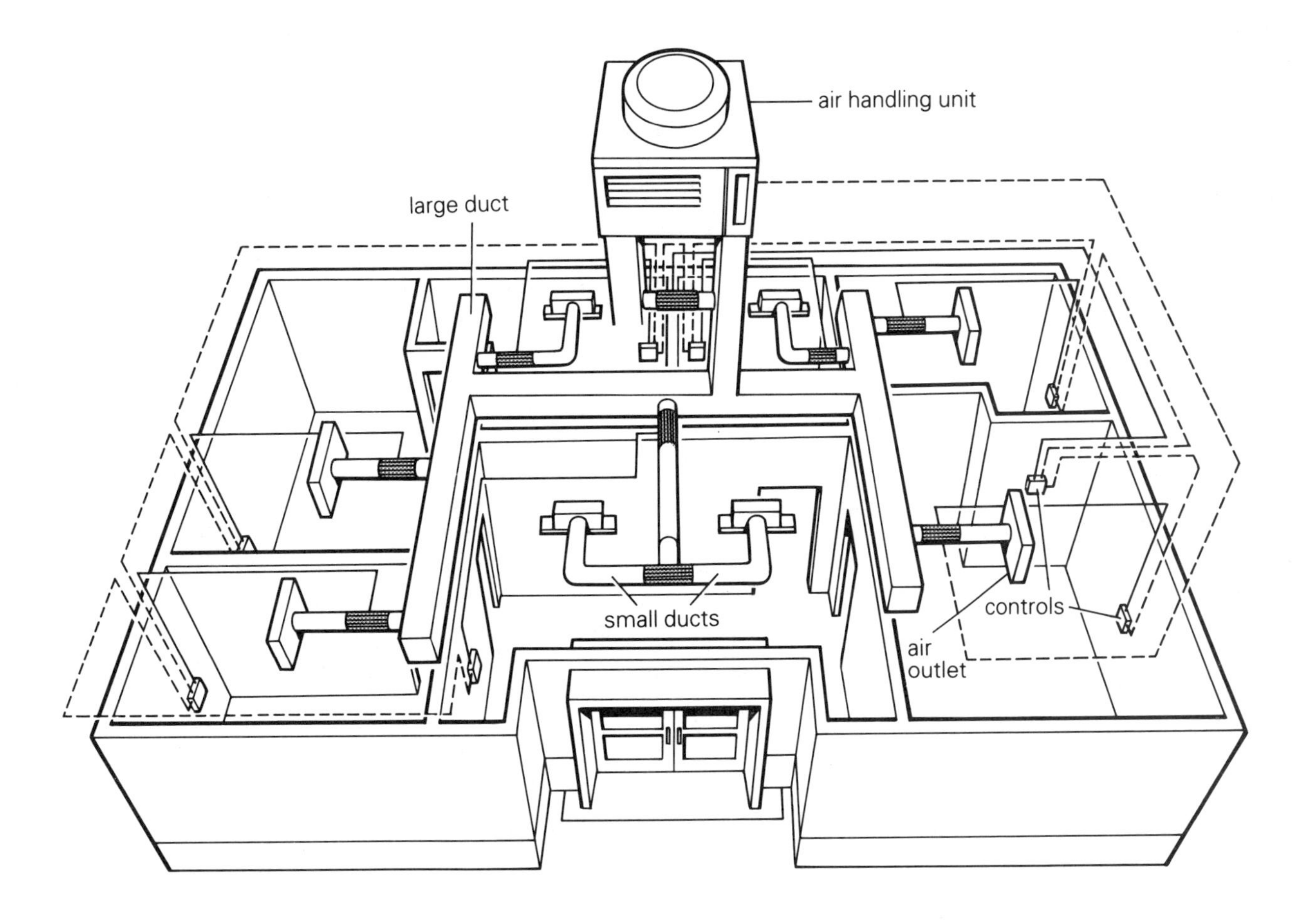

Figure 9.4 Air conditioning for individual rooms.

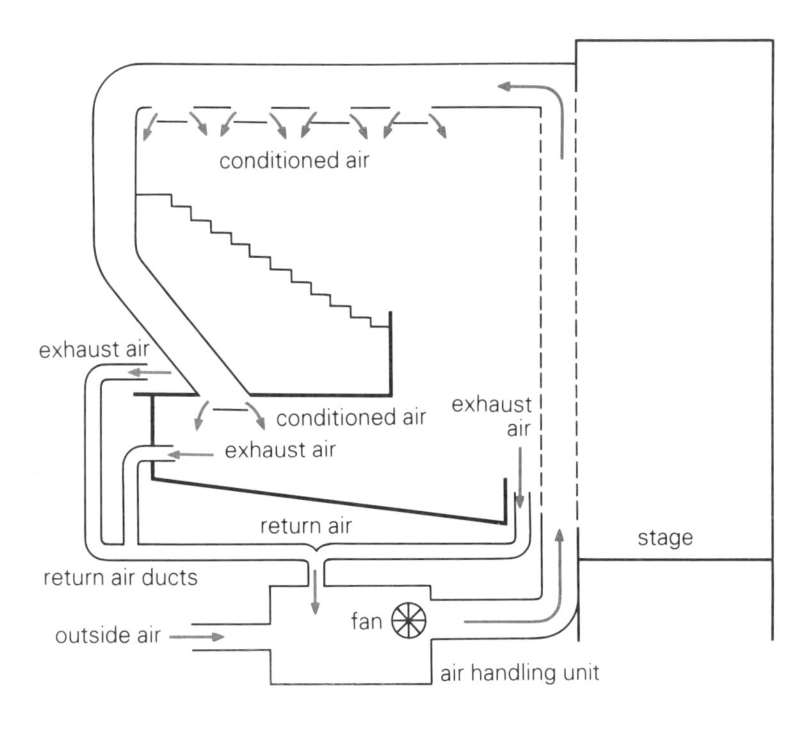

Figure 9.5 Return air ducts in a theatre.

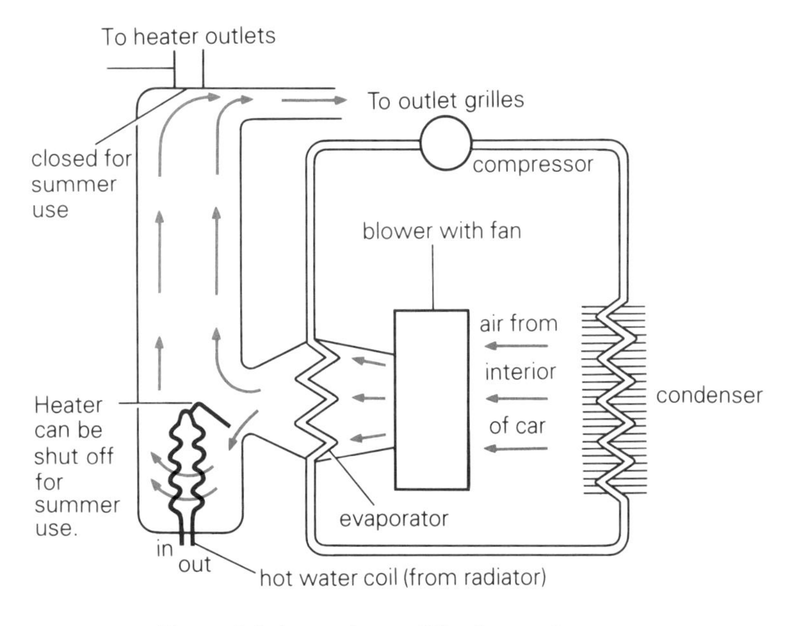

Figure 9.6 A car air-conditioning system.

Depending on the design of the system, ducts can run above ceilings, behind walls and under floors. Air which has been breathed in the air-conditioned space is called exhaust air, and this returns to the central unit as return air, through inlet grilles and along another system of (return air) ducts (see Figure 9.5). The return air is then mixed with outside air and the mixture is conditioned by the foregoing processes.

Some cars, taxis and buses have their own air-conditioning systems. Air from the inside of the car is blown by a fan over the evaporator of a refrigeration system. This cools the air which then re-enters the car through conditioned-air outlets. The direction of these outlets can be altered to blow air towards or away from the people in the car. The speed at which the air moves through the interior of the car is controlled by the fan. The fan also blows air over a heating coil when the weather is cold. Usually the heating coil gets its hot water from the car radiator. Figure 9.6 shows a car air-conditioning system.

Commercial air conditioning

Some **commercial air-conditioning** systems are really just very large comfort air-conditioning systems which can be used in hotels, office blocks, hospitals and other large buildings. In such systems, separate control of temperature is needed for each room. Hotels and hospitals are places where there are strong odours. It is important to stop the movement of odours from one room to another. People staying in a hotel do not want strong smells from the kitchen. Many commercial buildings were built before air conditioning was common. This means that ducts and grilles have to be placed in positions where they do not spoil the look of beautiful old rooms.

Often, special features are needed for commercial buildings. Offices, for example, often need a cigarette smoke removal system. Art galleries need very good filters to stop dirt and fumes; also humidity has to be just right or paintings will be damaged. Computers and computer equipment are easily damaged by excessive dust and this is one of the reasons why chalkboards should not be used for instruction in computer rooms. Air conditioning for computer rooms must filter out dust and also control the humidity very carefully. One place where noise control is important is in theatres.

Among other types of buildings which usually need to be air conditioned are restaurants, libraries, banks and television studios. Restaurants need odour control systems like those in hotels. Some types of fumes can damage books and these fumes need to be filtered from libraries. Banks often have two air-conditioning systems: one for customers and one for those working in the bank. The systems are different because bank workers are in the bank for longer than the bank is open to the public. When the bank is closed, but people are still there working, one system is switched off while the other is left on.

Note that in air-conditioning systems air can be cooled without change of moisure content, cooled and dehumidified, or cooled and humidified, depending on the method chosen. Cooling with humidification is called evaporative cooling.

Process air conditioning

In the manufacture of some types of goods it is important to keep the humidity at a steady level. Other types of goods need a steady temperature. **Process air-conditioning** systems are used in industry to produce these steady conditions.

Paper is a material which is affected as relative humidity changes. If paper is too dry its edges will curl and it will be impossible to print on it. If, however, relative humidity is too high the paper will swell and printer's ink will dry too slowly. In the printing industry, air conditioning is needed to keep the relative humidity just right. If the humidity is incorrect then good printing is impossible. Other industries where humidity is important are textiles, tobacco and plastics.

In some industries, such as part of the photographic industry, control of temperature is important. In other industries filter systems are needed to get rid of dust, dirt and fumes. Clean air must be used in food processing and dust-free air is very important in the manufacture of semiconductor devices, such as transistors, diodes and integrated circuits.

Humidity is usually kept at a steady level in the textile industry by using warm water sprays. These sprays are normally part of large air-conditioning units. Where very high relative humidities are needed, water is sprayed directly into the room.

Desert coolers

A **desert cooler** is an air conditioner that can only work where the relative humidity is low, as, for example, in a desert. A fan sucks outside air through a wet pad and the air causes some of the water to evaporate. This cools the air and also humidifies it, making conditions more comfortable for those in the room. The pad must be kept wet the whole time and this is done by means of water from a water pump.

Filters

Various small particles in the outside air, from factory fumes or trees and other plants cause the air to be contaminated. Some of these particles can cause discomfort and even illness to staff, and others can spoil industrial processes. Air-conditioning systems use **filters** to remove these damaging particles from the air.

Particle sizes vary according to the type of contamination and this will differ from area to area. Examples are fumes from industrial processes and smokes, also from industry but from tobacco too. These particles are very small. Dust particles are much larger as are those of pollen. Spores of fungi can also cause problems, and bacteria are germs which may cause illness among the staff of a company. Bacteria are often carried on dust particles.

Viscous filters

Viscous filters consist of a box containing small pieces of metal, known as the filtering medium, which are covered in oil. The dust and other particles stick to the oil so that air which passes through is cleaned. Some filters are designed to be thrown away after use but others can be cleaned and re-used.

An automatic form of viscous filter uses a continuous and moving roll of material which passes through a bath of oil. Metal plates are fixed to the roll and the dust sticks to the oil on these plates. Figure 9.7 shows both types of viscous filter.

Viscous filters are not very efficient compared with other types and are considered to be of most use in very polluted areas.

Dry filters

Dry filters use a material like glass fibre or cotton wool covered with a sticky substance. The particles stay on the sticky substance while the clean air

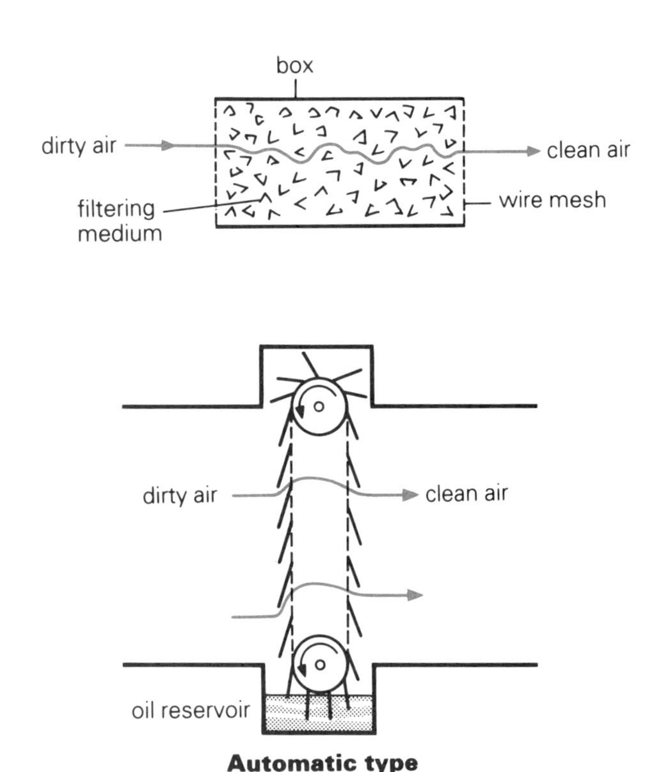

Figure 9.7 Viscous filters.

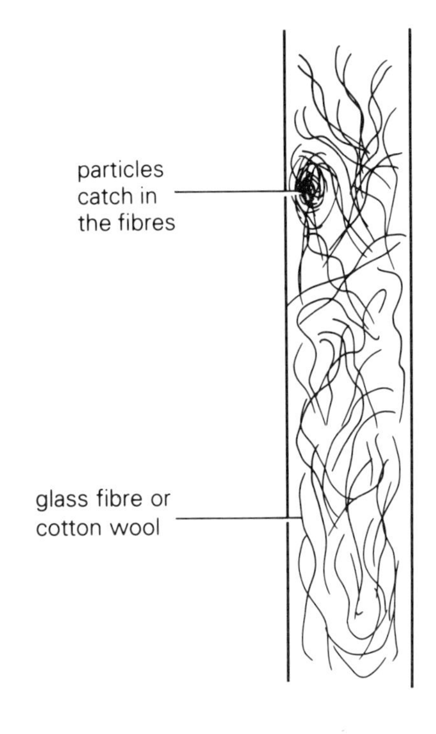

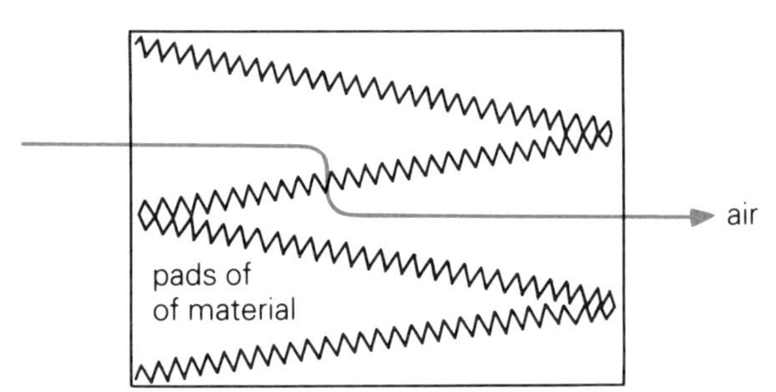

Figure 9.8 Dry filters.

passes through. Some of the particles are larger than the gaps in the fibre so that these are held by the fibres obstructing their movement (see Figure 9.8). In the filter, pads of the material are placed at different angles across the direction of air flow.

Dry filters also exist in automatic form and these use a system of two drums, similar to those employed for the viscous filter.

Electric filters

The dust, pollen or smoke particles, carried in the air stream, are passed between a series of electrodes. These electrodes have a high potential difference or voltage across them, usually in the region of 10 000 V. The high voltage removes some of the outer electrons from their atoms and this process is called ionisation. The atoms left behind are positively charged and are known as positive ions. A large proportion of the particles pick up positive ions and so become positively charged, while a much smaller proportion pick up electrons and become negatively charged.

The charged particles now pass between metal plates which are maintained at a lower potential difference than the electrodes. The negative particles are attracted to the positive plates and the positive particles to the negative plates. An **electric filter** is shown in Figure 9.9.

Electric filters are cheap to maintain, but one problem is that electric filters will only continue to operate well if they are washed regularly with water at high pressure. Another is the problem of insects in the system. Viscous and dry filters will stop the passage of insects into air-conditioning ducts, as insects cannot fly between the small gaps in the filtering material. However, this is not true of electric filters, and so a screen must be fitted somewhere in front of the filter in order to stop insects.

Other filters

Water sprays are sometimes used to remove polluting gases in industrial areas, such as hydrogen

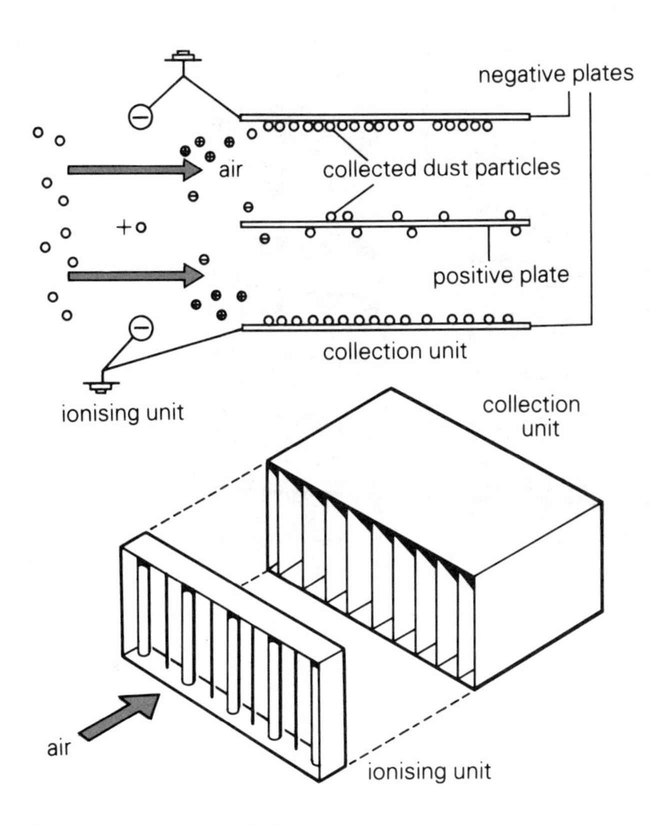

Figure 9.9 An electric filter.

sulphide and sulphur dioxide. However, they are not very good at removing dust.

Activated carbon filters are used for removing smells. The atoms of the gases that cause the smells stick to the carbon and so cannot pass into the air-conditioned room or building. The carbon must be removed from time to time and returned to the supplier where it is heated to a high temperature and re-activated. In the meantime a fresh filter from the stock is used.

Absolute filters

Filters which stop nearly all the particles in the air that passes through are called **absolute filters.** Absolute filters have very high efficiencies (95% up to nearly 100%) at stopping dust, compared with values of between 30% and 90% for ordinary filters. They are fixed where the supply air leaves the central unit.

Ultraviolet lamps

Some air-conditioning units have germicidal lamps in order to kill germs known as bacteria. These lamps give off a kind of electromagnetic radiation known as ultraviolet radiation. Ultraviolet is an invisible radiation that kills bacteria. This helps prevent people in an air-conditioned buildings from getting bacterial diseases.

Noise

Air-conditioning systems can be noisy. This can make life difficult in houses, where people naturally want to talk to one another. Noise causes particular problems in air-conditioning systems for offices, theatres and cinemas where it is important to hear what is being said. Sometimes noise is produced by machines, such as compressors or the fans that drive the air through the ducts. Sometimes it is produced by parts of the air-conditioning system which are not strongly fixed.

In good air-conditioning systems, installation engineers make sure that all parts are strongly fixed so that they cannnot vibrate and cause noise. The movement of machinery noise through the duct system can be stopped in a number of ways. One method is to line the inside of the ducts with material that absorbs sound. Such materials are called *acoustic absorbers* and one example is fibre glass. However, lining all the ducts in a system can be expensive and so, often, large acoustically-lined chambers, known as *plenums* are used. A plenum with, say, five times the cross-sectional area of the duct system, is placed between ducts and reduces the amount of noise (Figure 9.10)

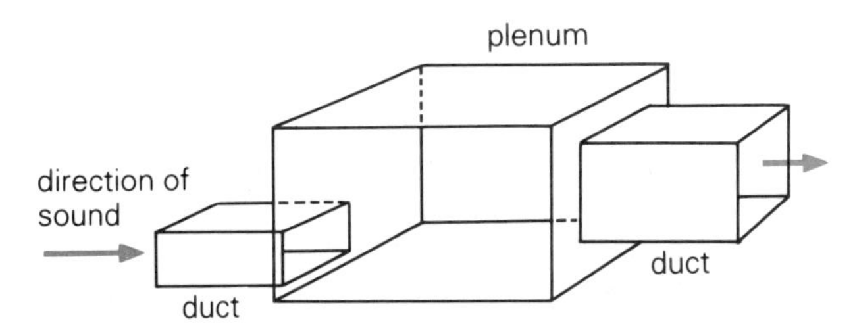

Figure 9.10 A plenum placed between ducts to reduce noise.

Another place where noise can be reduced is at the outside air intake . Here, special louvres with acoustic absorber inside can be used (see Figure 9.11(a)). Acoustic louvres can also be employed for the outlet grilles at the end of the ducts (Figure 9.11(b)).

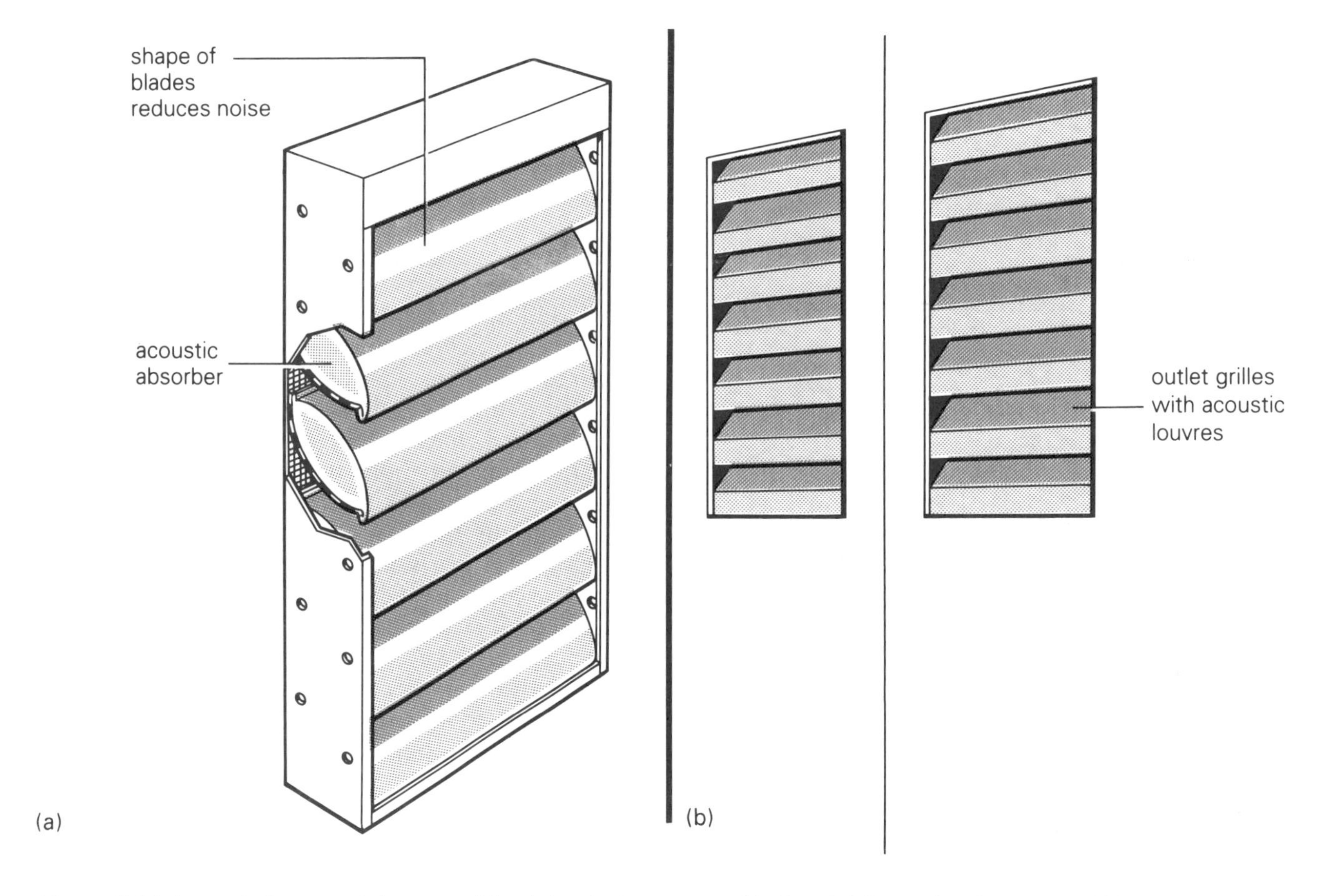

Figure 9.11 Acoustic louvres: (a) on outside air intake (courtesy of Industrial Acoustics Company); (b) on outlet grille.

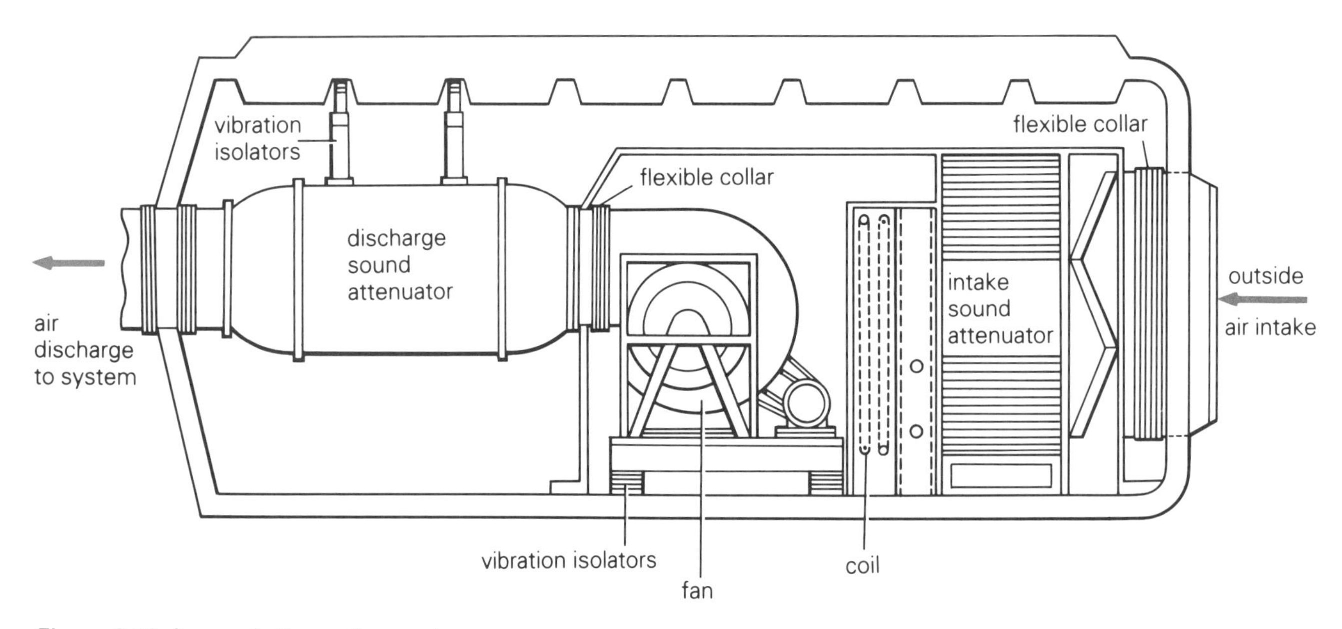

Figure 9.12 A sound attenuation system.

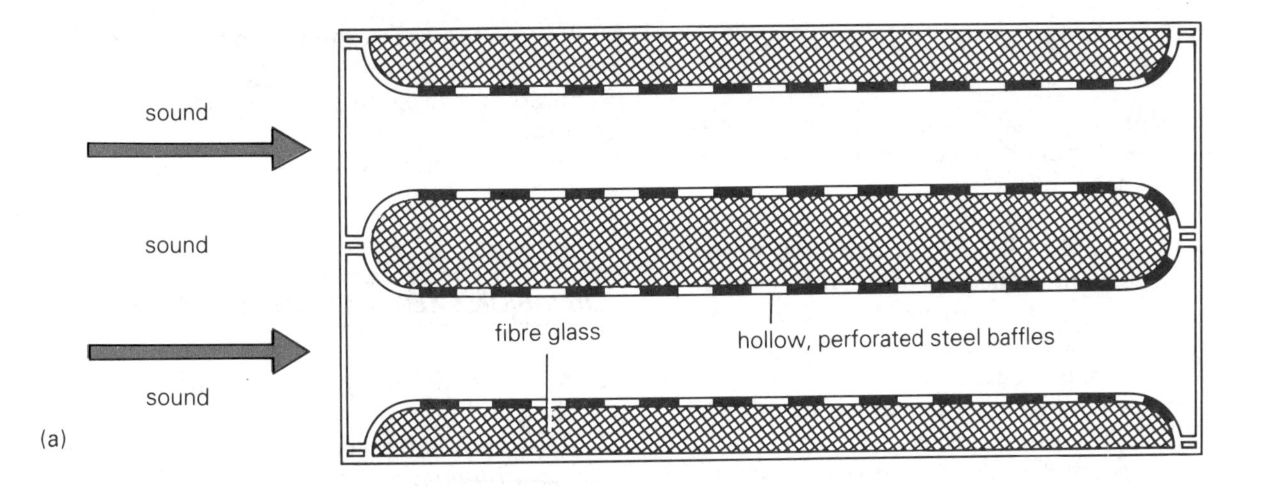

Figure 9.13 Some sound attenuators: (a) perforated hollow steel baffles with fibre glass inside; (b) absorbing material arranged round edge and in centre.

Some systems are equipped with devices known as *sound attenuators* or *silencers* which can be fitted in certain positions, such as where the return air enters, where the outside air enters and where the supply air leaves the central unit. A sound attenuator system is shown in Figure 9.12. The vibration isolators and flexible collars are there to reduce noise in the system further. Some attenuators contain perforated hollow steel baffles with fibre glass inside (Figure 9.13(a)), while others have the absorbing material arranged around the edges and in the centre (Figure 9.13(b)).

Air-conditioning systems can be noisy if they are badly designed. For example, the speed of air through the ducts may be too great. It is the task of the designer to make sure that this does not happen because it is very difficult for installation engineers to overcome bad design.

One noise problem that is not connected with air-conditioning machinery is that of noise between rooms in the workplace. For example, a conversation in one room may be carried through ducts to the next. This type of difficulty can be reduced by lining ducts with acoustic absorber in places where they pass through joining walls.

Dehumidification

When air is dehumidified by passing it over an evaporator or cooling coil the surface of the device becomes wet. The film of water does not conduct heat as well as the metal surface. Manufacturers take this into account by supplying evaporators and coils of greater capacity than would be necessary if the surface were not wet (see Chapter 12 Evaporators).

CHECK YOUR UNDERSTANDING

- Air conditioning is treating air in such a way that temperature, humidity and contamination are adjusted to suitable levels.
- Conditioned air supplied to the air-conditioned space is the supply air. Air which has passed through the air-conditioned space is called exhaust air, and the exhaust air returned to the air conditioning system is return air. Air taken in from outside the building is outside air or fresh air.
- Comfort air conditioning is making people feel comfortable in homes, offices, etc.
- For small rooms or shops a room air conditioner is used.
- Split units are larger than room air conditioners and central units control large systems of ducts which supply conditioned air to many rooms.
- Air can be humidified with warm water sprays. Humidistats control humidity.
- Air can be cooled and dehumidified.
- Thermostats are devices that control the temperature of conditioned air.
- Fans are used to blow the air along the ducts.
- Cars and other vehicles are sometimes fitted with air conditioning.
- Commercial air conditioning is special air conditioning for hotels, hospitals, etc.
- Process air conditioning is special air conditioning for industrial processes.
- Filters are used to remove damaging particles from the air.
- Air-conditioning systems should be designed to work as silently as possible.

REVISION EXERCISES AND QUESTIONS

1. What is meant by *cooling load* as applied to air-conditioning systems?
2. Distinguish between *comfort* and *process air conditioning*.
3. Explain the terms *supply air*, *exhaust air*, *return air* and *outside air*.
4. Explain the function of the air-conditioning filter.
5. What is an *absolute filter*?
6. Explain how air may be dehumidified.
7. Name two methods by which bacteria may be removed from an air-conditioned space.
8. Why must humidity be controlled in the printing industry?
9. What is a *humidistat*?
10. What is meant by the term *ionisation* with regard to air molecules?
11. What is a *thermostat*?

10 Compressors

Introduction

Compressors are machines that take refrigerant vapour flowing from the evaporator and compress it, causing a rise in temperature to take place. Compressors are also responsible for keeping the refrigerant circulating throughout the system, so that the hot vapour from the compressor is passed to the condenser, where it cools and flows back to the evaporator.

There are three types of compressor commonly used in refrigeration: these are the **reciprocating compressor**, the **centrifugal compressor** and the **rotary compressor**.

Reciprocating compressors

A reciprocating compressor has a piston moving up and down inside a cylinder which has valves at the top (see Figure 10.1). The **crankshaft** is being rotated in a clockwise direction by means of an electric motor and it is connected to the piston by a **crank pin**. In Figure 10.1(a) the piston has been pushed right to the top of the cylinder, to a position known as top dead centre (TDC). The **suction valve** is closed, the **discharge valve** is opened and the refrigerant has just been pushed into the discharge line by the compressing effect of the piston.

The rotation continues, the crankshaft pulls the crank pin down and the crank pin, in turn, pulls down the piston by means of the **connecting rod**. The volume of the cylinder above the piston increases and so the pressure decreases (see Chapter 5). The pressure of the refrigerant in the suction line is greater than the pressure in the cylinder and so the suction valve opens and refrigerant is sucked into the compressor. At the same time, the sucking effect of the pressure drop closes the discharge valve (Figure 10.1(b)). When the crank pin is vertically below the crankshaft (known as bottom dead centre, BDC) the volume of refrigerant in the cylinder is a maximum (Figure 10.1(c)). Further rotation now reduces the volume, compresses the vapour and forces it through the open discharge valve into the discharge line (Figure 10.1(d)). This compression is rapid enough for an adiabatic change in which there is a temperature rise to occur. The movement of the refrigerant through the compressor is shown by the arrows. The refrigerant cannot move directly from the suction line to the discharge line because there is a partition between them.

Figure 10.2 is the pressure–volume diagram for the whole cycle. From A to B the piston moves downwards in the cylinder allowing the hot vapour, compressed from the previous cycle, to expand. As the vapour expands, the pressure in the cylinder decreases, the pressure of the vapour in the suction line opens the suction valve and the fresh vapour is taken in (B to C). C represents bottom dead centre (BDC) and now the piston moves up, decreases the volume in the cylinder, puts the vapour under pressure and so raises the temperature. When the pressure is great enough (at D) the discharge valve is pushed open and vapour is forced into the discharge line.

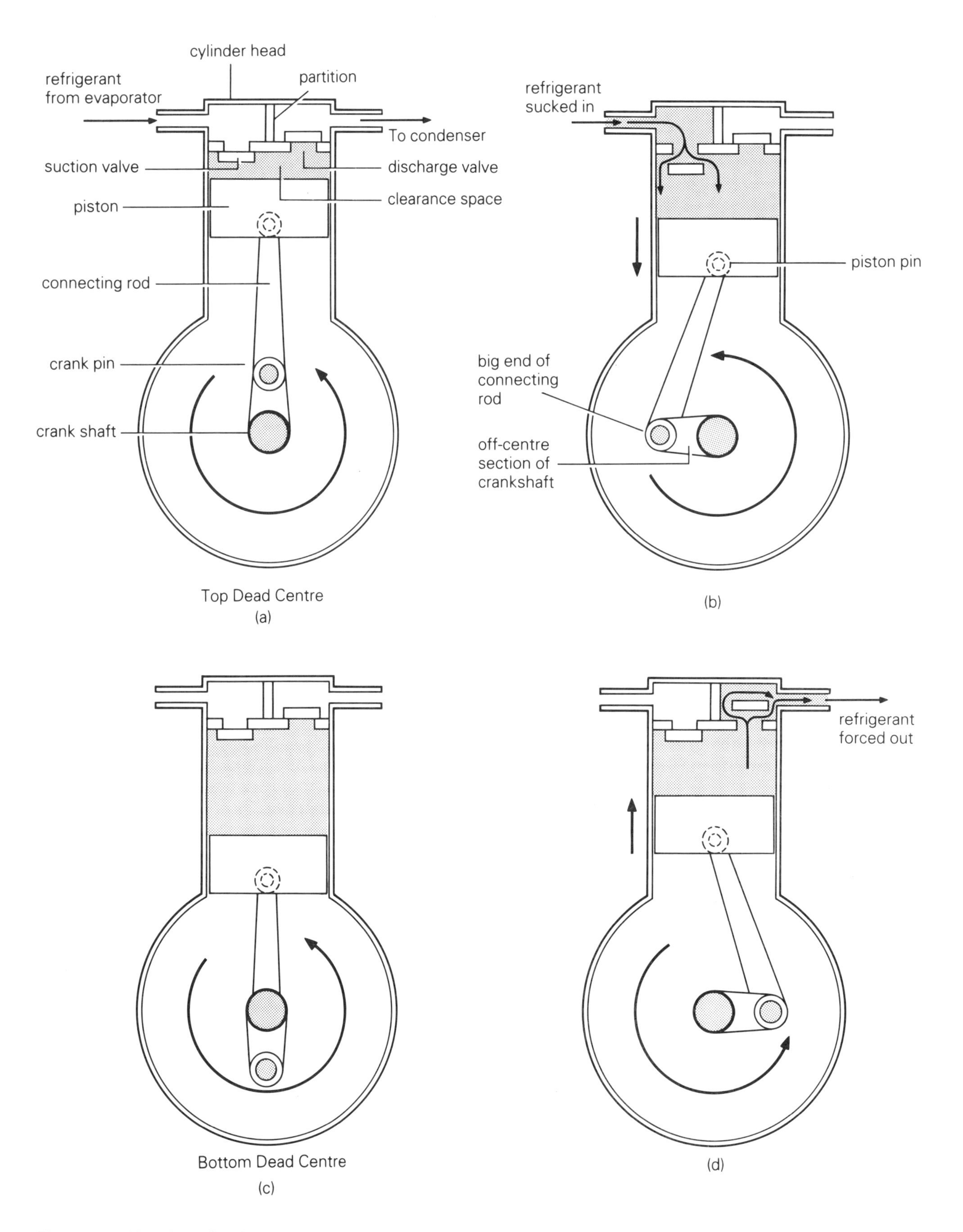

Figure 10.1 Working of a simple reciprocating compressor as the crankshaft is rotated clockwise [(a)→(d)].

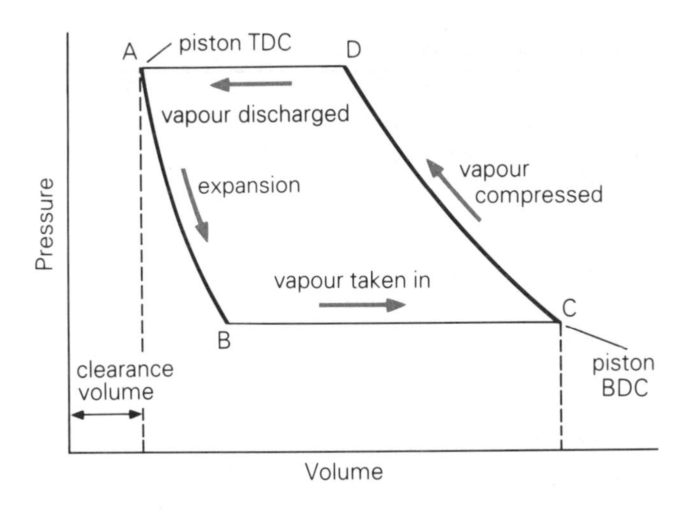

Figure 10.2 Pressure–volume diagram for reciprocating compressor cycle.

Refrigerating capacity

The **refrigerating capacity** or compressor capacity, the measure of the ability of a compressor to cause refrigeration, depends on two factors: the mass of refrigerant flowing through the compressor every second (the mass flow rate) and the refrigeration effect in kilojoules per kilogramme of refrigerant (see Chapter 6). Refrigerating capacity is measured in watts or kilowatts:

refrigerating capacity = mass flow rate × refrigerating effect

EXAMPLE 10.1

If the mass of refrigerant passing through a compressor is 0.1 kg/s and the refrigerating effect is 100 kJ/kg, calculate the refrigerating capacity of the compressor.

Solution
Refrigerating capacity = 0.1 × 100 = 10 kW.

The above example gives a theoretical value for refrigerating capacity which is greater than the actual value for two reasons:

1 as the piston comes down to suck in the vapour, less vapour is taken in than is apparent from theory; and
2 the density of vapour in the cylinder is less than that in the suction line.

The *total volumetric efficiency* is a measure of the actual volume of vapour coming into the cylinder (V_A) per second compared with the **piston displacement.** The piston displacement is the difference in volume between TDC and BDC divided by the time in seconds (V_p).

$$E_v = \frac{V_a}{V_p}$$

where E_v is the total volumetric efficiency. Expressed as a percentage:

$$E_v = \frac{V_a}{V_p} \times 100$$

The relationship between the actual and theoretical values of refrigerating capacity depends on E_v.

$$\text{Actual refrigerating capacity} = \text{theoretical refrigerating capacity} \times \frac{E_v}{100}$$

where E_v is the percentage value of total volumetric efficiency.

EXAMPLE 10.2

If the theoretical refrigerating capacity of a compressor is 10 kW and the total volumetric efficiency is 70%, calculate the actual refrigerating capacity.

Solution

$$\text{Actual refrigerating capacity} = 10 \times \frac{70}{100} = 7\ \text{kW}.$$

The value of the total volumetric efficiency depends on a number of factors. One factor is the compressor clearance or **clearance volume**, which is the space left between the top of the piston and the end of the cylinder, when the piston is TDC. Because of this, vapour is always left above the piston at the end of the discharge stroke. As the piston comes down again this vapour must be expanded sufficiently for the pressure to drop so that the suction valve opens. The first part of the movement is wasted because no vapour enters from the suction line. The volume of vapour that enters is less than would be expected from the size of the cylinder. The clearance volume should be as small as possible for maximum volumetric efficiency.

Changing the discharge and suction pressures will also alter the volumetric efficiency. If the discharge pressure is increased, the vapour in the clearance space will be at a greater pressure. This means that when expansion occurs the piston will have to move down further before vapour from the suction line enters. If the suction pressure is decreased, the piston will again have to move a greater distance before vapour enters. In both cases the volumetric efficiency goes down.

The **compression ratio** of a compressor is the ratio of the absolute discharge pressure to the absolute suction pressure, or

$$\text{compression ratio} = \frac{\text{absolute discharge pressure}}{\text{absolute suction pressure}}$$

EXAMPLE 10.3

The pressure in the discharge line is 10 bar A and the pressure in the suction line is 2.5 bar A. Find the compression ratio of the compressor.

Solution

$$\text{Compression ratio} = \frac{10}{2.5} = 4.$$

A high discharge pressure and a low suction pressure result in a high compression ratio and a low volumetric efficiency. When the compression ratio is high the volumetric efficiency is low and when the compression ratio is low the volumetric efficiency is high. In low-temperature refrigeration systems, such as deep freezes, the suction pressure (and temperature) are low. Hence the compression ratio is high and the volumetric efficiency is low. The refrigerating capacity is also low. If the same compressor is used at a high temperature, as in air conditioning, the refrigerating capacity will increase. The volumetric efficiency is also reduced by the small drop in pressure as the vapour leaves the suction line, enters the cylinder and expands rapidly. This process, which also occurs at the input of an evaporator is called throttling or wire-drawing. When the compressor is being used it gets hot and so the temperature of the cylinder increases, causing the vapour entering through the suction line to expand. This expansion reduces the volumetric efficiency. Leakage of the vapour through valves which should be shut tight and around pistons also reduces the volumetric efficiency. Leakage around pistons can be caused by dirt and contamination wearing away surfaces which should be in close contact.

Compressor power

Compressor power is the theoretical power required to drive a compressor and it is given by the formula:

compressor power = actual refrigerating capacity × theoretical power per unit refrigerating capacity

The theoretical power per unit refrigerating capacity or per kilowatt of refrigerating capacity, was discussed in Chapter 6 and the value calculated for the cycle shown in Figure 6.4 was 0.3070 kW/kW (under the heading *Refrigerating rate*).

EXAMPLE 10.4

A compressor has an actual refrigerating capacity of 7 kW and it operates under conditions where the theoretical power per kilowatt of refrigerating capacity is 0.2 kW/kW. Calculate the compressor power.

Solution
Compressor power = $7 \times 0.2 = 1.4$ kW.

The above value is a theoretical value and in practice the actual compressor power delivered by the electric motor to the crankshaft must be greater than this, as there is power loss due to friction inside the compressor. Electric motors, like all motors, are less than a hundred per cent efficient and the electric power delivered to the motor will be even greater than the actual compressor power.

EXAMPLE 10.5

The theoretical power of a compressor is 1.4 kW and there is a power loss of 0.4 kW due to friction and other causes while the compressor is working. If the compressor is driven by an electric motor which works at 70% efficiency, calculate the electrical power delivered to the motor.

Solution
Actual compressor power = $1.4 + 0.4 = 1.8$ kW.
1.8 kW is the power delivered to the compressor by the electric motor.
Power delivered by the motor = efficiency × electrical power.

$$1.8 = \frac{70}{100} \times \text{electrical power}.$$

$$\text{Electrical power} = 1.8 \times \frac{100}{70} = 2.6\ \text{kW}.$$

Compressor construction

In small compressors the cylinder is usually formed by boring a hole in the cast iron body of the compressor. The piston moves up and down inside the hole. In larger machines the hole is lined with a **cylinder sleeve** which can be removed and replaced once it is worn. This is preferable to replacing the whole of the compressor body. Pistons are cylindrical pieces of metal, made of cast iron or aluminium, which move up-and-down inside the cylinder. The piston should fit tightly in the cylinder but not so tightly as to restrict the up and down movement. A thin film of oil from the crankcase provides a gas-tight seal between the piston and cylinder so that no vapour leaks through to the crankcase oil. If the piston fits too loosely in the cylinder, the oil film will break and leakage will occur. Refrigerant in the oil causes problems in the system (see *Refrigerant contamination*, below).

In smaller compressors, contact with the inside of the cylinder is from the walls of the pistons themselves but with larger compressors, **piston rings** are used (Figure 10.3).

One advantage of using piston rings is that the area of contact between the rings and the cylinder is small, so that the amount of friction and therefore heating is reduced. Another advantage is that when the rings are worn, they can be replaced without replacing the whole piston. Piston rings have a gap at one point so they can be opened out, slipped over the cylinder and installed in grooves cut into the piston. Another type of ring called an **oil ring**, containing a groove to retain oil, is used to stop oil splashing up from the crankcase and mixing with refrigerant vapour (Figure 10.3).

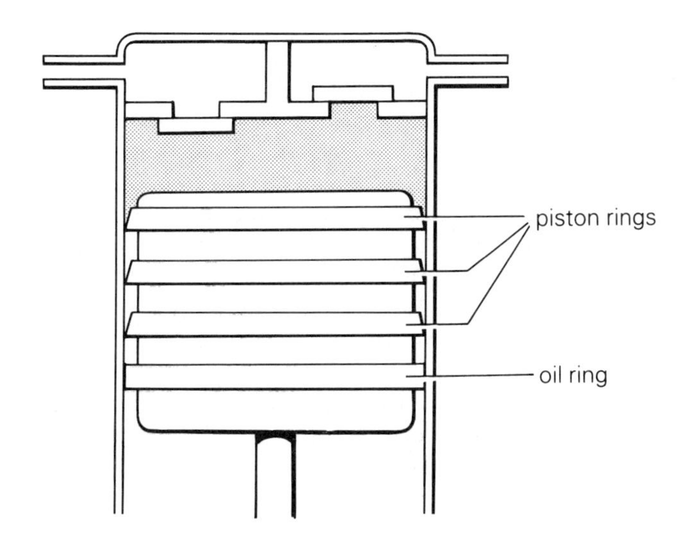

Figure 10.3 Piston rings and oil ring in a compressor.

An electric motor has a rotating shaft which connects to the crankshaft of the compressor (or else there is a single shaft). It is the function of the crankshaft to convert rotating motion to the up-and-down or reciprocating motion of the piston. Part of the shaft is constructed off-centre from the rest of the shaft and one end of the connecting rod, the **big end**, is connected to this off-centre section (see Figure 10.1). A bearing is a device which connects two moving parts together and a bearing is used between the big end and the crankshaft. This enables the crankshaft to rotate freely inside the big end. As the off-centre part of the shaft rotates with the rest of the crankshaft it swings round in a circle and causes the reciprocating motion of the piston. The other end of the connecting rod is connected by means of a piston pin to the piston. A bearing on the connecting rod enables free movement to take place between the rod and the pin. Figure 10.4 shows an exploded view of a reciprocating compressor.

Bearings

Compressor bearings are used not only on the connecting rod but on the crankshaft, where it passes through the compressor case, too. The bearings are in the form of sleeves, where the outer shell is often made of bronze. Inside the shell is a lining made of a fairly soft alloy which actually makes contact with the rotating crankshaft, or other moving part. In this way it is the bearing which wears, rather than the crankshaft, as bearings are fairly cheap and easy to replace compared with crankshafts.

The lubricating oil fills the small gaps between the bearings and the moving compressor parts and helps to keep them cool. The other function of the oil as it passes through the gaps is to remove grit and dirt. An oil filter stops the dirt from getting back in again and because of this oil filters become clogged. Filters need to be removed, inspected and if necessary cleaned, as part of normal maintenance. If oil is really dirty then it needs to be changed. As bearings and oil rings become worn, the gaps

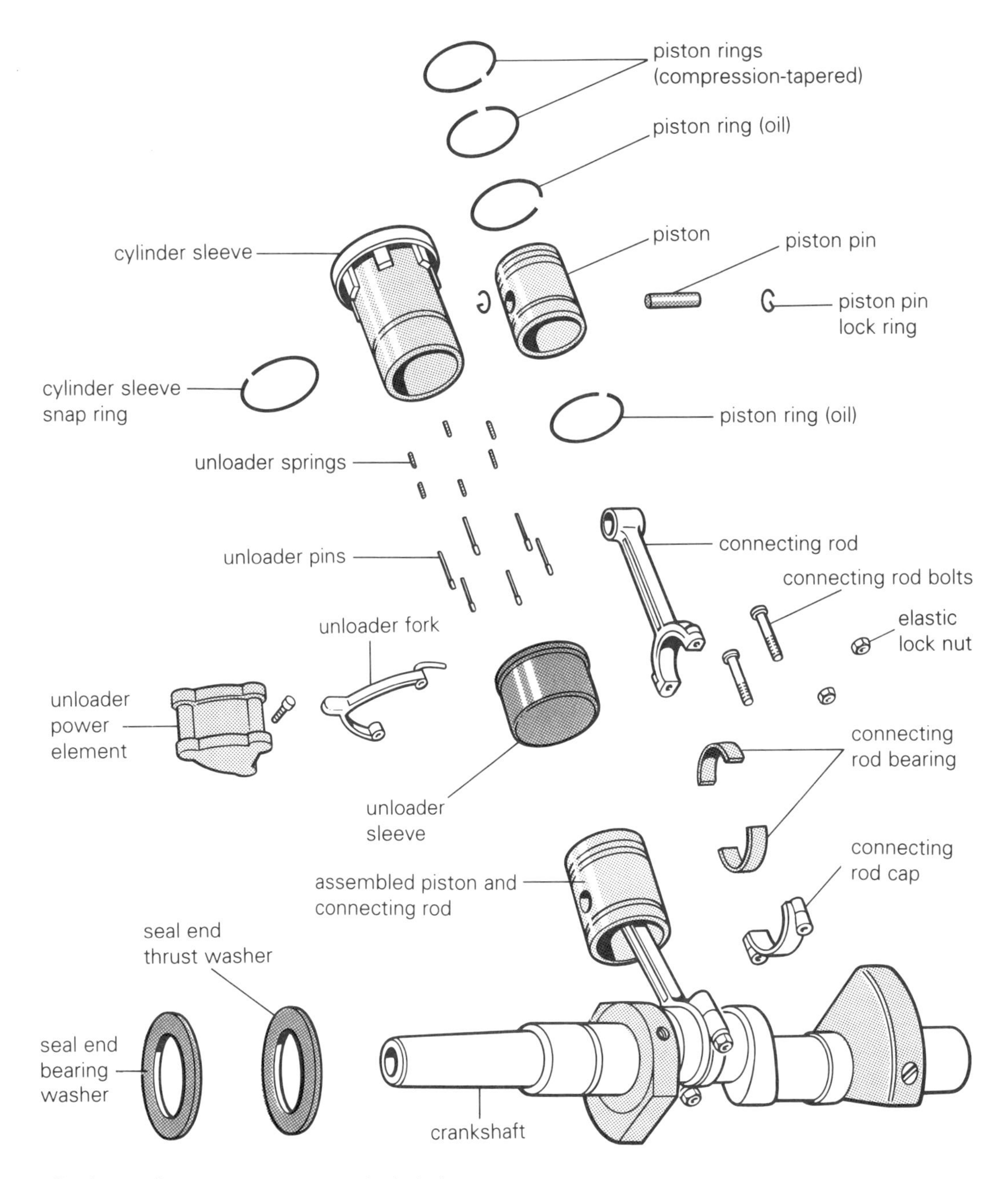

Figure 10.4 Reciprocating compressor – exploded view.

increase and more oil escapes from the compressor through the cylinder into the discharge line. If oil is being lost at a fast rate then the bearings and the oil ring should be replaced by new ones. In small compressors oil is stored at the bottom of the crankcase and as the crankshaft rotates it causes the oil to splash up and lubricate the moving surfaces in the compressor. In larger compressors oil pumps are used to circulate the oil through passages drilled in the crankshaft, connecting rod and compressor body.

Precautions have to be taken to make sure there is no leakage of oil from the crankcase. One type of seal which prevents leakage is a carbon ring which is held onto the crankshaft by means of a gasket made of an artificial rubber, such as neoprene. A spring holds the ring against the cover plate. A film of lubricating oil develops between the rotating face of the carbon ring and the stationary cover plate. This film stops vapour and filter oil from leaking away (see Figure 10.5).

There are a number of different types of valve used in compressors. One type is the ring plate valve, which consists of a flat disc with a cap that is

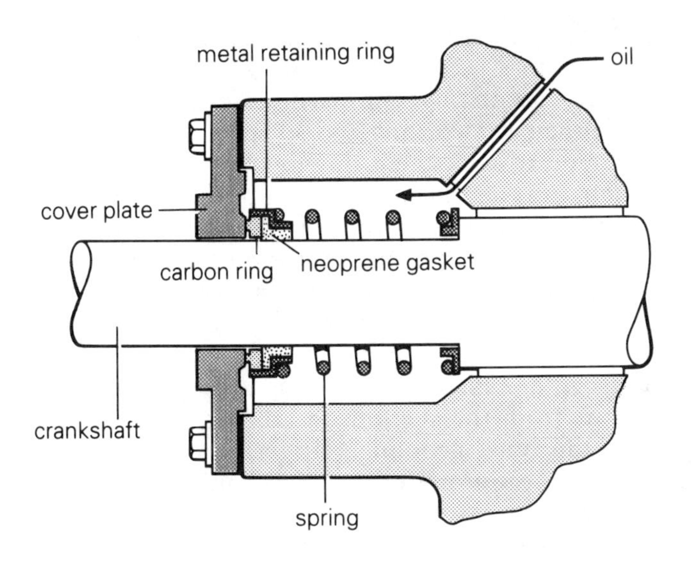

Figure 10.5 A crankcase seal: carbon ring held by gasket.

Figure 10.6 A two-cylinder compressor (courtesy of Carrier Air Conditioning).

held in position by a flat spring. The pressure difference between the two sides of the cap causes the cap to move up and down to allow the vapour through. Other types include poppet valves, used on slow speed compressors, and various types of flexing valve in which thin strips of metal respond to the pressure difference.

Multi-cylinder compressors

Small reciprocating compressors have just one cylinder but large compressors, used for industrial installations, can have as many as sixteen. A two cylinder compressor is shown in Figure 10.6.

The electrical power required to drive a compressor can vary from as little as 100 W to many kilowatts. Although, electric motors are normally used to drive compressors, in practice any machine, such as a petrol or diesel engine, which causes rotation could be used. In cases where there is no electrical supply these engines are sometimes used.

Open compressors

Electric motors and compressors can be supplied as two separate units which have to be joined together in some way, or they can be part of a complete motor–compressor unit. If they are supplied as separate units then the compressor crankshaft and the rotor shaft of the motor have to be connected so that the electric motor can drive the compressor.

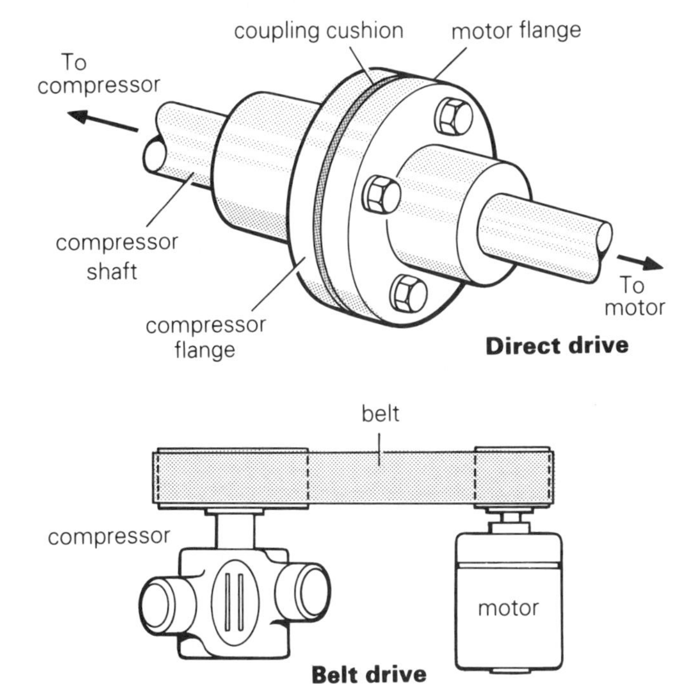

Figure 10.7 Connecting a compressor to its motor.

One way of doing this is by means of a belt drive, as shown in Figure 10.7. Another way is to bolt the two shafts together in a direct drive system. There is a cushion included in the coupling to absorb the shock developed by the compressor pumping (Figure 10.7).

A compressor and electric motor, together with a condenser and discharge line, are often supplied as a single unit known as a **condensing unit**.

These can be air or water cooled and in the air cooled type the electric motor drives a fan to cool the condenser.

Hermetic assemblies

Some condensing units employ an electric motor and compressor assembly which are mounted on the same rotor shaft. This has the advantage that no coupling has to be supplied between the motor and the condenser which are contained in a totally closed steel shell. Such containers are said to be hermetically sealed and the condensing unit is called a **hermetic condensing unit**. The hermetic sealing is achieved by welding. Hermetic condensing units are commonly used on domestic refrigerators. Semi-hermetic units in which the shell is bolted together have the advantage that they can be opened up for servicing. Semi-hermetic units of many kilowatts of power are used for large air-conditioning systems.

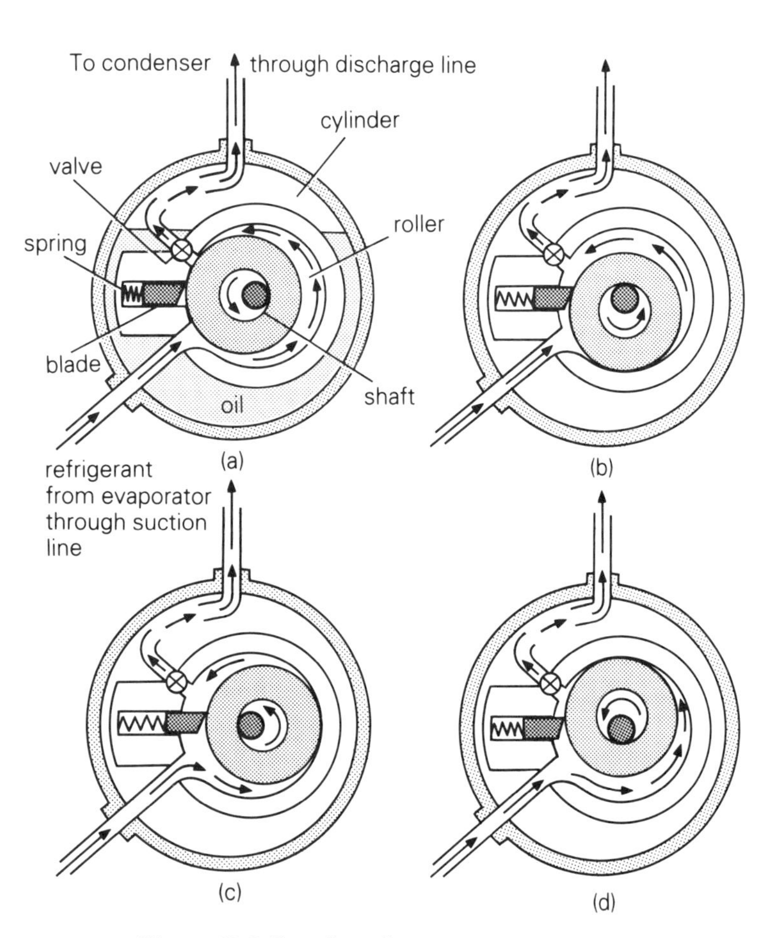

Figure 10.8 Rotating piston compressor.

Cooling

Electric motors, like all machines, tend to get hot while they are working and so some means has to be found to cool them down. One way is to use cooling fins on the outer surface of the motor case. Another way is to attach a fan on the end of the motor shaft to blow air over the motor windings.

In hermetic compressors the motor is contained inside a metal shell and this makes cooling difficult by the methods described above. In these compressors, one method of cooling is by passing cold vapour from the suction line through the motor. With this type of cooling, refrigerant leaks from the pipes can cause motors to burn out. Commercial refrigeration systems with hermetic compressors need to be checked frequently for leaks in order to avoid damage to the motor. Other methods of cooling include air, water, and oil cooling.

Rotary compressors

One type of rotary compressor consists of a **rotating piston** or roller which is attached to a rotating shaft. It is the way that the roller and the shaft are attached which enables the compressor to pump the refrigerant. Instead of the shaft being fixed to the centre of the roller it is fixed to one side. This is called eccentric fixing. As the roller rotates inside the cylinder it changes the pressure in such a way that refrigerant is sucked in through a pipe at the bottom and pushed out through a hole at the top. A spring-loaded blade pushes against the roller to ensure that it makes contact with the cylinder all the way round (Figure 10.8).

The pipe from the top of the cylinder protrudes above the level of the oil in the case and high pressure, high temperature vapour fills the space above the oil. A valve stops the high pressure vapour from entering the suction line and the rest of the low pressure part of the system. The vapour leaves the compressor through a pipe at the top of the case and then enters the discharge line.

Another kind of rotary compressor is the **rotating vane** type. Rotating vane compressors have spring loaded vanes fixed at four, or more, points around a rotating metal shaft known as a rotor. The rotor is again situated eccentrically. The springs push the vanes firmly against the inside of the cylinder and as the rotor rotates past the pipe from the suction line the volume of refrigerant vapour

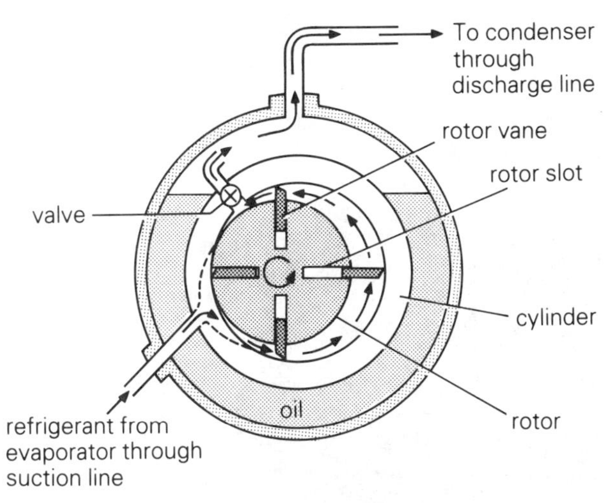

Figure 10.9 Rotating vane compressor.

trapped by the vanes increases, causing a decrease in pressure. Therefore more vapour is sucked in through the suction part (Figure 10.9).

By the time the vapour is discharged, the volume is small and the temperature and pressure are high. The high pressure pushes vapour into the space above the oil and from there it enters the discharge line. As in the rotating piston type of compressor, a valve stops high pressure vapour from entering the low pressure side.

The **scroll type** of rotary compressor, often used in air-conditioning systems uses two metal spirals, known as scrolls. One scroll is fixed, while the other rotates, so compressing the vapour against the fixed scroll. A scroll compressor is shown in Figure 10.10.

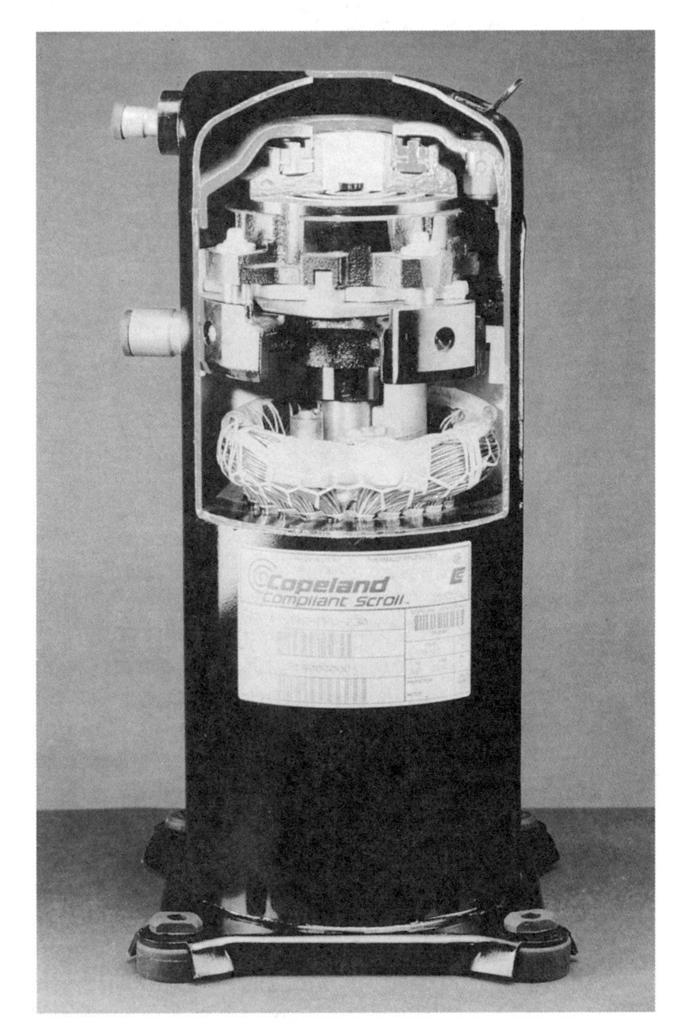

Figure 10.10 Hermetic motor-scroll compressor unit (courtesy of Copeland Corporation Ltd).

Centrifugal compressors

Centrifugal compressors consist of a series of vanes mounted on a wheel which is designed to rotate and is known as an impeller wheel. Refrigerant enters near the centre of the wheel and an outward force known as the centrifugal force exerted by the rotating vanes pushes the vapour outwards to the rim of the wheel and from there to the condenser (Figure 10.11).

By the time the vapour gets to the rim, its temperature and pressure has increased.

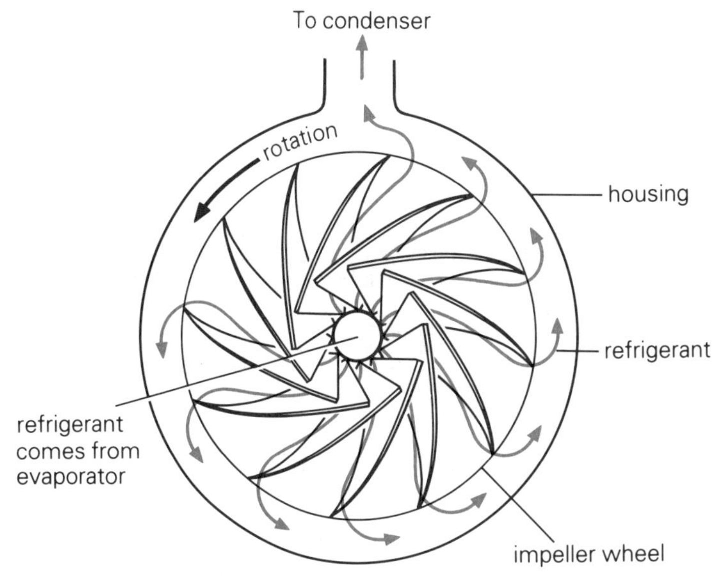

Figure 10.11 A centrifugal compressor.

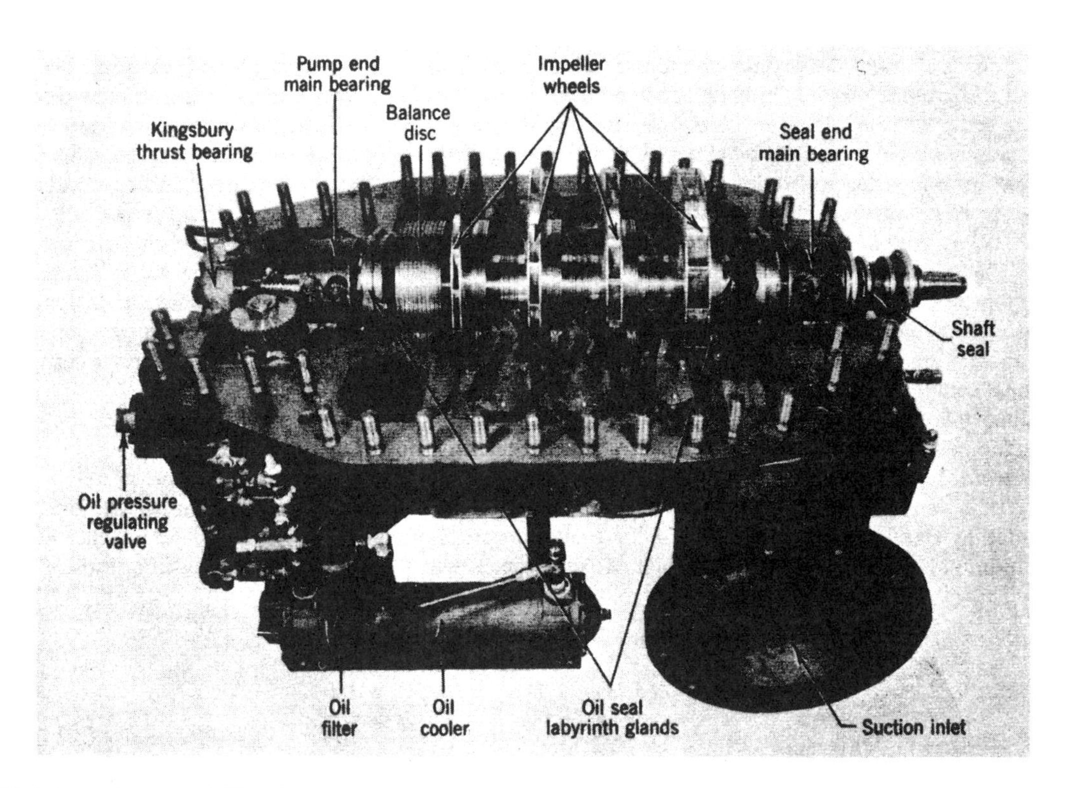

Figure 10.12 A four-stage centrifugal compressor.

Some centrifugal compressors employ more than one impeller wheel and as the vapour flows from wheel to wheel its pressure and temperature increase. A four-stage (four wheel) centrifugal compressor is shown in Figure 10.12 and an impeller wheel is shown in Figure 10.13.

In order to achieve the high vapour pressures necessary for the condenser, impeller wheels have to rotate at high speeds, above 3000 revolutions per minute (r.p.m.). This is 50 revolutions per second. Speeds up to 18 000 r.p.m. are sometimes used.

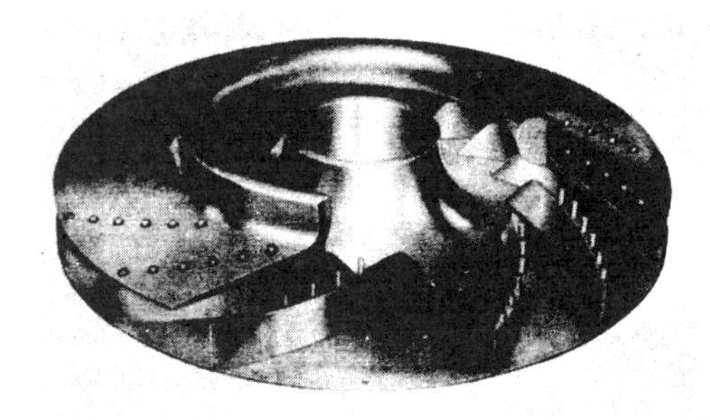

Figure 10.13 An impeller wheel.

Refrigerant contamination

Compressors have to be lubricated so that the moving parts, such as the crankshaft and the connecting rod can move freely. Without lubricating oil the friction between the moving parts would cause them to heat up, expand and eventually to seize solid. Refrigerant in the form of vapour passes through the compressor in order to move on to the condenser. As it does so, some of it will liquefy and mix with the oil at the bottom of the crankcase. There are a number of reasons why this happens.

1 Sometimes the flow of refrigerant through the evaporator is too great and liquid refrigerant will pass through the throttling valve, get into the suction line and drip into the oil. This can usually be prevented by the proper adjustment of the throttling valve. If it is caused by a faulty valve this can be repaired or replaced.
2 When the system control (see Chapter 21) switches the compressor off, the system is said to be in the *off cycle* and the refrigerant in the evaporator can condense and enter the oil through the suction line. If the crankcase temperature becomes too low when the system is off, vapour from the evaporator condenses inside the crankcase. This can be overcome by

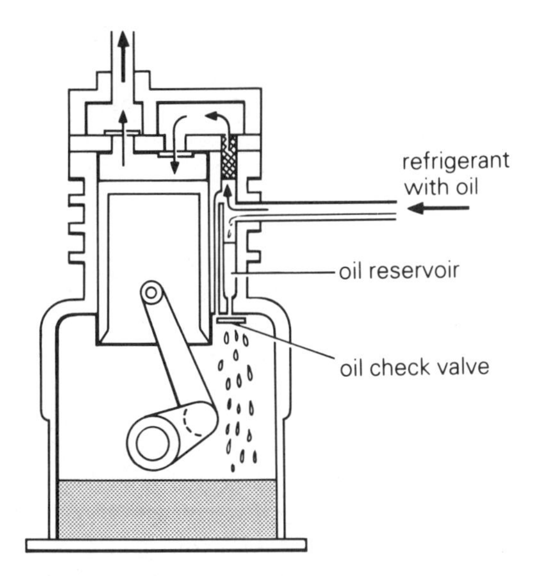

Figure 10.14 An oil check valve.

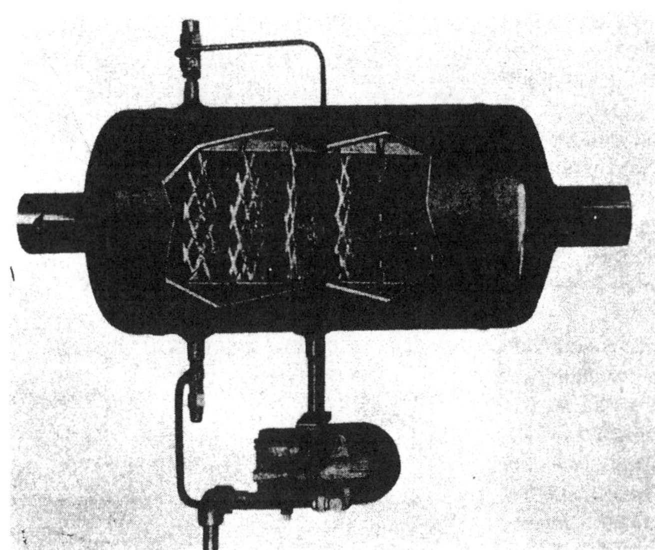

Figure 10.15 Oil separator.

using a compressor with a crankcase heater, which only comes on during the off cycle. The heater raises the temperature enough to stop refrigerant from condensing. Crankcase heaters also help prevent oil frothing up due to liquid refrigerant vaporising in the oil (see below).

A pump-down cycle is sometimes operated in conjunction with a crankcase heater in order to stop frothing. Close the receiver outlet valve and attach a pressure gauge to the suction service valve. Allow the compressor to lower the pressure to just above atmospheric. Switch off the compressor and the pressure gauge reading will rise as dissolved refrigerant boils out. When the gauge reading returns to just above atmospheric pressure the process is complete.

Another way of preventing frothing is to employ a compressor with a special valve, known as a check valve. If oil has passed round the system with the refrigerant, it will re-enter the compressor through the suction line. The oil, which is a liquid, passes through the check valve while the vapour continues to the suction valve (Figure 10.14). When a compressor restarts after the thermostat has switched it off there can be a sudden reduction in pressure in the crankcase which gives rise to frothing. The check valve prevents this from happening.

One effect that refrigerant in the oil has is to stop proper lubrication of the compressor and this can damage the compressor in the manner explained above. Another effect is that frothing occurs, causing oil to enter the discharge line. Once oil is in the discharge line it is carried throughout the system and becomes a problem. In the condenser the hot refrigerant vapour that leaves the compressor is converted into a liquid and the oil mixes very well with CFCs and HCFCs. Oil therefore causes little problem in the condenser. However in the evaporator the temperature is low and the oil is a liquid while the refrigerant is a vapour. The oil forms a layer on the inside of the evaporator. Oil is a poor conductor of heat so the efficiency of the evaporator is reduced (see Chapter 12). This problem can be overcome by means of *oil separators* in the discharge line. One type of separator uses screens that stop the oil but allow refrigerant to pass through. The oil then drains out and is passed back to the crankcase (Figure 10.15).

CHECK YOUR UNDERSTANDING

- Reciprocating compressors have a piston, which moves up and down inside a cylinder.
- Refrigerating capacity is a measure of the ability of a compressor to cause refrigeration. It is equal to mass flow rate × refrigerating effect.
- The total volumetric efficiency is a measure of the actual volume of vapour coming into the cylinder, compared with the piston displacement.
- Actual refrigerating capacity = theoretical refrigerating capacity × total volumetric efficiency as a percentage/100.

- Compression ratio is the ratio of the absolute discharge pressure to the absolute suction pressure.
- Compressor power = actual refrigerating capacity × theoretical power per unit refrigerating capacity.
- Larger reciprocating compressors have piston rings and an oil ring.
- Electric motors can be cooled by fins, fan or by cold vapour.
- The rotating piston compressor consists of a rotating piston which is attached to a rotating shaft.
- The rotating vane compressor has four spring-loaded vanes on a rotor.
- The scroll type compressor has one fixed and one rotating scroll.
- In centrifugal compressors, refrigerant is thrown outwards by the rotating vanes on the impeller wheel.
- Refrigerant passing through compressors can get into the oil and then carry it into the system.
- A check valve is one way of overcoming the problem of frothing and so is the crankcase heater.

REVISION EXERCISES AND QUESTIONS

1. If the mass of refrigerant passing through a compressor is 0.2 kg/s and the refrigerating effect is 80 kJ/kg, calculate the refrigerating capacity of the compressor.
2. If the theoretical refrigerating capacity of a compressor is 12 kW and the total volumetric efficiency is 60%, calculate the actual refrigerating capacity.
3. The pressure in the discharge line is 12 bar A and the pressure in the suction line is 2.0 bar A. Find the compression ratio of the compressor.
4. A compressor has an actual refrigerating capacity of 6 kW and it operates under conditions where the theoretical power per kilowatt of refrigerating capacity is 0.3 kW/kW. Calculate the compressor power.
5. The theoretical power of a compressor is 1.3 kW and there is a power loss of 0.2 kW due to friction and other causes while the compressor is working. If the compressor is driven by an electric motor which works at 60% efficiency, calculate the electrical power delivered to the motor.
6. What is meant by *compressor clearance* of a reciprocating compressor?
7. Name two advantages of using piston rings in a reciprocating compressor.
8. How is the electric motor cooled in a hermetic compressor?
9. Name two types of *rotary compressor.*
10. Briefly describe how the *centrifugal compressor* works.
11. Name one reason why refrigerant becomes contaminated with oil when it passes through the compressor.
12. How can the presence of refrigerant in the compressor oil damage the compressor?
13. In large compressors, how is the oil from the bottom of the crankcase circulated to other parts of the compressor?
14. What is the purpose of an *oil ring*?

Introduction

The condenser is that part of a refrigeration system in which the superheated vapour travelling along the discharge line from the compressor is condensed (or liquefied). Inside the condenser the hot refrigerant vapour cools as heat transfers by conduction through the metal walls. Outside the walls is the condensing medium, which can be either air or water. Condensers fall into three main groups: **air-cooled, water-cooled** and **evaporative**. In air-cooled types, the air-condensing medium removes heat from the outside of the condenser walls by convection. This convection can be either of the natural type in which air in contact with the walls is heated, rises and is replaced by cold air, or else it can be forced by a fan.

Air-cooled condensers

Condensers used on domestic refrigerators work by natural convection and they are mounted on the back of the refrigerator cabinet, which should not be obstructed so that the air can circulate properly. The metal used in manufacture is normally steel. Domestic refrigerator condensers are of two main types: **plate condensers** and **finned condensers**.

Plate condensers consist of steel tubing to which a metal plate is fastened. The metal plate helps to conduct heat away from the tubing. A gap is left between the refrigerator cabinet and the condenser in order to promote convection currents in the air.

Finned condensers are equipped with widely spaced cooling fins so as not to interfere with movement of convected air over the surface. Fins increase the surface area in contact with the air and so the amount of heat conducted away from the refrigerant is increased. In some cases, as in some kinds of domestic refrigerator, copper wires are soldered to the surface of the condenser to act as simple fins. Plate and finned condensers are shown in Figure 11.1.

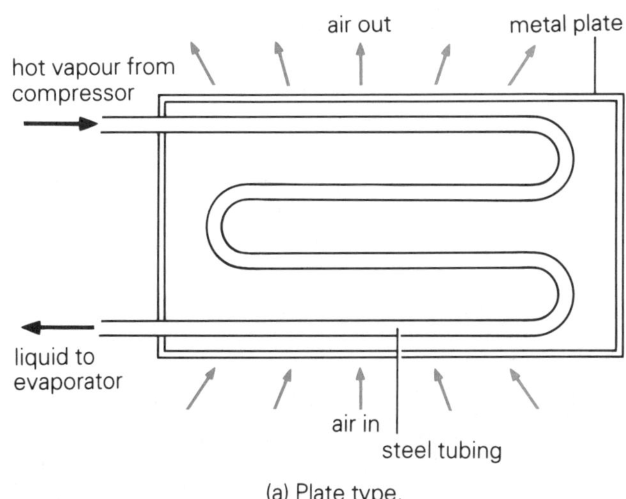

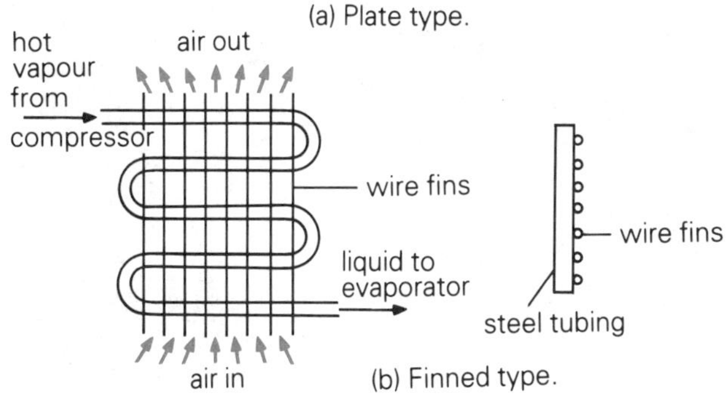

Figure 11.1 Condensers showing convection: (a) plate type; (b) finned type.

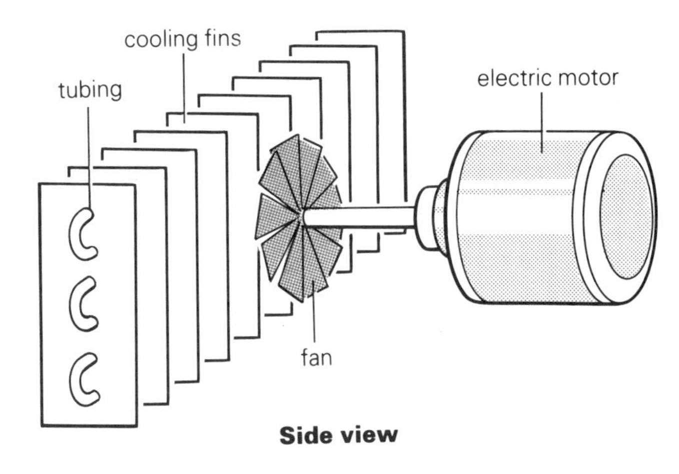

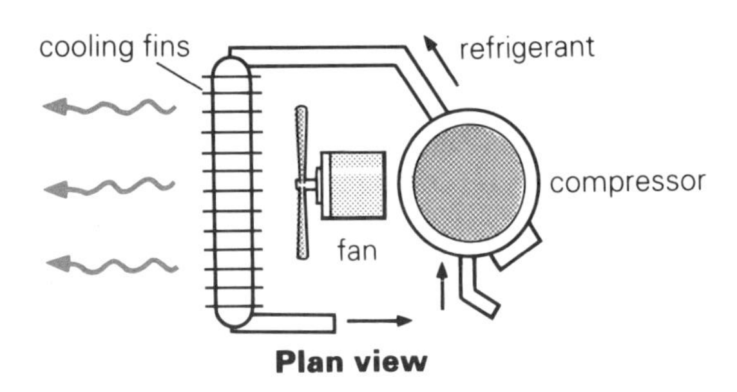

Figure 11.2 Forced air convection.

Figure 11.3 Remote air-cooled condensers (courtesy of Searle Manufacturing Company).

Forced air-convection type condensers fall into two groups: chassis-mounted types and remote types. Chassis types are usually mounted on the same chassis as the compressor and the whole item is termed a condensing unit. The fan is positioned close to the condenser coils and a separate electric motor is needed to drive the fan, see Figure 11.2.

The whole unit is attached to the refrigerator chassis. Remote types are mounted away from the the compressor and the other parts of the refrigerator system, either indoors or out of doors. The larger remote condensers are usually positioned on walls, roofs and even on the ground for very large units (see Figure 11.3).

Only the smaller condensers are suitable for indoor use because, indoors, there is a limited supply of air.

Water-cooled condensers

Water-cooled condensers fall into three categories: **double-tube**, **shell-and-coil** and **shell-and-tube**. In all water-cooled condensers, heat is conducted into the water, which is continuously pumped away to be replaced by cool water.

Double-tube condensers

Double-tube condensers consist of a narrow tube inside a wider one. The cooling water flows along the narrow inner tube while the refrigerant flows in the space between the tubes. The two fluids move in opposite directions to give the maximum heat transfer. Because the refrigerant is in the outer tube there is some cooling due to air as well as the water. Figures 11.4 and 11.5 show double-tube condensers.

Shell-and-coil condensers

Shell-and-coil condensers consist of a copper tube, wound into the shape of a coil, through which cooling water flows. Often fins are added to the coil which is surrounded by a hollow steel cover known as the shell. The refrigerant is in the shell (see Figure 11.6). Shell-and-coil condensers are used in smaller refrigeration systems.

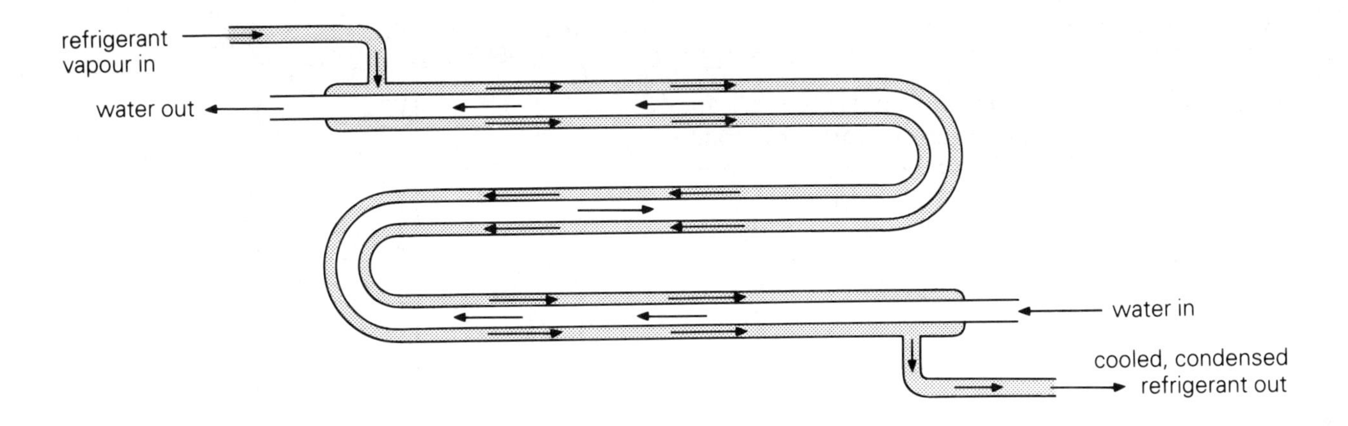

Figure 11.4 Diagram of double-tube condenser.

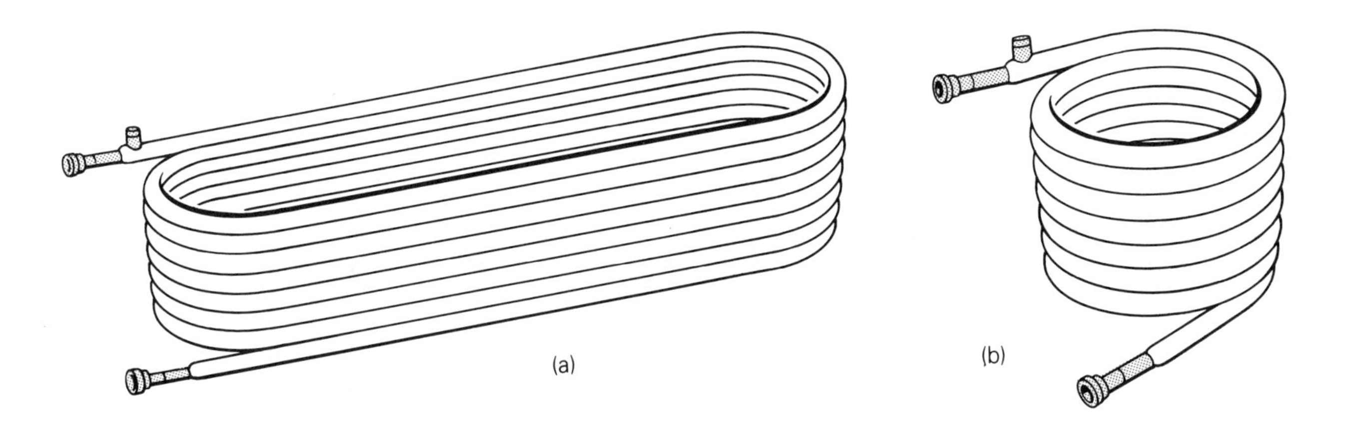

Figure 11.5 Double-tube condenser: (a) trombone configuration; (b) helix configuration.

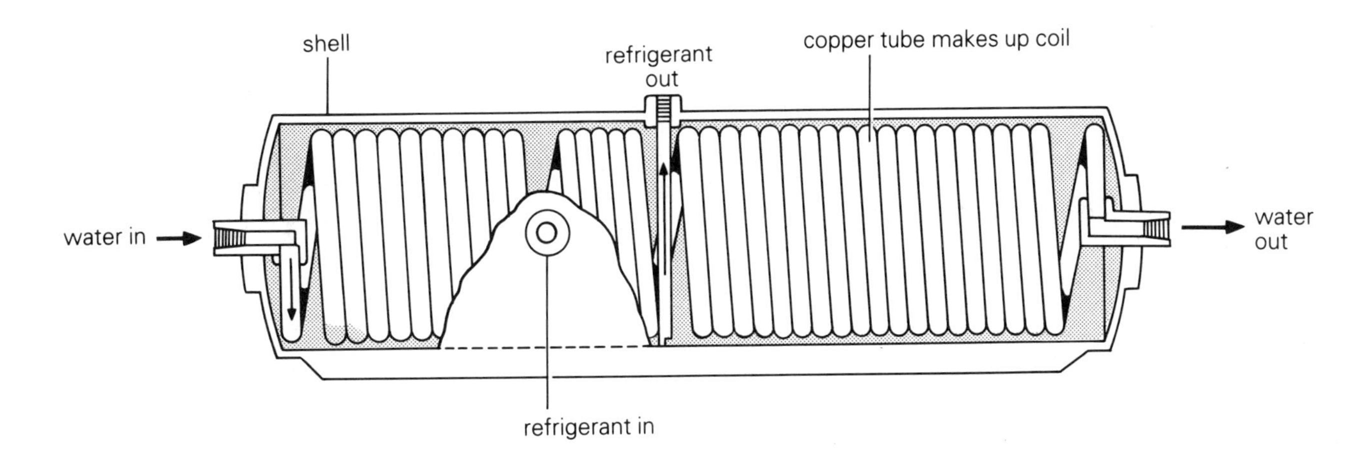

Figure 11.6 Shell-and-coil condenser.

Shell-and-tube condensers

Shell-and-tube condensers are similar to shell-and-coil types, except that there are a number of straight copper tubes arranged parallel to one another. Water flows through the tubes and the refrigerant flows in the space between the tubes and the shell (see Figure 11.7).

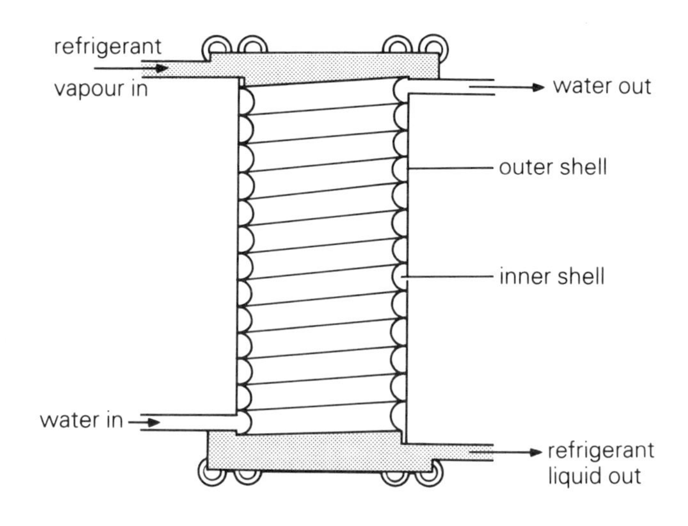

Figure 11.7 Shell-and-tube condenser.

Evaporative condensers

Evaporative condensers use both air and water as the condensing media (see Figures 11.8 and 11.9). Water is pumped up from a tank into a series of sprays which are above the condenser coil. The fine spray of droplets cools the coil. At the same time, air is drawn in by a fan and this passes over the condenser, extracting additional heat. The warm air, containing water vapour from the condenser surface, leaves through a vent at the top. An eliminator, which is a plate containing small holes, situated above the sprays, prevents water droplets escaping.

The disadvantage of the evaporative condenser is that of maintenance. One problem is that **scale** or **fur** tends to form on the condenser surface if hard water is used. Hard water exists in many parts of the world and it is caused by rainwater absorbing carbon dioxide as it falls through the atmosphere. The water, combined with carbon dioxide then passes through the ground and reacts with minerals, causing some of them to dissolve. When the water is later used and heated, minerals come out of solution and calcium carbonate (chalk), for example, is deposited. This is scale. In addition, air carries dirt and dust and this tends to deposit on the condenser, forming a hard crust. These deposits are poor conductors of heat and so decrease the efficiency of the condenser and, moreover, they are difficult to remove.

Because of this disadvantage, evaporative condensers are not used as much as other types and there is a preference for water-cooled condensers combined with cooling towers. These devices, together with the condenser, take up more space than the evaporative condenser and they use more power. However, they cause fewer maintenance problems.

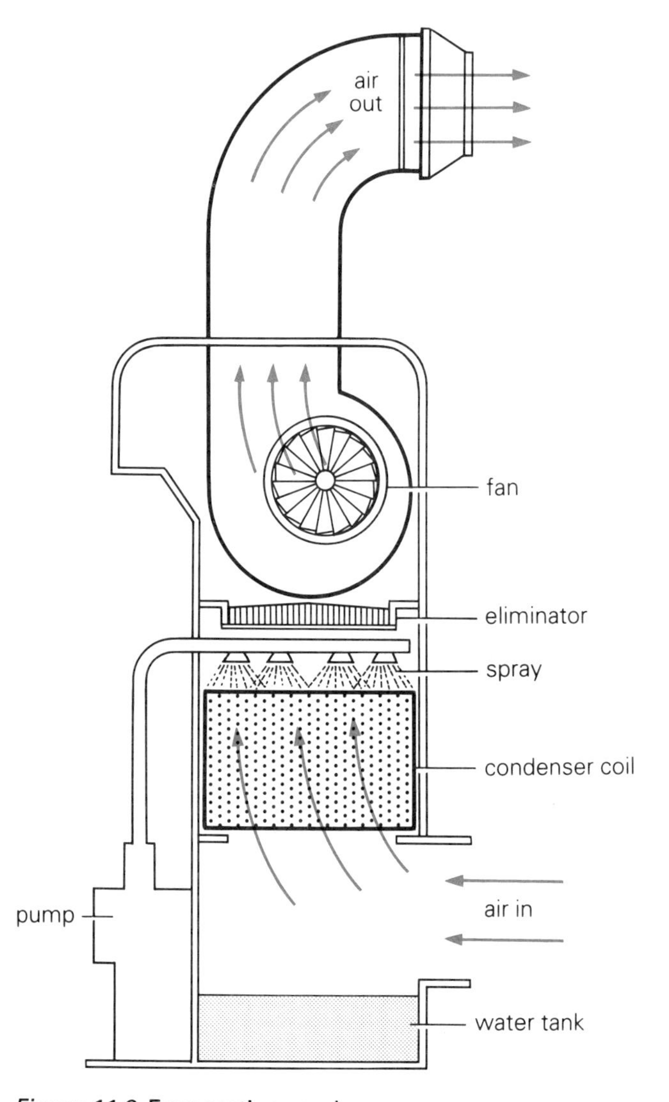

Figure 11.8 Evaporative condenser.

Figure 11.9 A low profile VCL evaporative condenser (courtesy of Baltimore Aircoil Ltd).

Cooling towers

Cooling towers are used to produce a constant supply of cool water for water-cooled condensers. The alternative would be to constantly supply cool water directly from the water main and then, when it gets heated, waste it by discharging it to the sewers. In an age which is increasingly concerned with conservation this is undesirable. A cooling tower is a device that saves water by constantly re-cycling it. Cooling towers can be grouped into two classes: **natural draught** or atmospheric types and **mechanical draught** types.

Atmospheric cooling towers

The hot water from the condenser passes through spray nozzles and is converted into fine droplets which then fall to the bottom of the tower (see Figure 11.10).

As the droplets fall they are cooled by the natural movement of air through the gaps in the sides of the tower. Cold water is piped out at the bottom. Atmospheric cooling towers are best situated on the roof of a building or at least in a convenient open space. The capacity of a cooling tower depends on wind speed. Any water lost in the cooling process, by evaporation or by droplets blowing away, is replaced by water from the main.

Mechanical draught towers

Mechanical draught towers produce the necessary draught of air by means of a fan. The air can either be sucked through, as in the induced draught type or blown through, as in the forced draught types. In both types the air that leaves is warm and nearly saturated and the condenser water, which gives up its heat to the air, is cooled. Because of the mechanical draught, droplets of water tend to be pushed out of the tower and so a spray eliminator must be

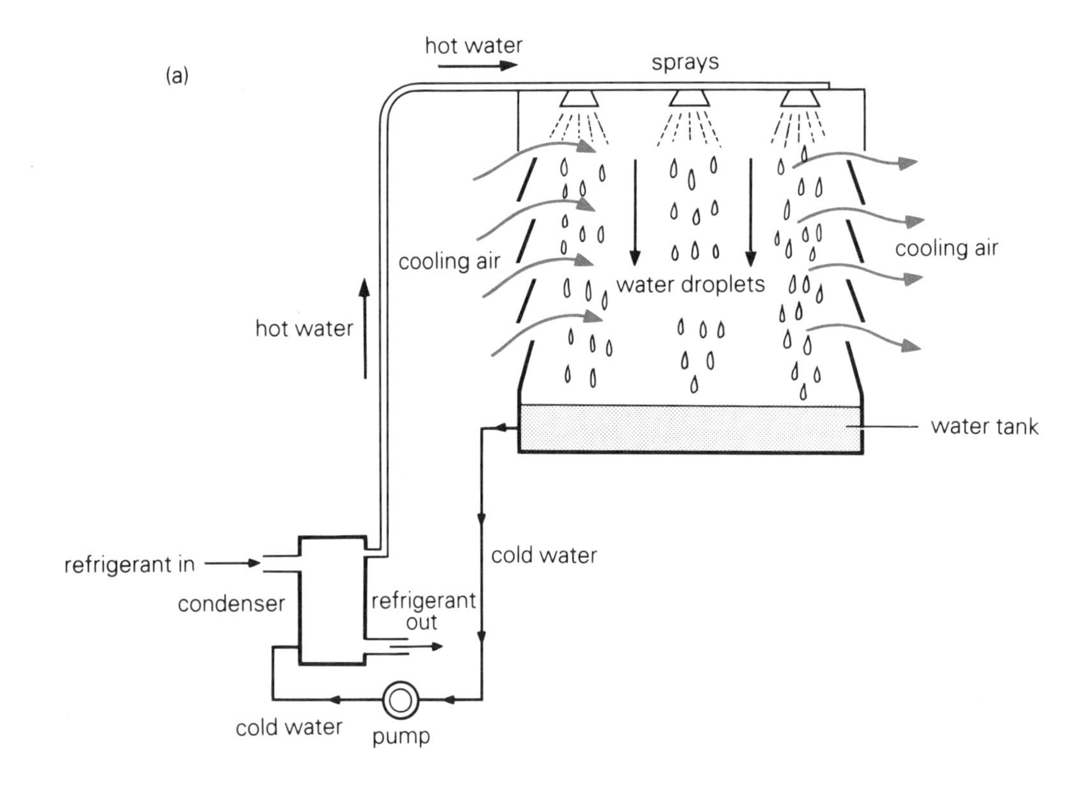

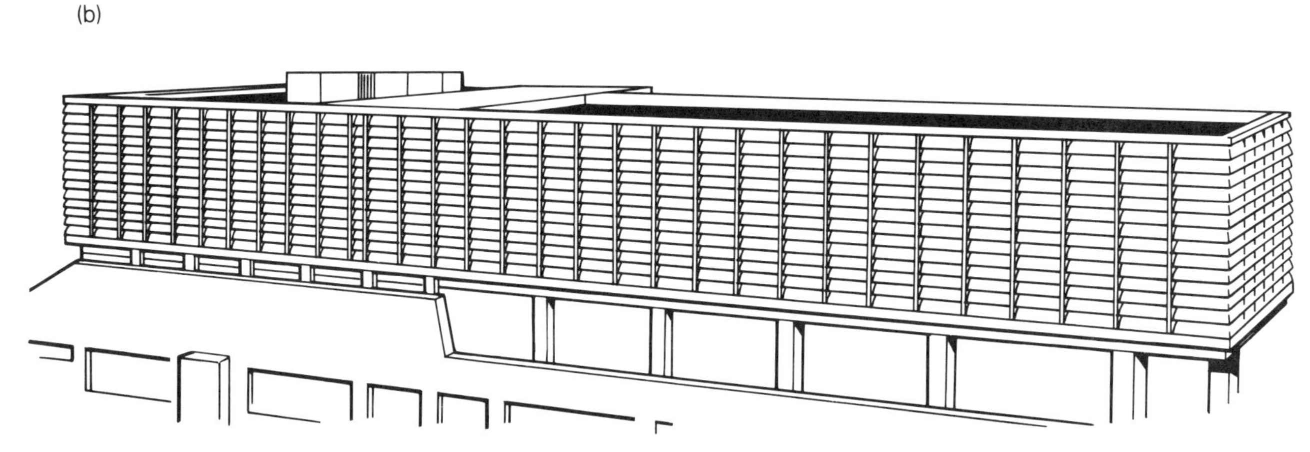

Figure 11.10 Atmospheric cooling tower; (a) diagram; (b) outside view of building.

fitted. Mechanical draught towers are shown in Figures 11.11 and 11.12. These towers are smaller than natural draught types and they can be used indoors as well as outdoors. They can be used for much larger systems.

Condenser capacity

When a manufacturer designs a condenser he must work to certain proven scientific principles. A service engineer must undersand these principles if he wants a thorough knowledge of refrigeration. Condenser capacity (Q), the rate in watts at which heat energy is conducted through the metal walls of the condenser, is one important consideration in condenser design, as it is in the evaporator (see Chapter 12). The difference between the two cases is that in the condenser, heat transfers outwards from the refrigerant, whereas, with the evaporator it travels in the opposite direction. However, this makes no difference to the choice of material, which is often copper or steel in both cases although aluminium is used for evaporators in

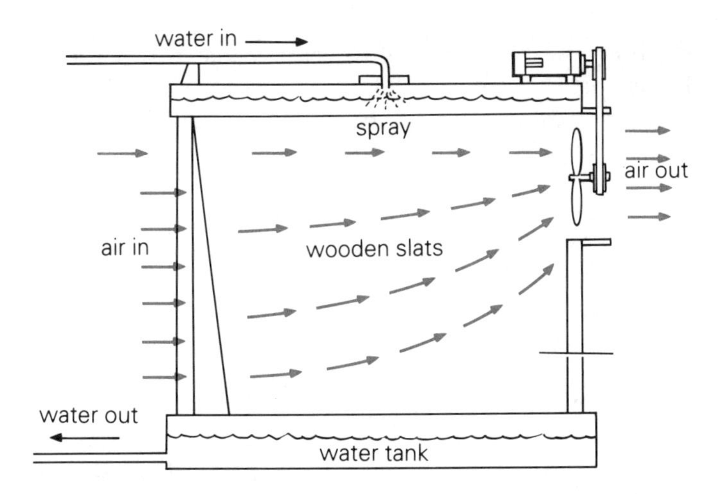

Figure 11.11 Induced draught cooling tower.

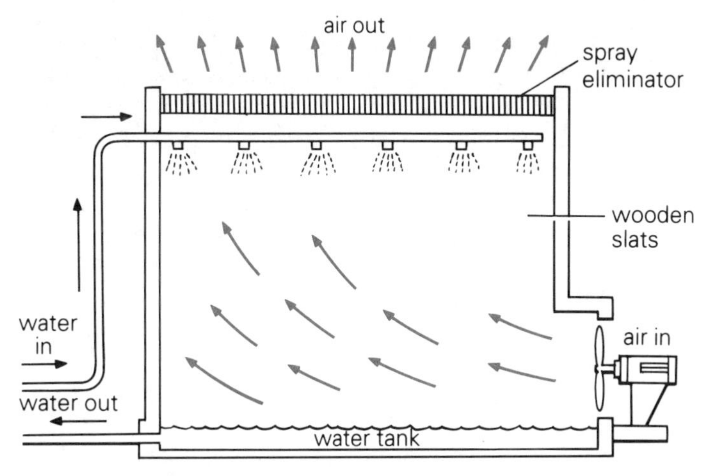

Figure 11.12 Forced draught cooling tower.

domestic refrigerators. Q is related to the properties of the condenser by the formula:

$$Q = A \times U \times TD$$

where A is the surface area of the condenser, in contact with the condensing medium, measured in m^2. U is the overall conductance factor in $W/m^2 K$, just as for the evaporator. It depends on the metal used for construction, the state of the refrigerant (liquid or vapour) and the condensing medium (air or water) and its speed of movement. TD is the mean effective temperature difference between refrigerant in the condenser and the condensing medium. This is not quite the same as the simple temperature difference (see Chapter 12).

EXAMPLE 11.1

If the surface area of a condenser is 9 m^2, the overall conductance factor is 800 $W/m^2 K$ and the mean effective temperature difference between the refrigerant and the condensing medium is 11°C, calculate the heat transferred through the condenser walls every second.

Solution

$Q = 9 \times 800 \times 11 = 79\,200\ W = 79.2\ kW.$

Heat rejection factor

Another factor which is important for condensers is the heat rejection factor (HRF). Heat is taken into a refrigeration system through the evaporator and through the compressor, and heat is rejected at the condenser. The total heat entering the system is equal to the total heat leaving. This means that the heat rejected in the condenser is always greater than the heat absorbed in the evaporator. Heat rejection factor is given by:

$$\text{HRF} = \frac{\text{heat energy per unit time rejected by the condenser}}{\text{heat energy per unit time absorbed by the evaporator}}$$

The value will depend on the compression ratio of the compressor and, typically, values vary between about 1.1 and about 1.5. The lower the evaporator temperature and the higher the condenser temperature the greater is the HRF.

EXAMPLE 11.2

A condenser rejects heat energy at the rate of 150 kW and an evaporator in the same refrigeration system absorbs heat at the rate of 100 kW. Find the heat rejection factor.

Solution

$$\text{Heat rejection factor} = \frac{150}{100} = 1.5.$$

Condenser maintenance

Air-cooled condensers, which work by natural convection, need little maintenance but those with finned outer surfaces need to be inspected for accumulations of grease and dust. Grease and dust will have two effects: air can no longer move freely over the finned surface, so that heat is not convected away properly, and conduction through the condenser wall is reduced because dust and grease are poor conductors. Dust on its own can be removed by brushing.

Accumulations of grease and dust can be removed by cleaning with cleaning fluids, of which kerosene, or paraffin, is a good example. Kerosene dissolves off grease which holds the dust in position but it has the disadvantage that it leaves behind a fine film on the condenser surface. This must also be cleaned off. Manufacturers produce special cleaners, which are useful for this purpose and they fall into two groups: spirit types and emulsion types. Specially manufactured items are known as proprietary brands. Spirits are thin liquids which evaporate very easily but they have the disadvantage that they are flammable and so should not be used in the presence of a naked flame. Emulsion cleaners mix with the grease to form a thick sludge or emulsion, which can then be removed using water.

▲ In the past, carbon tetrachloride has been used as a spirit cleaner but it should no longer be used as it is toxic. Petrol and alcohol are hazardous because they are highly flammable and they should not be used for cleaning purposes.

Forced convection condensers are maintained in the same way as natural convection types, except that the fan blades should be cleaned as described above. In addition the bearings of the motor that drives the fan should be lubricated regularly.

It was already mentioned (under the heading of *Evaporative condensers*) that they tend to fur up by the production of scale. This is also true of water-cooled condensers and it is particularly true of the top few tubes which receive the superheated vapour from the discharge line and are at a higher temperature. Scale is a poor conductor of heat, so the refrigerant cannot transfer its heat to the water so well. Water-cooled and evaporative condensers should be descaled, say, every six months.

The amount of scale can be reduced by using a technique known as **bleed off**, which is the removal of a small proportion of the water in the basin at the bottom of the cooling tower, because this has a higher proportion of chemicals that cause hardness than the rest of the water. This is because some spray water evaporates as it falls through the cooling tower leaving behind water with dissolved chemicals which drops down into the basin. The amount of water to be bled off depends on factors such as how much cooling is needed and the flow rate of the water. Manufacturers specify percentage of bleed off for their own equipment and it usually varies between about 0.1% and 1.0%. They also reccomend how often it should be done.

Draining and cleaning the basin at regular intervals also reduces the amount of scale. Once the basin has been refilled with fresh water a descaling compound is added and this is pumped through the system until all the scale is removed. The contaminated water is is then removed from the condenser–cooling tower system and it is refilled with fresh water.

Algae are plants which grow strongly in the presence of water and sunlight. They appear as green slime which looks ugly, but more importantly they can block the passage of water in condenser systems. Cooling towers are particularly prone to develop algae around water nozzles and this prevents the free flow of the water spray on to the hot condenser surface. Algae can be treated using chemicals specially designed to kill algae (algaecides). However, this is seldom completely successful and it is usually necessary to switch off the water supply and scrape away the algae.

It has recently been suggested that *Legionella* bacteria (as well as other types) exist in the water of some cooling towers. Bacteria form slime and clog water nozzles in the same way as algae. *Legionella* causes a serious disease called legionnaire's disease. The problem can be overcome by keeping water clean and free from dirt, scale and impurities. Chemical water treatments which control the growth of bacteria should be used. These treatments are often the same as those designed to control algae.

CHECK YOUR UNDERSTANDING

- The condenser is the part of a refrigeration system in which hot refrigerant vapour is condensed.
- Air cooled condensers can be cooled either naturally or by fan. There are plate and finned types.

- Water-cooled condensers can be double-tube, shell-and-coil, and shell-and-tube.
- Evaporative condensers use both air and water to cause the refrigerant to condense.
- Cooling towers maintain a constant supply of cold water for water-cooled condensers. There are two classes: natural draught and mechanical draught types.
- $Q = A \times U \times TD$, where Q is the condenser capacity in W, A is the surface area in m^2, U is the conductance factor in $W/m^2\,K$ and TD is the mean effective temperature in °C.
- Heat rejection factor is the ratio of the heat rejected by the condenser to the heat absorbed by the evaporator, over the same period of time.
- In maintenance, condensers should be kept clean to ensure good heat conduction. They should also be descaled. Algae can be a problem in cooling towers.

REVISION EXERCISES AND QUESTIONS

1. What is meant by the term *condensing medium*?
2. Some air-cooled condensers are fitted with fins. What is the advantage of fins?
3. Distinguish between *natural* and *forced convection*.
4. Why are some condensers situated out of doors, some distance from the compressor and evaporator?
5. What problem does hard water cause in water-cooled condensers?
6. Name the condensing mediums in the evaporative condenser.
7. What is the function of the cooling tower?
8. Explain the term *condenser capacity*.
9. Explain the term *heat rejection factor* of a condenser.
10. Explain why algae can be a problem in condenser systems.
11. If the surface area of a condenser is $10\,m^2$, the overall conductance factor is $750\,W/m^2\,K$ and the mean effective temperature difference between the refrigerant and the condensing medium is 8°C, calculate the heat transferred through the condenser walls every second.
12. A condenser rejects heat energy at the rate of 120 kW and an evaporator in the same refrigeration system absorbs heat at the rate of 90 kW. Find the heat rejection factor.

12 Evaporators

Introduction

The evaporator is that part of the refrigeration system in which the refrigerant reaches its saturation temperature and vaporises, taking its latent heat of vaporisation from the surrounding refrigerated space. Usually the refrigerated space is filled with air but in some air-conditioning systems it is water or brine.

Construction of evaporators

The three important types of construction are: **bare tube, plate surface** and **finned**.

Bare tube evaporators

These are the simplest types and they consist of a straightforward copper tube or pipe through which heat is conducted (see Figure 12.1).

Figure 12.1 Bare tube evaporator (flat coil).

If the refrigerant is ammonia, as in the case of an absorption refrigerator, steel is necessary as ammonia reacts with copper. Steel is often employed for large evaporators, such as those intended for frozen stores.

Aluminium tubing is commonly used in the manufacture of evaporators for domestic refrigerators.

Plate surface evaporators

One type of plate surface evaporator consists of two corrugated metal plates which are welded together in such a way that the corrugated surfaces form a pipe for the refrigerant to flow along. The large surface area of the metal provides a good conducting path for heat to be conducted (Figure 12.2).

This type of evaporator is commonly used in domestic refrigerators because it is cheap to make and is easily cleaned.

Another type of evaporator consists of a metal tube bent into a desired shape and enclosed between two metal plates. The metal plates are welded together to form an air-tight seal and then the air is removed from between them to form a vacuum. The pressure between the sealed plates is very small, so the outside pressure of the air pushes the plates very strongly on to the metal tube. This produces a good heat conduction path for outside heat to flow into the refrigerant.

Finned evaporators

Fins are metal plates, made of either copper or steel,

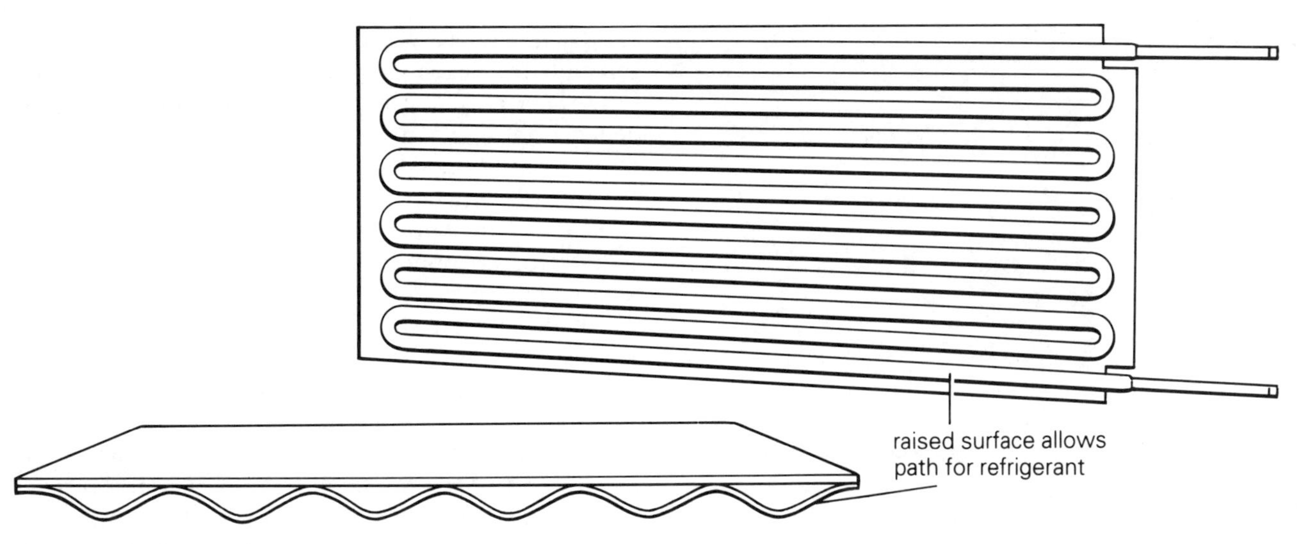

Figure 12.2 Plate surface evaporator.

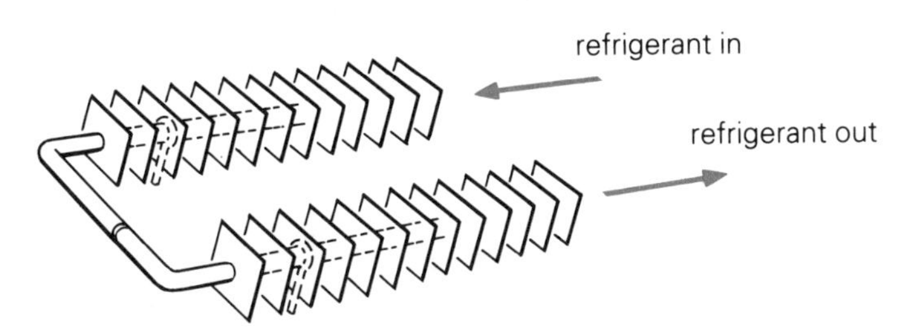

Figure 12.3 A finned evaporator.

which are fitted over the tube containing the refrigerant (see Figure 12.3). Evaporators fitted with fins are said to be finned.

Fins have the effect of increasing the area of the evaporator in contact with the air so that heat is conducted into the refrigerant more efficiently. However, the fins must be fitted tightly over the evaporator tube otherwise the efficiency of heat transfer will be lost. One method is to fix them in position by soldering and another is to place the fins over the tube and then expand the tube. Finned evaporators are smaller than other types for the same cooling capacity.

Refrigerant feed

There are two main ways in which refrigerant can be fed into an evaporator and so there are two main categories of evaporator. These are **dry expansion** and **flooded.**

Dry expansion evaporators

The flow of refrigerant into a dry expansion evaporator is controlled by the type of device described in Chapter 15; that is, some kind of expansion valve or else a capillary tube. As we saw in Chapters 5 and 6, upon entering the evaporator the refrigerant is mostly liquid but the proportion of vapour increases as it moves towards the outlet until it completely vaporises. By the time it leaves the outlet there will be a small amount of superheating and so the temperature will be higher then at the inlet end (see Figure 12.4).

The name 'dry expansion' is chosen in contrast to the term 'flooded evaporator' in which the evaporator is completely filled with liquid.

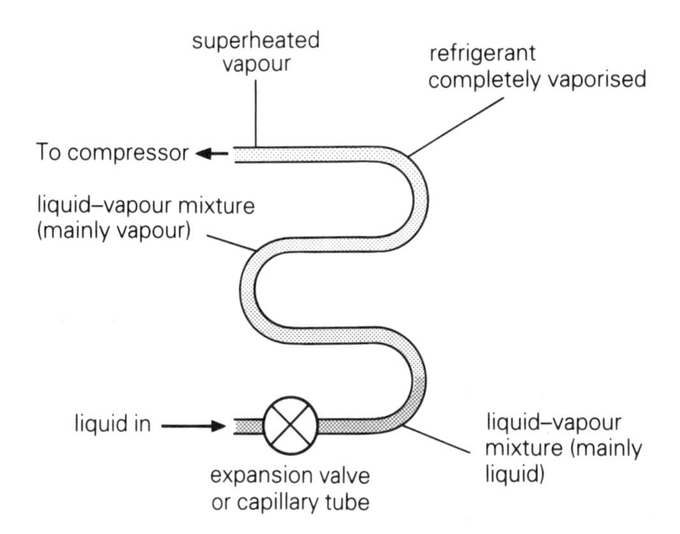

Figure 12.4 A dry expansion evaporator.

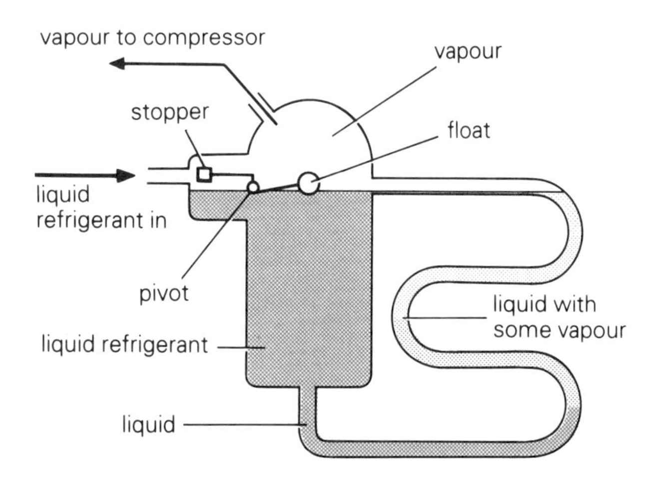

Figure 12.5 A flooded evaporator.

Flooded evaporators

Flooded evaporators often use a *float valve* to control the level of the liquid refrigerant in the evaporator. In a float valve a small ball floats on top of the liquid. As the refrigerant vaporises, when heat is conducted in from the refrigerated space, the liquid level goes down and the ball goes down with it. The ball is attached to a stopper through a pivot, so that when the ball drops the liquid line opens allowing in more refrigerant. When the liquid level is correct, the ball which has moved up with the liquid surface causes a pivoting effect and a stopper closes the pipe. A flooded evaporator is shown in Figure 12.5.

The inside of the pipe is always wetted with refrigerant liquid and so a good conducting path is provided for heat to be conducted in through the walls. The flooded evaporator is more efficient than the dry expansion type but it requires more refrigerant. At the outlet, the refrigerant enters an *accumulator*, which is a hollow cylinder used for storing liquid refrigerant in the bottom and above contains the float valve. Vapour from the refrigerant flows into the top of the accumulator and from there enters the suction line. A *baffle* prevents liquid droplets from entering the suction line.

Evaporator capacity

All evaporators work by conducting heat into the refrigerant and it is convenient to measure the ability of a capacitor to do this. This ability is called **evaporator capacity**. The capacity of an evaporator is the rate (Q) in watts, at which heat flows through the walls to reach the refrigerant inside. One factor that the evaporator capacity must depend on is the surface area (A) that is in contact with the fluid (usually air) to be cooled. The greater the area of contact the greater is the amount of heat conducted in. Another factor is the ability of the evaporator to conduct heat, which should be as high as possible. This depends in part on the metal that makes up the walls of the evaporator, although because all metals are good conductors of heat compared with non-metals, this actually has little effect on resistance to heat flow. The ability to conduct heat is called **conductance**. Resistance is the opposite to conductance; the lower the resistance to heat flow, the higher is the conductance and the higher the resistance the lower is the conductance. The same relationship exists between electrical conductance and resistance (see Chapter 4). The important effects on the conduction of heat are caused by a thin film of refrigerant fluid on the inner wall of the evaporator and a thin layer of air between the refrigerated space and the outer wall.

The inner film of refrigerant is in close contact with the wall and it is mainly liquid near the input of the evaporator. At the suction line end of dry evaporators it is all vapour. In flooded evaporators there is liquid refrigerant all along the pipe. Liquids are much better conductors of heat than vapours. Sometimes the fluid in the refrigerated space is air but in some cases it is a liquid, such as brine or water. These latter two substances are much better conductors than air. The ability to conduct heat, the conductance, is also affected by the speed at which fluid in the refrigerated space moves over the surface of the evaporator. The speed of the refrigerant inside the evaporator is important, too. In both cases the higher the speed, the greater is the conductance. Taking into account all the above effects on conductance, there is an overall conductance factor (U) for the evaporator.

Heat conduction and any other form of heat transfer depends upon the temperature difference (TD) between the outside of the evaporator and the refrigerant inside. The capacity (Q) is related to area, conductance and temperature difference by the following equation:

$$Q = A \times U \times TD$$

where A is the surface area of the evaporator, in contact with the fluid to be cooled, in m^2; U is the overall conductance factor in $W/m^2\,K$ and TD is the temperature difference in kelvin (or °C).

The temperature difference is not constant over

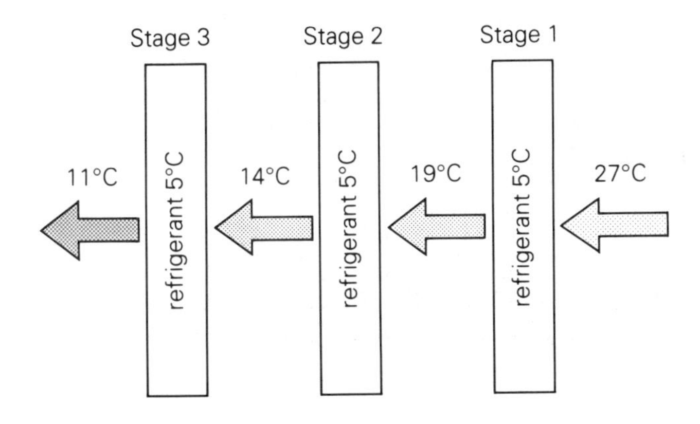

Figure 12.6 Change of air temperature through three-stage evaporator.

the whole of an evaporator. Some large evaporators, for example, consist of a number of plates joined together or manifolded. Air flows over the first row of plates at a high temperature and by the time it leaves the last row it is at a much lower temperature (see Figure 12.6).

In such a large evaporator, used for, say, air conditioning, let the temperature of the air entering the evaporator be t_1 and the temperature of the air leaving be t_2. Then the temperature difference between the incoming air and that of the refrigerant at a temperature t_r is $(t_1 - t_r)$. For the air leaving, the temperature difference is $(t_2 - t_r)$. The **mean temperature difference** (MTD) is given by:

$$MTD = \frac{(t_1 - t_r) + (t_2 - t_r)}{2}$$

EXAMPLE 11.1

The air entering an air-conditioning evaporator is at a temperature of 27°C and it leaves at 11°C. If the refrigerant is at 5°C, calculate the mean temperature difference.

Solution
$t_1 = 27°C$, $t_2 = 11°C$, $t_r = 5°C$.

$$MTD = \frac{(27 - 5) + (11 - 5)}{2}$$

$$= \frac{22 + 6}{2} = \frac{28}{2} = 14°C \ (14K).$$

In practice the temperature across the evaporator does not vary in a simple way and for very accurate calculations the **mean effective temperature difference** (METD) must be used. This can be calculated from a more complex formula than the one given above or it can be looked up in tables. The METD for the temperatures used in Example 11.1 is about 12.3°C.

EXAMPLE 11.2

A large evaporator designed to produce a low temperature for a large quantity of frozen meat has a total surface area of $80\,m^2$. If the overall conductance factor, U, for the temperature required is $12\,W/m^2K$ and the METD is 7K, calculate the evaporator capacity.

Solution
$Q = A \times U \times TD$
$= 80 \times 12 \times 7 = 6720$ W or 6.72 kW.

Evaporators and air movement

Air can be made to pass over the evaporator either by natural or forced convection. Natural convection occurs in a domestic refrigerator where the evaporator and the freezing compartment are at the top. Warm air rises from the bottom of the food compartment and then cools at the evaporator, so setting up convection currents. In air-conditioning systems the air is blown over the evaporator by means of a fan.

Chillers

Chillers or liquid cooling evaporators are devices which have a number of applications, from the cooling of milk and wine to the cooling of liquids known as **secondary refrigerants**. One application of secondary refrigerants is, for air-conditioning systems and for other refrigeration systems, in situations where the evaporator is some distance from the compressor. With normal (primary) refrigerants, pressure drops would occur in the long pipes that are needed, and so in a refrigeration

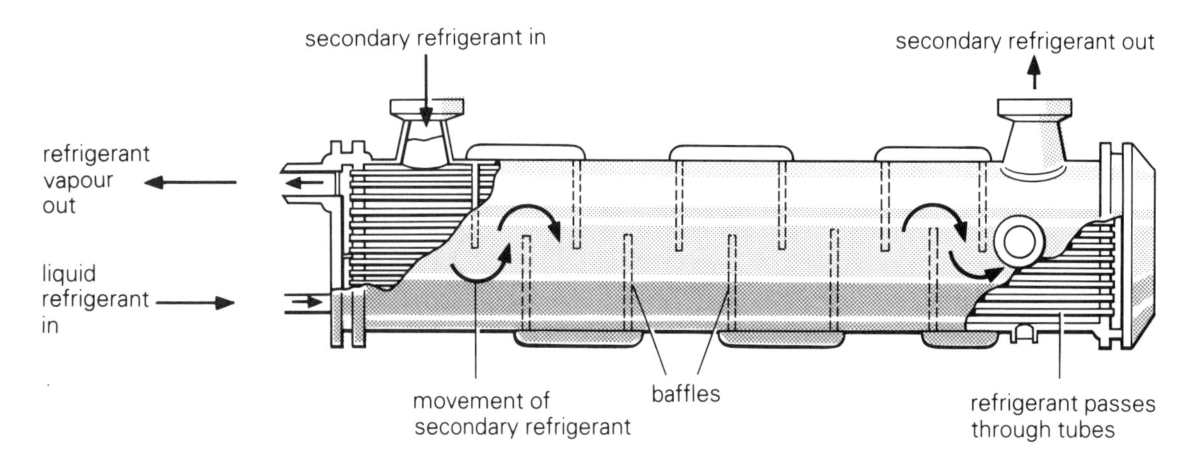

Figure 12.7 A dry expansion chiller.

system for air conditioning, the condenser, compressor and evaporator are positioned separately from the **cooling coil** which is used to lower the temperature of the air being conditioned. Secondary refrigerant, which can be water or brine, is pumped through the chiller and cooled. From the chiller the secondary refrigerant is then pumped through the cooling coils, or it may be used to cool the water in a water spray unit. Brine is a salt water solution designed for use at temperatures lower than 0°C, where water would freeze.

Dry expansion chillers

The **dry expansion chiller** works on the same principle as the dry expansion evaporator. Liquid primary refrigerant passes through a throttling valve and vaporises in a large number of tubes contained within a metal shell. The secondary refrigerant circulates through the shell and is cooled by contact with the tubes. Flat plates called baffles control the speed of flow of secondary refrigerant through the chiller. If the incoming speed is high, widely spaced baffles are used to reduce the speed, whereas if the speed is low the baffles are close together to increase the speed. Figure 12.7 shows a dry expansion chiller.

Flooded chiller

In this type of chiller the primary refrigerant is contained in the shell while the secondary refrigerant flows through the pipe. A float valve controls the flow of primary refrigerant into the shell. The tubes in the **flooded chiller** are fixed close together for maximum heat transfer. A variation on the flooded chiller is the spray chiller in which refrigerant is sprayed over the brine or water tubes. This type is shown in Figure 12.8.

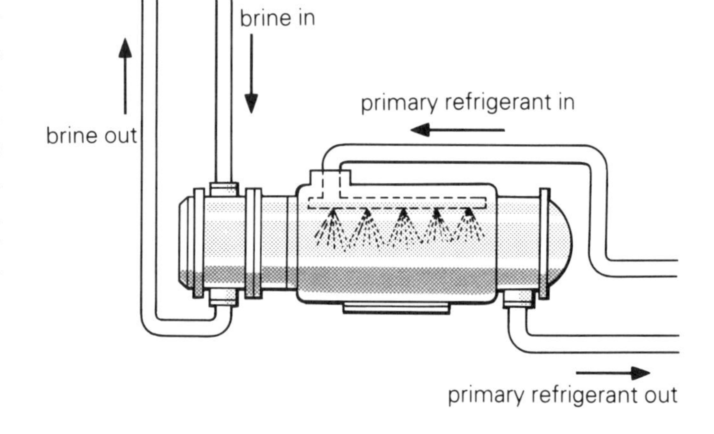

Figure 12.8 A flooded chiller.

Double-pipe cooler

A **double-pipe cooler** consists of two tubes, one arranged inside the other. The brine or water flows in one direction through the inner tube while the refrigerant flows in the opposite direction in the other. Double-pipe coolers can be operated either as dry expansion types or as flooded types. The disadvantage of this type of cooler is that it is more bulky than other coolers so that its use is limited.

Baudelot cooler

The **Baudelot cooler** consists of a number of parallel tubes arranged close together in such a way that a large flat plate is produced. This plate is held vertically with the tubes horizontal as shown in Figure 12.9.

Refrigerant is passed through the tubes and a thin film of the liquid to be cooled is passed through small holes above the plate and allowed to trickle down over the surface of the tubes. The liquid can be secondary refrigerant or else it can be something like milk or wine that needs to be cooled.

Figure 12.9 A Baudelot cooler (courtesy of Omega Engineering B.V.).

Tank and coil coolers

An evaporator coil is placed in a tank full of the liquid which is to be chilled. Warm liquid comes in at the top of the tank and flows over the evaporator. Cool liquid leaves at the side. The movement of liquid within the tank is forced by a fan-like agitator which is driven by an electric motor. Tank coolers have the advantage that they can store cooled secondary refrigerant for use during periods when the air-conditioning system is being heavily used. During such periods there is a tendency for secondary refrigerants not to have time to be cooled properly, since the system is being used to the limit.

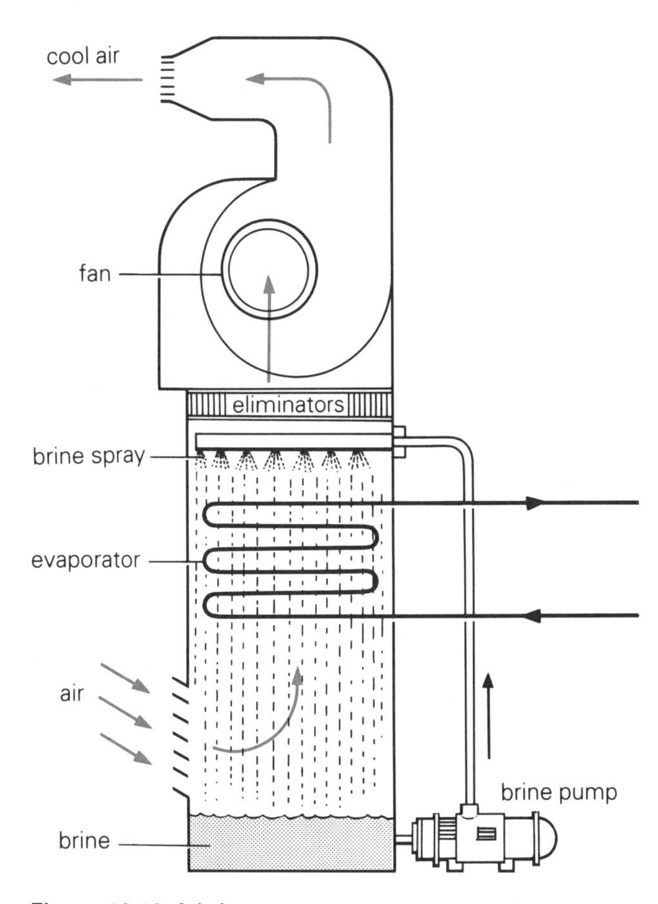

Figure 12.10 A brine spray.

Air-conditioning coils

In air-conditioning systems, an evaporator coil is sometimes placed in brine solution, contained in a tank. The brine is pumped through a cooling coil which is placed in an air-conditioning duct (see Figure 9.2). Air is blown over the coil using a fan and the air is then guided to the air-conditioned space through the duct. This system does not apply only to air-conditioning systems, it applies also where cold air is needed in large freezers or cold stores.

Brine sprays

Cool air may also be produced by a brine spray cooler. A fan sucks air over an evaporator coil and at the same time a spray of brine cools as it cascades over the coil. This cools the air further and a duct at the top conducts the cool air to the refrigerated space (see Figure 12.10). Eliminators stop water droplets from entering the duct.

Evaporator maintenance

A major problem with evaporators is that water from the air condenses and then freezes to form ice or frost on the evaporator surfaces. The lower the temperature of the evaporator the faster is the rate of frost formation. Of course, there is no frost formation on those evaporators where the working temperature is greater than 0°C.

Frost is a poor conductor of heat and so the rate of heat conduction from the refrigerated space into the refrigerant is reduced. This means that the refrigerant temperature is lower than it ought to be and so more frost forms making it even more difficult for heat to enter. The evaporator capacity is thus reduced. In finned evaporators frost forms between the fins and reduces the area of contact between the fins and the air. This reduces heat conduction and so reduces the temperature, again leading to more frost. Water expands as it freezes and this expansion can damage the fins.

Defrosting the evaporator

The frost that collects on evaporators must be removed from time to time and the process is called defrosting. In small domestic refrigerators defrosting is usually achieved by switching off the apparatus for a period until the ice melts. Some of the frost may be carefully chipped away and removed in order to speed up the process so that food does not spoil.

In larger systems a number of methods may be used. One method is to spray warm water on the frost. Another is to use specially constructed evaporators which have electric elements fixed inside them. The frost is melted by switching on the element. A third way is to use discharge vapour from the compressor. This vapour is hot enough to melt the ice.

Refrigeration systems should be defrosted at intervals according to the manufacturers' instructions. In general, the lower the temperature is, the more frequently the system needs defrosting. Some methods involve simply shutting down the system until the frost melts, as in the case of domestic refrigerators and freezers; while other systems are more complex and involve removing the refrigerant, followed by heating the evaporator. Methods of defrosting are given below.

Water defrosting

A valve in the liquid line is closed and the compressor pumps the refrigerant out, the compressor is then switched off, followed by the evaporator fan to stop water being sprayed into the refrigerator.

The water spray, which is situated above the evaporator, is turned on for a few minutes until the frost is melted and the water has been allowed to drain away.

Electrical defrosting

Again the liquid line is closed and the compressor is switched off as soon as the refrigerant is pumped out. The heating element is switched on, the fan switched off and heating continues until the frost is melted (see Figure 12.11). The heating element is then switched off, the compressor is started, a valve is opened to allow the refrigerant back and the fan is switched back on. The process can be performed either manually, by an operator, or automatically, using a timer.

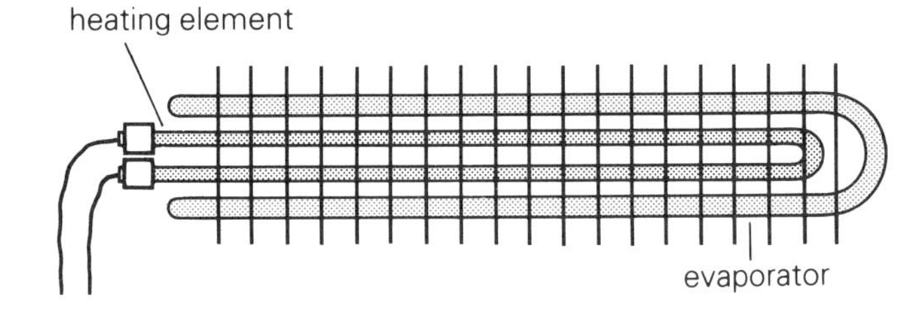

Figure 12.11 Electrical defrosting.

Hot gas defrosting

A tube, known as the by-pass line, runs from the discharge line to the evaporator. When the valve in the by-pass line is opened, hot gas travels to the evaporator and melts the ice around it.

One disadvantage of this method is that because the hot gas condenses into a liquid in the evaporator, there is a danger that liquid refrigerant will return to the compressor along the suction line and damage the compressor. This problem can be overcome by using a second evaporator, known as a re-evaporator, which is switched into the system by a valve when defrosting occurs. After defrosting it can be switched out again, usually by a timer.

Other maintenance

In addition to defrosting, the surfaces of evaporators should be cleaned regularly using a solvent (see Chapter 11).

The accumulation of oil, which has come from the compressor, in the evaporator can be a problem (see Chapter 10). This is because oil is a poor conductor of heat and heat is not conducted in from the refrigerated space so readily. The refigeration system becomes less efficient. The presence of oil in the pipes can be checked by making sure that the oil level in the compressor has not dropped. If it has, it may be a sign that oil has been deposited inside the evaporator. The compressor should also be checked for leaks to eliminate that possibility of oil loss.

CHECK YOUR UNDERSTANDING

- The evaporator is the part of the refrigeration system in which liquid refrigerant vaporises.
- The three important types of construction are: bare tube, plate surface and finned.
- Refrigerant feed can either be dry expansion or flooded.
- Chillers are designed to cool secondary refrigerants. Dry expansion and flooded are two types of chiller.
- Coolers include double-pipe, tank and coil, and Baudelot.
- $Q = A \times U \times TD$, where Q is the evaporator capacity in W, A is the surface area in m^2, U is the overall conductance factor in $W/m^2\,K$ and TD is the temperature difference in kelvin (or °C).
- Mean effective temperature difference METD is a better way of measuring temperature difference.
- Defrosting methods include water, electrical and hot gas defrosting.
- Evaporators should be cleaned regularly.

REVISION EXERCISES AND QUESTIONS

1. One type of plate surface evaporator has a vacuum between two welded plates. Why is the vacuum necessary?
2. What is a *secondary refrigerant*?
3. What is a *chiller* used for?
4. How does a *dry expansion evaporator* work?
5. How does a *flooded evaporator* work?
6. A large evaporator, designed to produce a low temperature for a large quantity of frozen meat, has a total surface area of $70\,m^2$. If the overall conductance factor, U, for the temperature required is $10\,W/m^2\,K$ and the METD is 8°C, calculate the evaporator capacity.
7. The air entering an air-conditioning evaporator is at a temperature of 25°C and leaves at 10°C. If the refrigerant is at 6°C, calculate the mean temperature difference.
8. What is meant by the term *frost* as applied to evaporators?
9. What is meant by the term *defrosting evaporators*?
10. Name three ways in which an evaporator may be defrosted.

13 Driers

Introduction

It is important that refigerant is dry and therefore contains no water. Moisture in a refrigeration system can cause acids to be formed and these can corrode and weaken the metals that make up the pipes and other parts. Sludge, which blocks the system, can also be a problem. Moisture can also cause ice to form in throttling valves.

Liquid line driers

One type of **drier** is fitted into the liquid line of a system, as shown in Figure 13.1.

Because this is in the high pressure side of the system, these are sometimes called **high side driers**. Modern **liquid line driers** not only remove water, they also filter to remove sludge and other impurities; in addition they take out acids. These driers are placed in the liquid line because moisture is concentrated into a smaller volume when the refrigerant is a liquid.

The right size of drier is selected by consulting manufacturers' tables. Factors that influence the size are type of refrigerant, amount of refrigerant and the size of the refrigeration system. A drier normally consists of a cylindrical cartridge which has a connection for the liquid line tube at each end, as shown in Figure 13.2.

Inside the cartridge are filters and the dehydrating material or **dessicant**. One kind of dessicant is the **adsorption type**.

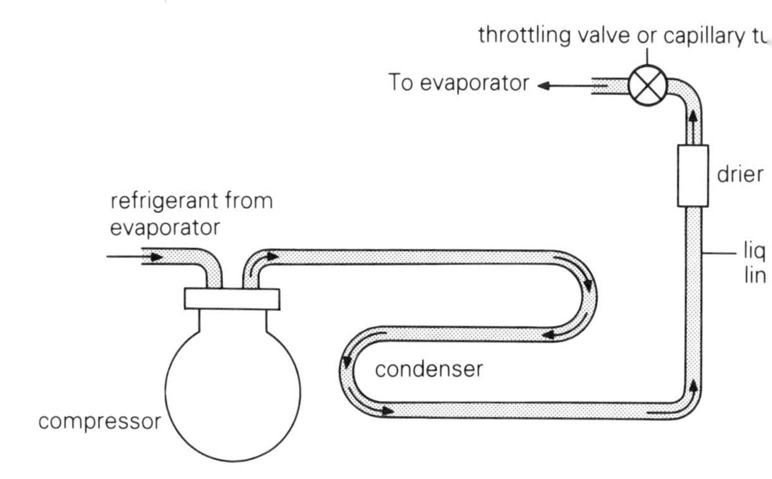

Figure 13.1 The position of a liquid line drier in the liquid line.

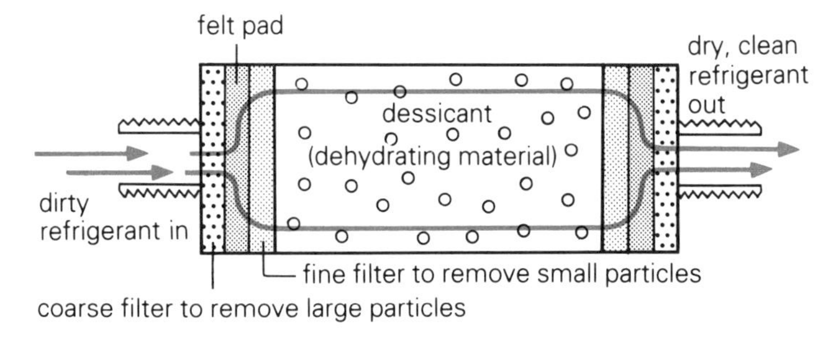

Figure 13.2 A liquid line drier.

Adsorption dessicants

Adsorption is where one chemical sticks to the surface of another. As the moist refrigerant passes through the dessicant, which has microscopic holes in it for liquid to pass, water sticks to the surface and stays behind. Dry refrigerant passes into the throttling valve. After the drier has been used for some time and it no longer works efficiently, it can be removed from the system, heated to drive away the water and then re-used. This can be done many times. Some common adsorption materials are *silica gel* and *activated alumina*. Silica gel is silicon dioxide and alumina is aluminium oxide. Another kind of dessicant is the **absorption type**.

Absorption dessicants

Absorption dessicants are chemicals that react with water and so form another chemical compound. The new compound behaves differently from the original one. Some form a powder and others become wet and eventually liquefy. *Calcium oxide* is one absorption dessicant and this forms a fine dust. *Calcium chloride* is another and it liquefies as it absorbs water. Absorption driers should be installed only for short periods, say half a day to a day and then replaced. They are often used when a system has just been repaired and it needs to be dried quickly. The absorption drier is then removed and relaced by an adsorption type.

Suction line driers

Suction line driers or **low side driers** are placed in the suction line near to the compressor (see Figure 13.3). Their function is to filter out any foreign matter in the refrigerant and to dry it, so that only clean, dry refrigerant passes into the compressor.

Moisture indicators

Moisture indicators are preventive maintenance devices, which are placed in the liquid line part of the refrigeration system. A glass viewing port enables the liquid refrigerant to be seen. The service technician can then observe problems, such as bubbles in the refrigerant which might indicate a lack of refrigerant, or some kind of restriction in the liquid line.

A moisture sensing element, usually consisting of a filter paper or a piece of soft cloth containing a chemical, is used to determine whether the refrigerant has water in it. One such chemical is called *anhydrous calcium sulphate*. Salts of cobalt are also used and they turn blue when the refrigerant contains water. Figure 13.4 shows the position of a moisure indicator in the refrigeration system.

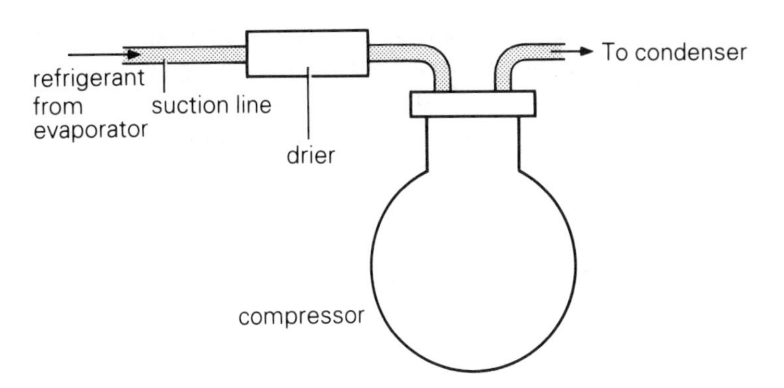

Figure 13.3 A suction line drier.

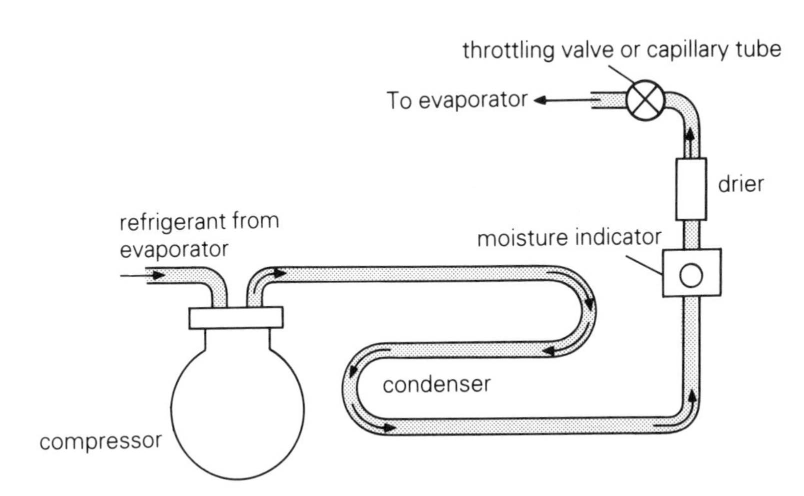

Figure 13.4 The position of a moisture indicator in the refrigeration system.

CHECK YOUR UNDERSTANDING

- Driers are used to remove moisture from the refrigerant.
- Moisture in refrigerant can cause the formation of acids, the formation of sludge and the formation of ice in valves.
- Liquid line or high side driers fit in the liquid line.
- Suction line or low side driers fit in the suction line.
- Common dessicants in adsorption driers are silica gel or activated alumina.
- Common dessicants in absorption driers are calcium oxide and calcium chloride.

● Moisture indicators are used to reveal the presence of moisture in refigerant. They do this by means of a chemical that changes colour. Common chemicals are anhydrous calcium sulphate and salts of cobalt.

REVISION EXERCISES AND QUESTIONS

1. Why are driers used in refrigeration systems?
2. In which part of the refrigeration system is a *high side drier* fitted?
3. How does an *adsorption dessicant* work?
4. How does an *absorption dessicant* work?
5. In which part of the refrigeration system is a *low side drier* fitted?
6. What is a *moisture indicator*?

14 Refrigerants

Introduction

Refrigerants are the working fluids used in refrigeration and air conditioning. At certain times, during a cycle, they evaporate and so absorb heat and at other times they condense and reject heat. Most refrigerants boil at low temperatures so that they are gases at normal atmospheric pressure. One exception to this is water which is used as a refrigerant in one of the absorption systems.

Refrigerants should be non-flammable, non-explosive and not be poisonous. They should flow easily and be able to conduct heat well. The freezing point should be lower than the working temperature of the evaporator. As we have seen, refrigerant vapour comes into contact with oil (or other lubricants) in the compressor and dissolves in it. Some of the refrigerant dissolves in the oil and can affect compressor performance. The miscibility, or ability to mix with oil, is very important

An internationally recognised system of numbering has been developed for refrigerants. Each number begins with R, for refrigerant. Probably the most commonly used refrigerant is R12. R22 is also common and R717 is ammonia, used in absorption systems. R744 is carbon dioxide, which is used in some high pressure refrigeration systems on board ships.

It is now considered that some types of refrigerant cause damage to the environment. R12, for example, is a compound which is made entirely of chlorine, fluorine and carbon and is known as a **chlorofluorocarbon** or **CFC**. CFCs are very stable and if they get into the atmosphere they drift upwards until they destroy ozone in the upper atmosphere. They may also be responsible for a rise in the temperature of the earth, or so-called global warming.

> To combat environmental damage, a meeting of individual countries was arranged in Montreal by the United Nations and the so-called **Montreal Protocol** came into force.

The Montreal Protocol was revised and strengthened in 1992 and the manufacture of the CFCs R11, R12, R113, R114 and R115 is to be first limited and then stopped completely by 1996. Another group of refrigerants is going to replace CFCs in the short term; these are the **hydrochlorofluorocarbons** or **HCFCs**. Probably the most common HCFC is R22. However, even HCFCs may do some damage to the environment and they also are to be phased out by the year 2030.

Although the foregoing refrigerants are to be phased out there are many millions of refrigerators and air-conditioning systems still in existence which use them. These will continue to be used and they will have to be maintained until well into the next century.

Throughout the world, scientists and engineers are working to find replacement refrigerants which do not damage the atmosphere at all. R134a is a **hydrofluorocarbon** (**HFC**), one of a group of compounds that has been developed that has no effect on the ozone layer. ICI, a large chemical company, have produced their version of R134a, tradenamed KLEA 134a, as their contribution to cleaner refrigerants. The Mollier diagram and tables of thermodynamic properties for R134a are given in Chapter 6, where the vapour-compression cycle is based on its behaviour. The Mollier diagram (Figure 14.1) and tables for R22 are given at the end of this chapter, for use as reference.

Secondary refrigerants

The common secondary refrigerants are water and brines. Water is used frequently in air-conditioning systems, where it is passed over the surface of an evaporator and then pumped through pipes to a cooling coil or a water spray (see Chapter 9). Water flows easily and has a high specific heat capacity, so it makes a very good secondary refrigerant. It is also used in some types of coolers (see Chapter 12). Water is unsuitable for use where the temperature drops below 0°C.

Brines

Originally **brine** was the name for a mixture of common salt and water. Sea water is mainly brine. Brine has a lower freezing point than water, so in cold countries, salt is thrown on to frozen and snowy roads, brine is formed, and the snow melts. Common salt is a chemical compound called sodium chloride. Brines used in refrigeration systems can either be sodium chloride or calcium chloride. Both calcium and sodium chloride belong to a group of compounds known as salts.

Up to a point, the more salt (sodium or calcium chloride) that is added to water, the lower is the freezing point, although if too much is added, the freezing point rises again. Calcium chloride brine is used where temperatures of less than about −18°C are needed and it is used for freezing a variety of products, including food. A disadvantage of calcium chloride brine is that, if it leaks from the system, it makes food taste bitter. Where such contamination may occur, sodium chloride brine is used. Temperatures as low as −21°C can be obtained with a mixture of 23% by mass of sodium chloride and 77% water.

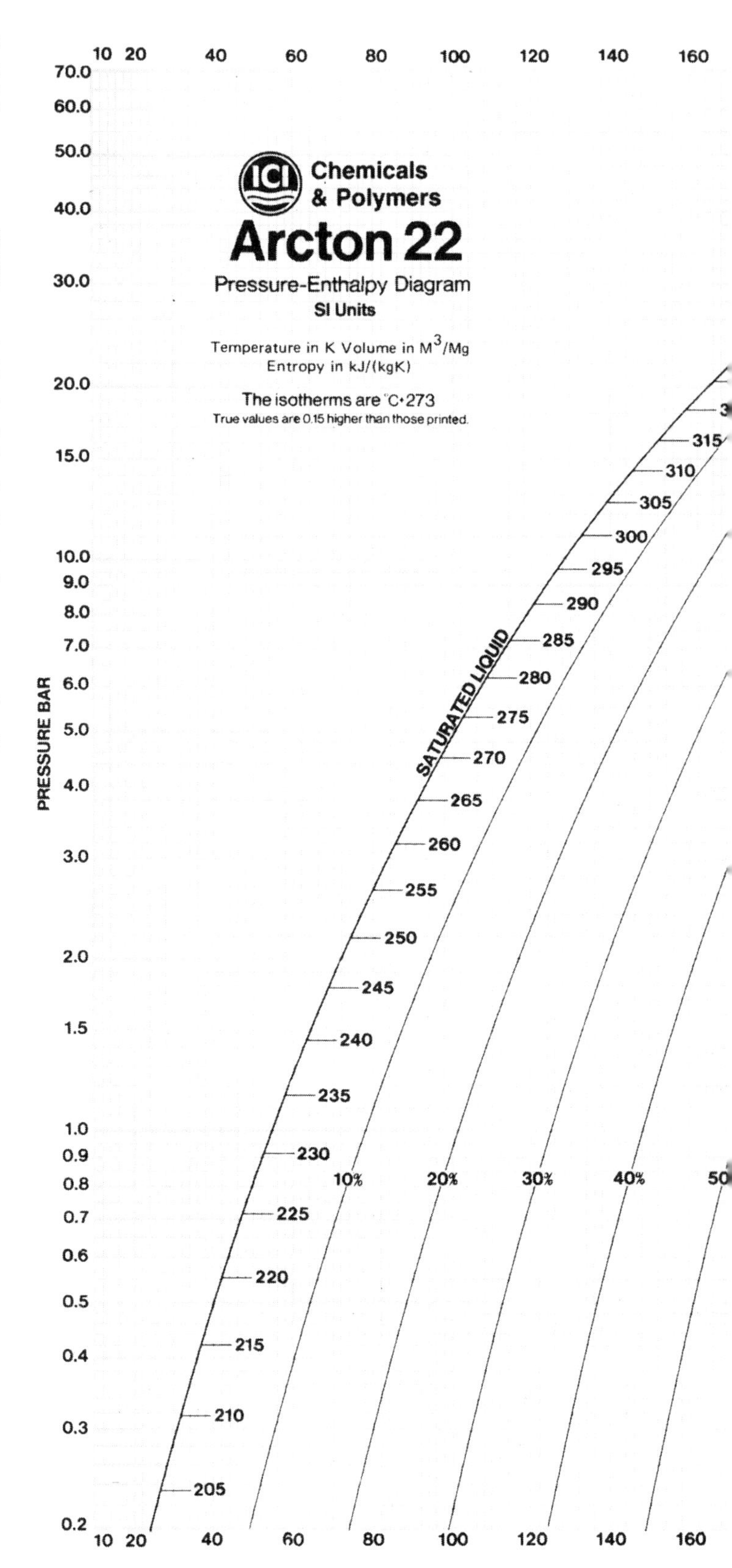

Figure 14.1 Mollier diagram for R22.

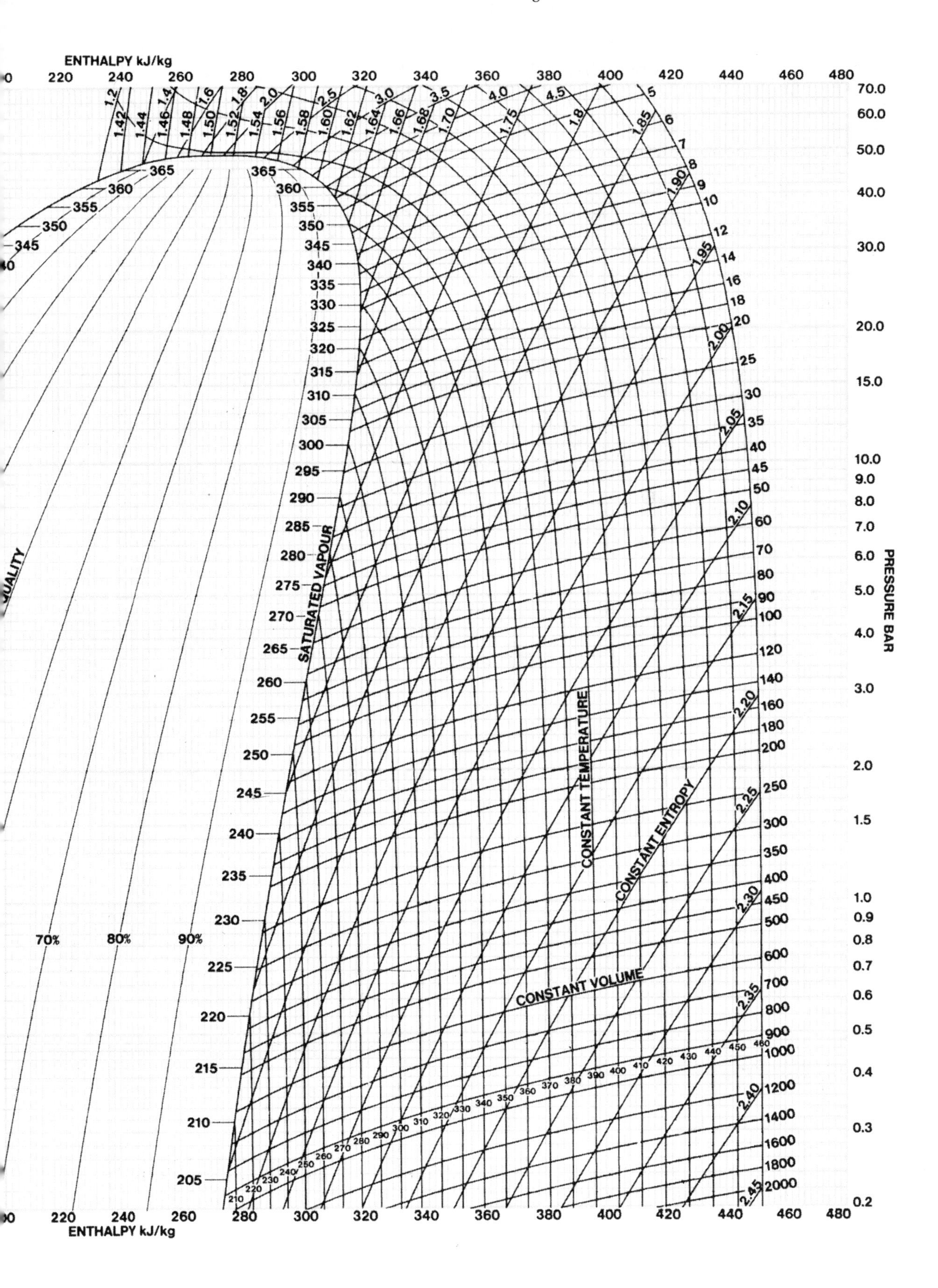
ENTHALPY kJ/kg
PRESSURE BAR
SATURATED VAPOUR
CONSTANT TEMPERATURE
CONSTANT ENTROPY
CONSTANT VOLUME
70%
80%
90%

Table 14.1 Arcton 22: Saturation properties (SI units)

Temp. (K) 0.15	Absolute pressure (bar)	Volume (m^3/Mg) Liquid	Volume (m^3/kg) Vapour	Density (Mg/m^3) Liquid	Density (kg/m^3) Vapour	Enthalpy (kJ/kg) Liquid	Enthalpy (kJ/kg) Latent	Enthalpy (kJ/kg) Vapour	Entropy (kJ/kg K) Liquid	Entropy (kJ/kg K) Vapour	Temp. (K) −0.15
275	5.29424	0.78193	0.044504	1.2789	22.4698	102.309	204.426	306.735	1.00833	1.75128	275
276	5.46624	0.78404	0.043141	1.2754	23.1799	103.468	203.634	307.102	1.01248	1.74987	276
277	5.64244	0.78618	0.041827	1.2720	23.9081	104.629	202.835	307.464	1.01663	1.74848	277
278	5.82289	0.78834	0.040561	1.2685	24.6544	105.794	202.029	307.822	1.02077	1.74709	278
279	6.00770	0.79052	0.039340	1.2650	25.4197	106.962	201.215	308.177	1.02491	1.74571	279
280	6.19690	0.79272	0.038162	1.2615	26.2040	108.132	200.395	308.527	1.02905	1.74434	280
281	6.39055	0.79495	0.037026	1.2579	27.0078	109.306	199.567	308.873	1.03317	1.74298	281
282	6.58875	0.79721	0.035930	1.2544	27.8316	110.483	198.732	309.215	1.03730	1.74163	282
283	6.79153	0.79949	0.034873	1.2508	28.6757	111.664	197.888	309.552	1.04141	1.74028	283
284	6.99898	0.80180	0.033852	1.2472	29.5405	112.847	196.038	309.885	1.04553	1.73894	284
285	7.21115	0.80413	0.032866	1.2436	30.4266	114.034	196.180	310.214	1.04964	1.73761	285
286	7.42816	0.80650	0.031914	1.2399	31.3345	115.224	195.314	310.537	1.05374	1.73629	286
287	7.65002	0.80889	0.030994	1.2363	32.2645	116.418	194.439	310.857	1.05784	1.73497	287
288	7.87684	0.81131	0.030105	1.2326	33.2172	117.615	193.557	311.171	1.06194	1.73365	288
289	8.10864	0.81376	0.029246	1.2289	34.1929	118.815	192.666	311.481	1.06603	1.73234	289
290	8.34556	0.81624	0.028415	1.2251	35.1924	120.020	191.766	311.786	1.07013	1.73104	290
291	8.58762	0.81875	0.027612	1.2214	36.2160	121.227	190.859	312.086	1.07421	1.72974	291
292	8.83487	0.82129	0.026835	1.2176	37.2642	122.439	189.942	312.381	1.07830	1.72844	292
293	9.08749	0.82387	0.026084	1.2138	38.3380	123.654	189.016	312.670	1.08238	1.72714	293
294	9.34544	0.82648	0.025357	1.2100	39.4374	124.874	188.081	312.955	1.08646	1.72585	294
295	9.60881	0.82912	0.024653	1.2061	40.5632	126.097	187.137	313.234	1.09054	1.72457	295
296	9.87772	0.83180	0.023972	1.2022	41.7162	127.325	186.183	313.508	1.09461	1.72328	296
297	10.15218	0.83452	0.023312	1.1983	42.8966	128.556	185.220	313.776	1.09869	1.72200	297
298	10.43233	0.83727	0.022673	1.1944	44.1055	129.792	184.247	314.039	1.10276	1.72072	298
299	10.71822	0.84006	0.022054	1.1904	45.3433	131.032	183.264	314.295	1.10683	1.71944	299
300	11.00990	0.84289	0.021454	1.1864	46.6108	132.277	182.270	314.547	1.11091	1.71816	300
301	11.30750	0.84576	0.020873	1.1824	47.9088	133.526	181.266	314.792	1.11498	1.71688	301
302	11.61106	0.84867	0.020310	1.1783	49.2380	134.780	180.251	315.031	1.11905	1.71560	302
303	11.92061	0.85162	0.019763	1.1742	50.5987	136.039	179.225	315.264	1.12312	1.71432	303
304	12.23630	0.85462	0.019234	1.1701	51.9923	137.302	178.188	315.490	1.12719	1.71304	304
305	12.55814	0.85766	0.018720	1.1660	53.4192	138.571	177.140	315.711	1.13127	1.71176	305
306	12.88627	0.86074	0.018221	1.1618	54.8805	139.845	176.080	315.924	1.13534	1.71047	306
307	13.22074	0.86388	0.017738	1.1576	56.3771	141.124	175.007	316.131	1.13942	1.70919	307
308	13.56165	0.86706	0.017268	1.1533	579099	142.409	173.923	316.332	1.14350	1.70790	308
309	13.90904	0.87030	0.016812	1.1490	59.4797	143.700	172.825	316.525	1.14758	1.70661	309
310	14.2630	0.87358	0.0163700	1.14471	61.087	144.996	171.715	316.711	1.15167	1.70531	310
311	14.6236	0.87692	0.0159402	1.14035	62.734	146.298	170.592	316.890	1.15576	1.70402	311
312	14.9909	0.88032	0.0155228	1.13595	64.421	147.607	169.455	317.062	1.15986	1.70271	312
313	15.3651	0.88377	0.0151173	1.13151	66.149	148.922	168.305	317.226	1.16396	1.70140	313
314	15.7461	0.88729	0.0147232	1.12703	67.920	150.243	167.139	317.382	1.16806	1.70009	314
315	16.1342	0.89086	0.0143400	1.12251	69.735	151.571	165.959	317.531	1.17217	1.69877	315
316	16.5292	0.89450	0.0139677	1.11795	71.594	152.906	164.764	317.671	1.17629	1.69744	316
317	16.9315	0.89820	0.0136055	1.11334	73.500	154.249	163.554	317.802	1.18042	1.69611	317
318	17.3409	0.90197	0.0132533	1.10868	75.453	155.599	162.327	317.926	1.18455	1.69476	318
319	17.7577	0.90581	0.0129107	1.10398	77.455	156.957	161.084	318.040	1.18869	1.69341	319
320	18.1818	0.90973	0.0125772	1.09923	79.509	158.323	159.823	318.146	1.19285	1.69205	320
321	18.6135	0.91372	0.0122528	1.09442	81.614	159.697	158.545	318.242	1.19701	1.69068	321
322	19.0526	0.91779	0.0119369	1.08957	83.774	161.080	157.249	318.329	1.20118	1.68930	322
323	19.4994	0.92195	0.0116294	1.08466	85.989	162.472	155.934	318.406	1.20537	1.68791	323
324	19.9539	0.92619	0.0113299	1.07970	88.262	163.872	154.600	318.472	1.20957	1.68650	324
325	20.4163	0.93051	0.0110382	1.07467	90.595	165.283	153.246	318.529	1.21378	1.68508	325
326	20.8865	0.93494	0.0107539	1.06959	92.989	166.704	151.870	318.574	1.21801	1.68365	326
327	21.3647	0.93946	0.0104769	1.06445	95.448	168.135	150.473	318.608	1.22225	1.68220	327

Table 14.1 (continued) Arcton 22: Saturation properties (SI units)

Temp. (K) 0.15	Absolute pressure (bar)	Volume (m^3/Mg)	Volume (m^3/kg)	Density (Mg/m^3)	Density (kg/m^3)	Enthalpy (kJ/kg)			Entropy (kJ/kg K)		Temp. (K) −0.15
		Liquid	Vapour	Liquid	Vapour	Liquid	Latent	Vapour	Liquid	Vapour	
328	21.8510	0.94408	0.0102069	1.05924	97.973	169.577	149.054	318.631	1.22651	1.68073	328
329	22.3455	0.94880	0.0099435	1.05396	100.568	171.031	147.611	318.642	1.23079	1.67925	329
330	22.8482	0.95364	0.0096867	1.04861	103.234	172.496	146.145	318.640	1.23509	1.67775	330
331	23.3593	0.95860	0.0094362	1.04319	105.975	173.973	144.653	318.626	1.23941	1.67623	331
332	23.8788	0.96367	0.0091916	1.03770	108.794	175.464	143.134	318.598	1.24376	1.67468	332
333	24.4068	0.96888	0.0089530	1.03212	111.695	176.968	141.588	318.556	1.24813	1.67312	333
334	24.9434	0.97422	0.0087199	1.02646	114.680	178.486	140.014	318.500	1.25252	1.67153	334
335	25.4887	0.97970	0.0084923	1.02072	117.754	180.019	138.409	318.428	1.25694	1.66991	335
336	26.0428	0.98534	0.0082698	1.01488	120.922	181.567	136.773	318.340	1.26139	1.66827	336
337	26.6058	0.99113	0.0080524	1.00895	124.187	183.132	135.104	318.236	1.26587	1.66659	337
338	27.1779	0.99709	0.0078398	1.00291	127.555	184.714	133.399	318.113	1.27039	1.66488	338
339	27.7589	1.00324	0.0076318	0.99677	131.031	186.314	131.659	317.973	1.27494	1.66314	339
340	28.3492	1.00957	0.0074282	0.99052	134.621	187.933	129.879	317.812	1.27954	1.66136	340
341	28.9486	1.01610	0.0072290	0.98416	138.332	189.572	128.059	317.631	1.28417	1.65954	341
342	29.5576	1.02285	0.0070337	0.97766	142.173	191.234	126.194	317.428	1.28885	1.65767	342
343	30.1759	1.02983	0.0068423	0.97103	146.149	192.917	124.284	317.201	1.29358	1.65576	343
344	30.8038	1.03706	0.0066547	0.96427	150.271	194.625	122.325	316.949	1.29836	1.65379	344

Table 14.2 Arcton 22: Properties of superheated vapour (SI units)

Temp. (K) −0.15	Absolute pressure (bar) 9.5 Satn. temp. = 294.74K			10.0 Satn. temp. = 296.60K			10.5 Satn. temp. = 298.39K			11.0 Satn. temp. = 300.12K		
	V	H	S	V	H	S	V	H	S	V	H	S
360	0.033647	364.04	1.8811	0.031817	363.51	1.8751	0.030160	362.99	1.8693	0.028653	362.46	1.8638
362	0.033891	365.61	1.8855	0.032051	365.10	1.8795	0.030386	364.58	1.8737	0.028870	364.06	1.8682
364	0.034135	367.19	1.8898	0.032285	366.68	1.8838	0.030610	366.17	1.8781	0.029087	365.66	1.8726
366	0.034377	368.77	1.8941	0.032517	368.27	1.8882	0.030834	367.77	1.8825	0.029303	367.27	1.8770
368	0.034619	370.35	1.8984	0.032749	369.86	1.8925	0.031057	369.37	1.8869	0.029518	368.87	1.8814
370	0.034860	371.94	1.9027	0.032980	371.45	1.8968	0.031279	370.97	1.8912	0.029732	370.48	1.8857
372	0.035100	373.52	1.9070	0.033210	373.05	1.9011	0.031500	372.57	1.8955	0.029945	372.09	1.8901
374	0.035339	375.11	1.9113	0.033440	374.64	1.9054	0.031721	374.17	1.8998	0.030158	373.70	1.8944
376	0.035577	376.70	1.9155	0.033668	376.24	1.9097	0.031941	375.78	1.9041	0.030370	375.31	1.8987
378	0.035815	378.30	1.9197	0.033896	377.84	1.9139	0.032160	377.38	1.9083	0.030581	376.92	1.9030
380	0.036052	379.89	1.9239	0.034124	379.45	1.9181	0.032378	378.99	1.9126	0.030791	378.54	1.9072
382	0.036289	381.49	1.9281	0.034350	381.05	1.9224	0.032596	380.61	1.9168	0.031000	380.16	1.9115
384	0.036524	383.09	1.9323	0.034576	382.66	1.9265	0.032813	382.22	1.9210	0.031209	381.78	1.9157
386	0.036760	384.70	1.9365	0.034801	384.27	1.9307	0.033029	383.84	1.9252	0.031417	383.40	1.9199
388	0.036994	386.30	1.9406	0.035026	385.88	1.9349	0.033244	385.45	1.9294	0.031624	385.03	1.9241
390	0.037228	387.91	1.9448	0.035250	387.49	1.9390	0.033459	387.08	1.9336	0.031831	386.65	1.9283
392	0.037461	389.52	1.9489	0.035473	389.11	1.9432	0.033674	388.70	1.9377	0.032037	388.28	1.9325
394	0.037694	391.14	1.9530	0.035695	390.73	1.9473	0.033887	390.32	1.9419	0.032243	389.92	1.9366
396	0.037926	392.75	1.9571	0.035918	392.35	1.9514	0.034100	391.95	1.9460	0.032448	391.55	1.9408
398	0.038157	394.37	1.9611	0.036139	393.98	1.9555	0.034313	393.58	1.9501	0.032652	393.19	1.9449
400	0.038388	395.99	1.9652	0.036360	395.61	1.9596	0.034525	395.22	1.9542	0.032856	394.82	1.9490
402	0.038618	397.62	1.9693	0.036580	397.24	1.9636	0.034736	396.85	1.9582	0.033059	396.46	1.9531
404	0.038848	399.25	1.9733	0.036800	398.87	1.9677	0.034947	398.49	1.9623	0.033262	398.11	1.9571
406	0.039078	400.88	1.9773	0.037020	400.50	1.9717	0.035157	400.13	1.9664	0.033464	399.75	1.9612
408	0.039306	402.51	1.9813	0.037238	402.14	1.9757	0.035367	401.77	1.9704	0.033665	401.40	1.9653
410	0.039535	404.14	1.9853	0.037457	403.78	1.9797	0.035576	403.42	1.9744	0.033866	403.05	1.9693
412	0.039763	405.78	1.9893	0.037674	405.42	1.9837	0.035785	405.07	1.9784	0.034067	404.71	1.9733
414	0.039990	407.42	1.9933	0.037892	407.07	1.9877	0.035993	406.72	1.9824	0.034267	406.36	1.9773
416	0.040217	409.07	1.9972	0.038109	408.72	1.9917	0.036201	408.37	1.9864	0.034467	408.02	1.9813
418	0.040443	410.71	2.0012	0.038325	410.37	1.9957	0.036408	410.02	1.9904	0.034666	409.68	1.9853
420	0.040669	412.36	2.0051	0.038541	412.02	1.9996	0.036615	411.68	1.9943	0.034864	411.34	1.9893

Table 14.2 (continued) Arcton 22: Properties of superheated vapour (SI units)

Temp. (K) −0.15	Absolute pressure (bar)											
	11.5			12.0			12.5			13.0		
	Satn. temp. = 301.79K			Satn. temp. = 303.40K			Satn. temp. = 304.97K			Satn. temp. = 306.49K		
	V	H	S	V	H	S	V	H	S	V	H	S
Satn.	0.020512	314.94	1.7161	0.019628	315.32	1.7140	0.018811	315.67	1.7120	0.018054	316.00	1.7100
302	0.020560	315.24	1.7171									
304	0.020821	316.89	1.7225	0.019723	315.94	1.7160						
306	0.021079	318.52	1.7278	0.019976	317.60	1.7215	0.018958	316.66	1.7152	0.018255	317.41	1.7146
308	0.021334	320.15	1.7331	0.020227	319.26	1.7269	0.019204	318.34	1.7207	0.018495	319.10	1.7201
310	0.021586	321.78	1.7384	0.020474	320.90	1.7322	0.019447	320.01	1.7261	0.018731	320.79	1.7255
312	0.021836	323.40	1.7436	0.020718	322.55	1.7375	0.019687	321.68	1.7315	0.018965	322.47	1.7309
314	0.022083	325.02	1.7488	0.020960	324.19	1.7427	0.019924	323.34	1.7368	0.019195	324.15	1.7362
316	0.022327	326.64	1.7539	0.021200	325.82	1.7479	0.020159	324.99	1.7420	0.019423	325.82	1.7415
318	0.022570	328.25	1.7590	0.021436	327.45	1.7530	0.020391	326.64	1.7472	0.019649	327.48	1.7467
320	0.022810	329.86	1.7640	0.021671	329.08	1.7581	0.020621	328.29	1.7524	0.019872	329.14	1.7519
322	0.023048	331.47	1.7690	0.021904	330.70	1.7632	0.020848	329.93	1.7575	0.020092	330.80	1.7570
324	0.023284	333.07	1.7740	0.022134	332.33	1.7682	0.021074	331.57	1.7625	0.020311	332.45	1.7621
326	0.023519	334.68	1.7790	0.022363	333.95	1.7732	0.021297	333.20	1.7676	0.020527	334.10	1.7671
328	0.023751	336.28	1.7839	0.022589	335.56	1.7781	0.021518	334.84	1.7726	0.020742	335.75	1.7721
330	0.023982	337.88	1.7887	0.022814	337.18	1.7831	0.021738	336.47	1.7775	0.020955	337.39	1.7771
332	0.024211	339.49	1.7936	0.023037	338.80	1.7879	0.021955	338.10	1.7824	0.021166	339.03	1.7820
334	0.024439	341.09	1.7984	0.023259	340.41	1.7928	0.022171	339.73	1.7873	0.021375	340.67	1.7869
336	0.024665	342.69	1.8031	0.023478	342.03	1.7976	0.022386	341.35	1.7922	0.021583	342.31	1.7918
338	0.024889	344.29	1.8079	0.023697	343.64	1.8024	0.022598	342.98	1.7970	0.021789	343.95	1.7966
340	0.025112	345.89	1.8126	0.023914	345.25	1.8071	0.022810	344.60	1.8018	0.021994	345.59	1.8014
342	0.025334	347.49	1.8173	0.024129	346.86	1.8119	0.023019	346.23	1.8066	0.022197	347.22	1.8062
344	0.025555	349.09	1.8220	0.024343	348.48	1.8166	0.023228	347.85	1.8113	0.022399	348.86	1.8109
346	0.025774	350.69	1.8266	0.024556	350.09	1.8212	0.023435	349.48	1.8160	0.022599	350.49	1.8156
348	0.025992	352.30	1.8312	0.024768	351.70	1.8259	0.023641	351.10	1.8208	0.022798	352.13	1.8203
350	0.026208	353.90	1.8358	0.024978	353.31	1.8305	0.023845	352.72	1.8253	0.022996	353.76	1.8250
352	0.026424	355.50	1.8404	0.025187	354.93	1.8351	0.024048	354.35	1.8300	0.023193	355.40	1.8296
354	0.026639	357.11	1.8449	0.025395	356.54	1.8397	0.024251	355.97	1.8346	0.023388	357.03	1.8342
356	0.026852	358.71	1.8495	0.025602	358.16	1.8442	0.024452	357.60	1.8391	0.023583	358.67	1.8388
358	0.027065	360.32	1.8539	0.025808	359.77	1.8487	0.024651	359.22	1.8437	0.023776	360.30	1.8433
360	0.027276	361.93	1.8584	0.026013	361.39	1.8532	0.024850	360.85	1.8482	0.023969	361.94	1.8478
362	0.027486	363.54	1.8629	0.026217	363.01	1.8577	0.025048	362.47	1.8527	0.024160	363.57	1.8523
364	0.027696	365.15	1.8673	0.026420	364.63	1.8622	0.025245	364.10	1.8572	0.024350	365.21	1.8568
366	0.027904	366.76	1.8717	0.026622	366.25	1.8666	0.025441	365.73	1.8616	0.024540	366.85	1.8613
368	0.028112	368.37	1.8761	0.026823	367.87	1.8710	0.025636	367.36	1.8661			

Antifreezes

Compounds known as **antifreezes** are being used to replace brines in a number of systems. Propylene glycol is the most widely used of the antifreezes and, like brines, it reduces the freezing point of water. It has the advantage over brines in that it does not corrode metal surfaces. Other antifreezes are ethylene glycol, methanol and glycerine.

Antifreezes are used to protect closed circuit coolers which cool condenser refrigerant. Closed circuit coolers, like cooling towers, are installed on roofs or walls and antifreeze is used to ensure that the water employed as a coolant does not freeze in winter.

CHECK YOUR UNDERSTANDING

- Refrigerants should be non-flammable, non-explosive and non-toxic.
- The amount by which a refrigerant mixes with the lubricant is an important consideration in choosing both refrigerant and lubricant.
- Refrigerants are given numbers beginning with R.
- CFCs may destroy the ozone layer.
- The Montreal Protocol limits the use of CFCs and HCFCs and they will be phased out over a period.
- HFCs which do not damage the ozone layer are now being brought in.
- Secondary refrigerants include water, brines and antifreezes.

REVISION EXERCISES AND QUESTIONS

1 What is meant by the term *refrigerant*?
2 List some of the properties that a refrigerant should have.
3 In what ways do CFCs damage the environment?
4 What is the *Montreal Protocol*?
5 Under what circumstances can water be used as a secondary refrigerant?
6 What is meant by the term *brine*?
7 What is the advantage of *propylene glycol* over *brine*?

15 Throttling valves

Introduction

Throttling is the conversion of liquid refrigerant into a vapour by the rapid expansion of the refrigerant as it passes through a small hole. The function of a **throttling valve** is to control the rate at which refrigerant passes from the liquid line into the evaporator and to maintain the pressure difference between high and low pressure sides of the refrigeration system. The simplest type of throttling control is the **capillary tube** and it is the kind used in most domestic refrigerators and freezers.

Capillary tubes

A capillary tube is a length of small diameter tubing which is normally connected directly between the condenser and the evaporator (Figure 15.1).

Because of the small diameter of the tubing and because of friction between the refrigerant and the sides of the tube the capillary limits the flow of refrigerant through the system. If the system is to operate efficiently, the rate at which refrigerant can pass through the tube must be equal to the rate at which the compressor is capable of pumping the refrigerant. If the capillary tube is too wide or too narrow or if it is too long or too short, the refrigeration system will still operate but at a low level of efficiency. However, once a capillary tube has been selected by the manufacturer for a particular set of operating conditions, it will operate with reasonable efficiency over a range of conditions: as the outside temperature changes or the refrigerator is loaded with different amounts of food. As the refrigerant passes through the tube it partly vaporises or flashes prior to entering the evaporator (Figure 15.2).

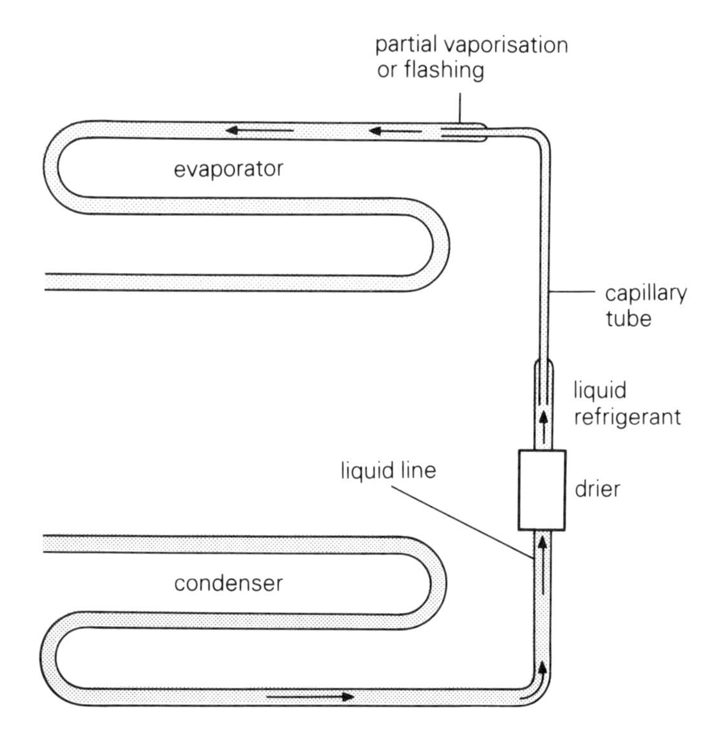

Figure 15.1 A capillary tube.

Part of the capillary tube is fixed to the suction line because the cool suction line reduces the temperature of the refrigerant before it enters the evaporator.

One disadvantage of the capillary tube is that when the thermostat switches the refrigerator off (see Chapter 21) the tube does not close and the pressures on the high and low sides of the system become the same. As this process occurs any surplus liquid refrigerant in the compressor will be sucked through to the evaporator. This is not desirable because the liquid is at the same high temperature as that of the condenser and food will defrost. This causes the compressor to come on too frequently and so the motor is overloaded. Because of this problem, domestic refrigerators have no receiver in which refrigerant collects as it leaves the condenser. Instead the amount of refrigerant in the system should be the minimum amount that is possible, consistent with keeping it running efficiently. Then only a small quantity of hot refrigerant will enter the evaporator when the system is switched off.

Once the amount of refrigerant is correctly adjusted the fact that the tube does not close becomes an advantage, because the pressure in the compressor drops to the same level as the evaporator when the system switches off. This means that there is less strain on the compressor as it starts up again and a cheaper type of electric motor can be used to drive it. Capillary tubes also have the advantage that they are cheap.

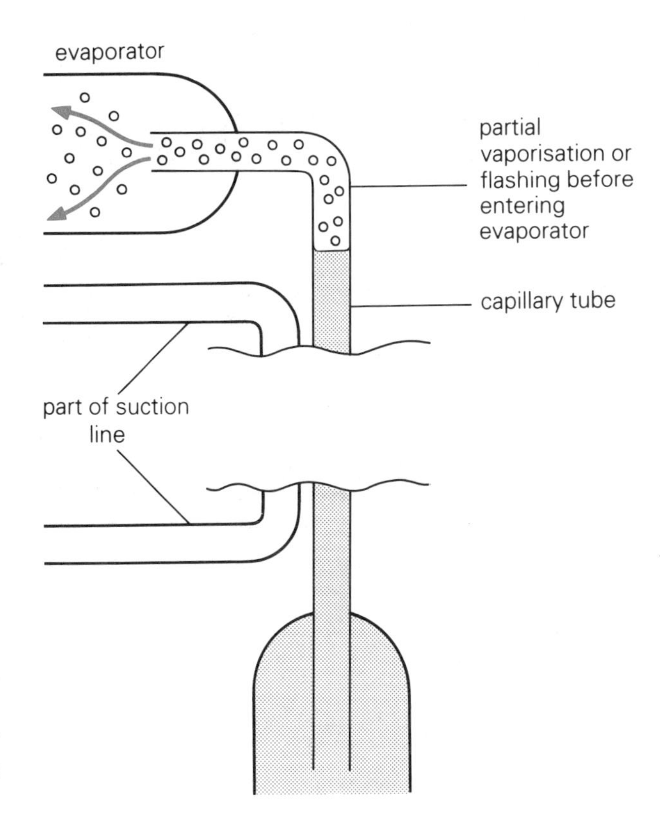

Figure 15.2 Vaporisation in a capillary tube.

The hand expansion valve

Next to the capillary tube, the **hand expansion valve** is the simplest type (see Figure 15.3).

A shaft can be screwed up and down to alter the size of the orifice and so control the flow of refrigerant. The hand expansion valve can only be used on larger refrigeration systems, where an operator is employed to look after the plant the whole time.

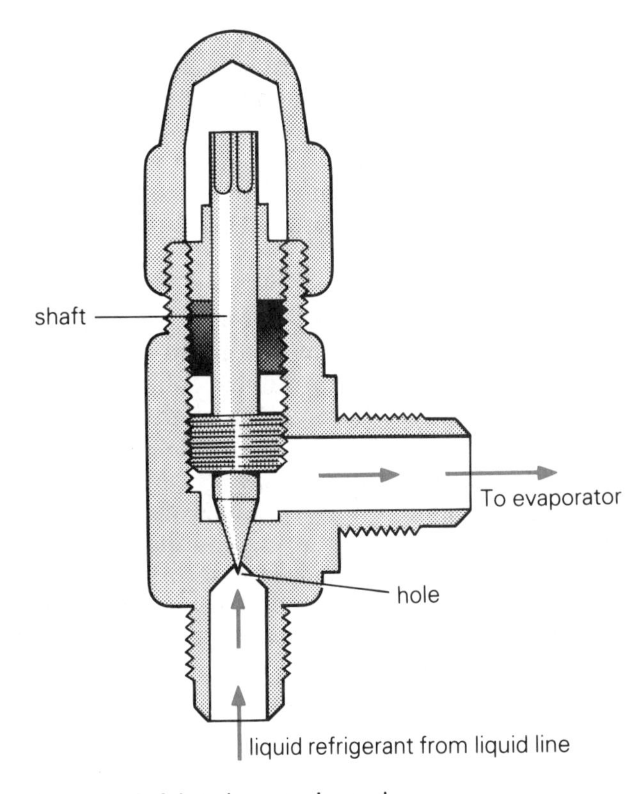

Figure 15.3 A hand expansion valve.

Thermostatic expansion valve (TEV)

The **thermostatic expansion valve** controls the flow of refrigerant in the system by maintaining a constant **superheat temperature** at the suction line end of the evaporator. This is the temperature difference between points A and B on the evaporator. It does this by means of a bulb, which contains refrigerant and is known as the **remote**

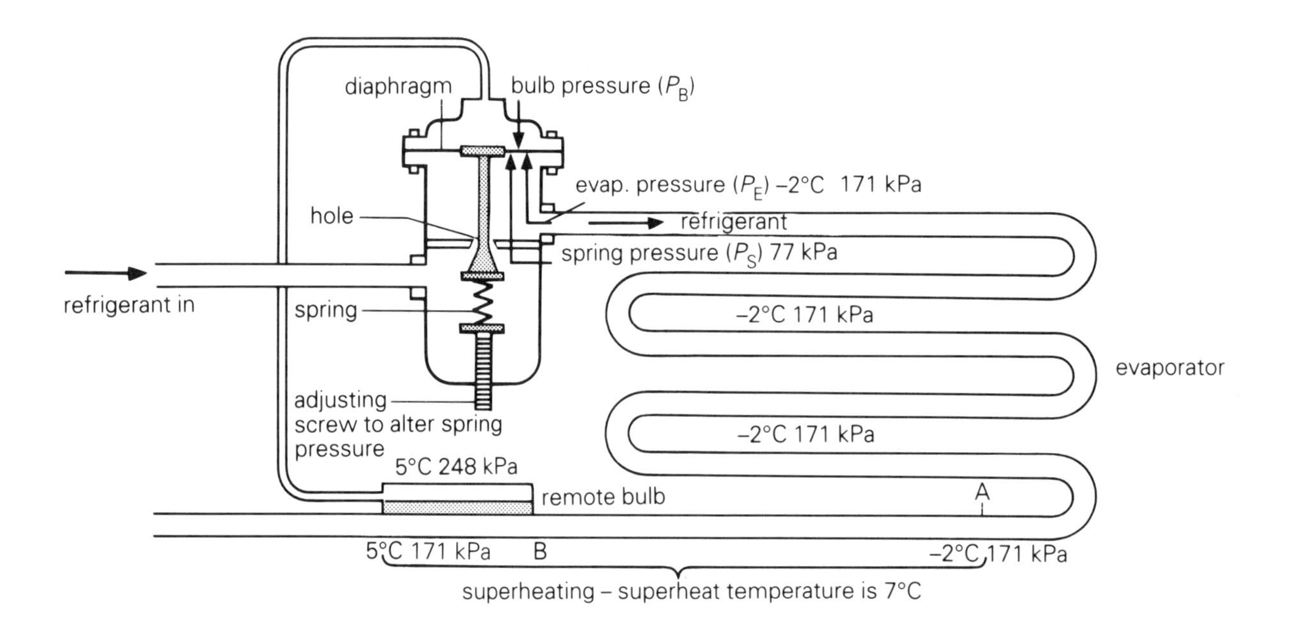

Figure 15.4 A thermostatic expansion valve.

bulb or **phial**. The remote bulb is attached to the end of the evaporator and so is at the same temperature as the vapour inside. It is assumed that the temperature and pressure of the liquid–vapour mixture are the same throughout the evaporator and then, when all the liquid has vaporised, superheating begins to occur. Although the temperature goes up, the pressure remains the same as that in the evaporator. A thermostatic expansion valve is shown in Figure 15.4.

Suppose the refrigerant is R134a and the temperature of the superheated vapour in the line at C is 5°C. This means the temperature in the remote bulb is also 5°C. From the R134a Mollier diagram or from the tables, the pressure of the saturated vapour in the bulb is 3.49 bar A or 2.48 bar G (or 248 kPa G). This is also the pressure exerted on top of the diaphragm. Inside the valve there are two pressures: one due to the spring and the other due to the pressure of the liquid–vapour mixture inside the evaporator. The pressure of the vapour from the remote bulb acts downwards (P_B) while the other two pressures P_S and P_E act upwards.

If the temperature in the evaporator is −2°C then from the R134a table the pressure P_E is 272 kPa A or 171 kPa G. This means that if the spring pressure is 77 kPa, the pressures acting on the diaphragm exactly balance because $P_B = P_E + P_S$ (248 = 171 +77). Now suppose that, for some reason, the superheat temperature goes down. This may happen, for example, if the surrounding air temperature decreases. When the superheat temperature goes down the pressure in the remote bulb decreases and any decrease in pressure causes suction (see Chapter 3). The diaphragm is sucked upwards and the upward pressure of the spring partly closes the hole between the top and bottom parts of the valve. This has the effect of restricting the flow of refrigerant into the evaporator and the smaller amount of refrigerant is more easily superheated as it leaves the evaporator on the outlet side. The superheat temperature increases and so the pressure in the remote bulb increases. The diaphragm returns to its balance condition.

If, instead of decreasing, the superheat temperature goes up, and so the remote bulb pressure increases, then the hole between the two parts opens more. A greater amount of refrigerant now passes into the evaporator and less superheating occurs at the outlet end. The pressure in the remote bulb decreases and the diaphragm returns to balance. The thermostatic expansion valve acts to keep the evaporator supplied with refrigerant by keeping the superheat temperature constant.

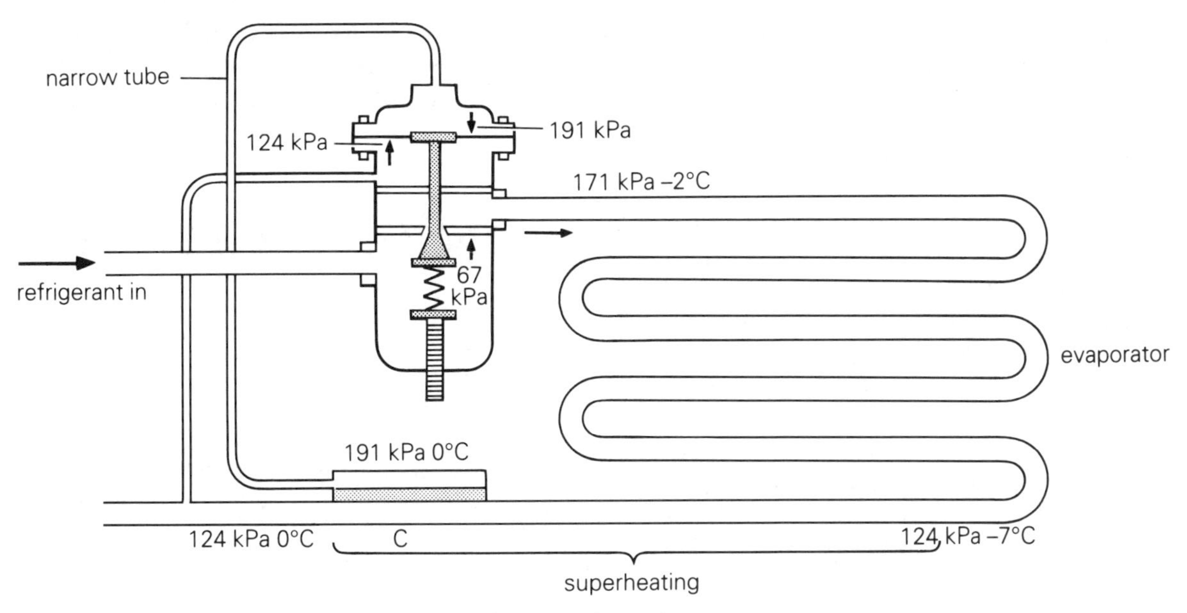

Figure 15.5 Externally equalised thermostatic expansion valve.

Externally equalised TEVs

The ordinary thermostatic expansion valve works on the assumption that the pressure at the outlet of the evaporator is the same as that at the input. However, in practice, friction between the refrigerant and the walls of the evaporator and friction inside the refrigerant itself causes a drop in pressure. The lower the pressure, the lower is the saturation temperature and so the refrigerant tends to vaporise completely, before it gets to the outlet of the evaporator, and starts to superheat. This means that the last part of the evaporator becomes ineffective in cooling food or in cooling the air-conditioned space.

To overcome this problem, an **externally equalised TEV** is used. This differs from the ordinary TEV in that a narrow tube runs from a point along the suction line just beyond the remote bulb to a point below the diaphragm in the valve. This is shown in Figure 15.5. The pressure of the refrigerant at the input of the evaporator does not act on the diaphragm at all.

In the example given on the ordinary TEV, the rise in temperature due to superheating is 7°C. If the pressure at the input of the evaporator is 171 kPa G and it drops to 124 kPa G, then the saturation temperature drops from −2°C to −7°C. With superheating, the temperature at C becomes 0°C at the same pressure of 124 kPa. The temperature of the remote bulb is also 0°C but the pressure exerted by the saturated vapour is greater than this, at 191 kPa. If the spring pressure is 67 kPa, then because $P_B = P_E + P_S$ (191 = 124 + 67), balance is maintained at the diaphragm using the new figures.

Thermostatic expansion valves are normally adjusted by the manufacturer for a superheat temperature of between about 5°C and 8°C. This may have to be altered, if necessary, by the installation engineer.

The constant pressure expansion valve

This valve maintains a constant pressure in the evaporator. Figure 15.6 shows an adjustable spring

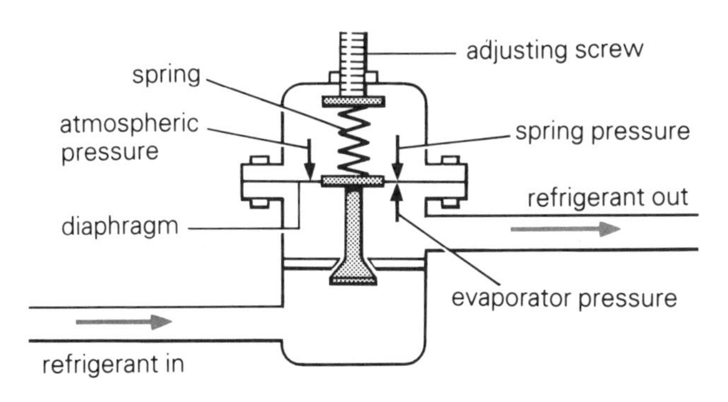

Figure 15.6 Constant pressure expansion valve.

which exerts downward pressure on a metal diaphragm. At the same time, refrigerant from the liquid line expands through the hole and exerts an upward pressure on the diaphragm.

Suppose the spring exerts a downward pressure of 200 kPa and the atmosphere, also acting downwards, exerts a pressure of 1.01 bar or 101 kPa, then the total downward pressure is 301 kPa. Liquid refrigerant, after passing through the hole, starts to vaporise beneath the diaphragm and develops an equal upward pressure of 301 kPa G. If, for some reason, the refrigerant pressure drops below 301 kPa, the downward pressure exceeds the upward pressure, the needle is pushed down, and the hole opens up. This allows in more refrigerant and the pressure goes up again. If, on the other hand, the evaporator pressure increases, the upward pressure becomes greater, the valve starts to close, and the pressure goes down. In this way the valve exerts a constant pressure.

CHECK YOUR UNDERSTANDING

- Liquid expands into a vapour and at the same time the temperature goes down, when it expands through a small hole. This process is throttling.
- The simplest throttling device is a narrow tube called a capillary tube.
- The simplest throttling valve is the hand expansion valve, which has to be adjusted by an operator.
- The thermostatic expansion valve maintains a constant superheat temperature by means of a remote bulb at the suction line end of the evaporator.
- The constant pressure expansion valve maintains a constant pressure by means of a spring acting on a diaphragm and balancing out the evaporator pressure.

REVISION EXERCISES AND QUESTIONS

1. Explain the term *throttling*, as applied to liquids and vapours.
2. What is a *capillary tube* and how is it used as a throttling device?
3. If a capillary tube is used for throttling what happens to the high and low side pressures when the thermostat switches the compressor off?
4. How does the *thermostatic expansion valve* keep a constant superheat temperature?
5. What is the main disadvantage of the *hand expansion valve*?
6. Why should a domestic refigerator with capillary tube throttling not use a receiver?
7. Why does refrigerant pressure in the evaporator tend to decrease between the input and the output?
8. If the pressure drop between the input and the output of the evaporator is large and so effectively reduces the evaporator surface, what kind of TEV is it best to use?
9. If the remote bulb pressure in a TEV is 350 kPa G and the spring pressure is 85 kPa, what is the value of the evaporator pressure?
10. How does a constant pressure expansion valve maintain constant pressure in the evaporator?

16 Fluid flow

Introduction

A fluid is any substance that flows and so it can be either a liquid or a gas. Refrigerant is cycled through a refrigeration system and as it does so it changes in temperature, in pressure and in phase from liquid to vapour and back again. Because of this it is necessary for the technician to know something of the laws of fluid flow along refrigeration pipes.

Fluid pressure

A fluid which is not moving will exert a pressure known as the **static pressure**. For example, the atmosphere will exert a static pressure, at sea level, of about 1 bar. Water in a pool will exert a static pressure which increases with depth. The pressure 10 m below the surface will be 1 bar greater than that at the surface, while at 20 m it will be 2 bar. The water at 10 m is said to have a **head** of water of 10 m above it. At 20 m the head of water is 20 m (see Figure 16.1).

As the pressure doubles, so does the head. The head is directly proportional to the pressure and so it can be used as a measure of pressure for water and for other liquids. However, the density of a gas is not constant and so the head cannot be used for pressure.

> Static pressure is exerted equally in all directions.

The head of liquid associated with static pressure is called the **static head**.

A fluid which is moving exerts another pressure in addition to the static pressure. This is called the **velocity pressure**, or, in terms of head, the **velocity head**.

> Velocity pressure is exerted only in the direction in which the fluid flows.

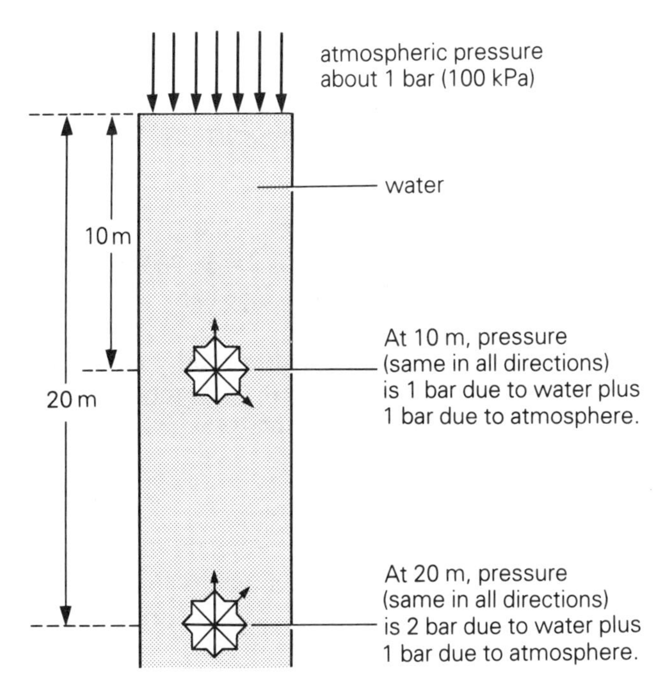

Figure 16.1 Static head.

The relationship between velocity and velocity head is given by the formula:

$$h = \frac{v^2}{2g}$$

where h is the velocity head, v is the velocity of the fluid and g is the acceleration of free fall.

EXAMPLE 16.1

What is the velocity of the flow of water along a tube if the head of water is 5 m? Take the acceleration of free fall to be 10 m/s^2.

Solution
$h = v^2/2g$, so that $v^2 = 2gh$ and $v = \sqrt{2gh}$.
Substituting into the formula
$v = \sqrt{2 \times 10 \times 5} = \sqrt{100} = 10$ m/s.
The velocity pressure of a liquid can be calculated from the velocity head, using the formula:

pressure = density $\times g \times$ head

(see Chapter 3).

Note, this relationship does not hold for a gas as the density is not constant (see above).

EXAMPLE 16.2

A velocity head of 7 m causes a liquid to flow at 11.8 m/s. Calculate the value of the velocity pressure, if the density of the liquid is 800 kg/m^3. Take the acceleration of free fall to be 10 m/s^2.

Solution
Velocity pressure = density $\times g \times$ head
= $800 \times 10 \times 7$ = 56 000 Pa
= 56 kPa or 0.56 bar.

The total head of a liquid is obtained by adding the static head to the velocity head. The total pressure can then be calculated from the total head.

EXAMPLE 16.3

The static head of a liquid in a pipe is 15 m and the velocity head is 7 m. If the density of the liquid is 750 kg/m^3 and the acceleration of free fall is 10 m/s^2, calculate:
i) the total head, and
ii) the total pressure.

Solution
i) Total head = static head + velocity head
= 15 m + 7 m = 22 m.
ii) Total pressure = density $\times g \times$ head
= $750 \times 10 \times 22$ = 165 000 Pa
= 165 kPa = 1.65 bar.

Measuring fluid pressure

The pressure exerted by a moving fluid inside a pipe can be measured by means of a manometer. This is shown in Figure 16.2.

One manometer is fixed with its opening at the side and at right angles to the direction of flow. Because velocity pressure is only exerted in the direction of flow, it has no effect on the liquid level in the manometer. It is only the static pressure, acting in all directions, that will affect the manometer. The difference in liquid levels is a measure of the static pressure.

The other manometer has its opening in the centre of the pipe and along the direction of flow. It therefore measures the velocity pressure because the fluid flows directly into it. But the static pressure is exerted equally in all directions, so that it also measures static pressure. This manometer measures total pressure. The velocity pressure is calculated from the difference in the readings of the two manometers.

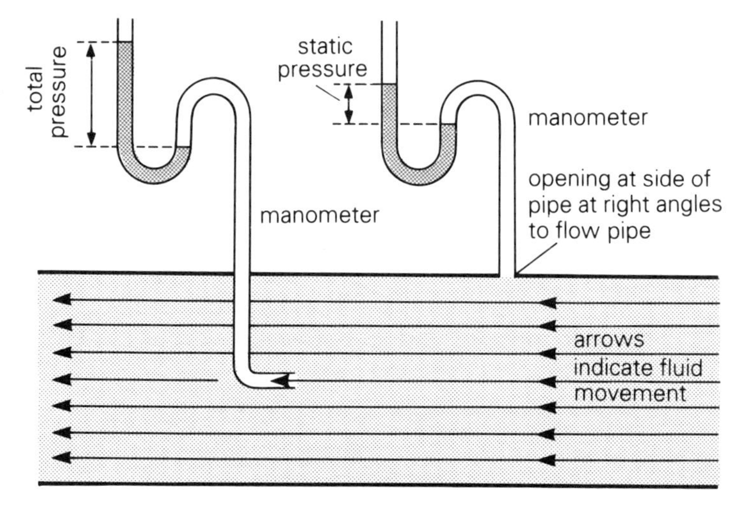

Figure 16.2 Manometers measure fluid pressure.

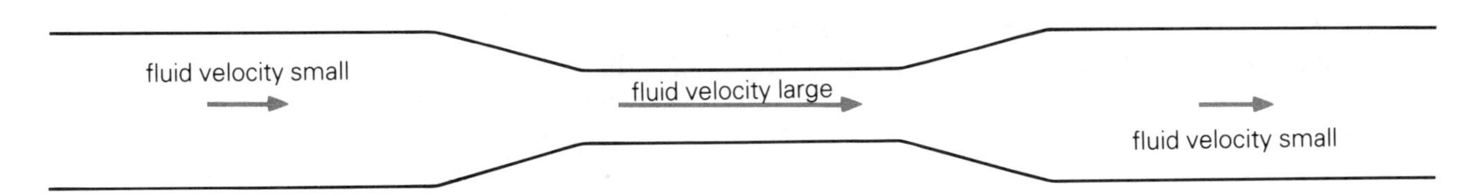

Figure 16.3 Variation of fluid velocity along a pipe.

Velocity changes

The velocity of a fluid is not a constant along a pipe but will vary according to the cross-sectional area of the pipe. If the cross-sectional area is small, the velocity is large and if the area is large, the velocity is small (see Figure 16.3).

The relationship between velocity and area is given by:

$$v = \frac{V}{A}$$

where v is the velocity in m/s, V is the volume flow rate in m^3/s and A is the cross-sectional area in m^2.

EXAMPLE 16.4

A quantity of water is flowing through a pipe with a cross-sectional area of 5 cm^2 and the velocity of flow is 12 m/s. What is:

i) the volume flow rate, and
ii) the new velocity of flow when the pipe narrows to 2.5 cm^2?

Solution

i) $v = V/A$, so that $V = v \times A$
$= 12 \times 5 \times 10^{-4} = 60 \times 10^{-4}$
$= 6 \times 10^{-3}\ m^3/s$ (6 L/s).

ii) $v = \dfrac{6 \times 10^{-3}}{2.5 \times 10^{-4}} = 24$ m/s.

Friction

So far we have ignored the effects of friction as the fluid passes along the pipe. When there is no friction, the total pressure (static + velocity) will be the same everywhere in the pipe. However, this is not true of the individual pressures and as the velocity pressure varies the static pressure also varies but in such a way that the total is constant. As the fluid passes along the pipe there is a force of friction between the walls and the fluid. There is also friction between the layers of fluid and this fluid friction is called **viscosity**. Because of the forces of friction, heat is generated, so the fluid loses energy and there is a pressure drop along the pipe.

The amount of the pressure drop depends on factors such as the viscosity of the fluid (friction within the fluid), the density of the fluid, its velocity, the inner sufaces of the pipe (rough or smooth) and the length of the pipe. Any joints in the pipe, such as tee joints, elbows and valves also have to be allowed for.

All of the above factors can be taken account of by tables which give pressure drops for various joints, rough and smooth pipe, different lengths of pipe and different refrigerants. These tables can be obtained from manufacturers, but their use is beyond the scope of this book.

CHECK YOUR UNDERSTANDING

- A fluid is any substance that flows and it can be either a liquid or a gas.
- Static pressure in a fluid is the same in all directions.
- Velocity pressure is exerted in the direction of fluid flow.
- The depth of a column of fluid is called the head. Head is used as a measure of pressure.
- Velocity head is given by the formula $v^2/2g$, where v is the velocity of the fluid and g is the acceleration of free fall.
- Head can be converted to pressure by the formula: pressure = density × g × head.
- Total head = static head + velocity head.
- Total pressure = static pressure + velocity pressure.

- Static pressure in a pipe can be measured using a manometer with its opening at right angles to the fluid flow.
- Total pressure in a pipe can be measured using a manometer with its opening along the direction of fluid flow. Velocity pressure is the difference of the manometer readings.
- The velocity of a fluid is related to the cross-sectional area of the pipe by the relationship: $v = V/A$, where v is the velocity in m/s, V is the volume flow in m^3/s and A is the area in m^2.
- Friction between the fluid and the walls of the pipe and within the fluid causes a drop in total pressure along the pipe.

REVISION EXERCISES AND QUESTIONS

1. What is the velocity of the flow of water along a tube if the head of water is 8 m? Take the acceleration of free fall to be 10 m/s^2.
2. A velocity head of 6 m causes a liquid to flow at 11.0 m/s. Calculate the value of the velocity pressure if the density of the liquid is 850 kg/m^3. Take the acceleration of free fall to be 10 m/s^2.
3. The *static head* of a liquid in a pipe is 13 m and the velocity head is 6 m. If the density of the liquid is 700 kg/m^3 and the acceleration of free fall is 10 m/s^2, calculate:
   i) the total head, and
   ii) the total pressure.
4. A quantity of water is flowing through a pipe with a cross-sectional area of 4 cm^2 and the velocity of flow is 16 m/s. What is:
   i) the volume flow rate, and
   ii) the new velocity of flow when the pipe narrows to 2 cm^2?
5. Name four factors which cause a pressure drop along a pipe containing a moving fluid.
6. How can the *velocity pressure* of the fluid in a pipe be measured?
7. Distinguish between *static* and *velocity pressure* in terms of the direction in which the pressure is exerted.
8. Explain what is meant by the term *fluid*.
9. What is the *viscosity* of a fluid?
10. Why is it that a fluid loses energy because of friction?

17 Food spoilage and preservation

Introduction

As we saw in Chapter 1, food is spoiled by very small organisms called germs. One type of germ is the **bacterium**.

Bacteria

Living things such as animals and plants are called *organisms* and they are made up of very small units known as *cells*. Each cell contains genetic material, which is responsible for the next generation of organisms. For example, the seeds of an apple tree contain genetic material which enables them to grow into apple trees and not, say, plum trees. Cells also contain protein and the fibres that make up our muscles are made of protein. Meat is made up of muscle fibres and so contains a large amount of protein. Human beings, most animals and most plants contain many millions of living cells. However, some organisms are made up of just one cell. Such an organism is the bacterium, which is a single-celled plant.

Bacteria reproduce, to create more bacteria, when they split into two equal cells each containing the genetic material for that type of bacterium. This cell splitting, or division, can occur very quickly and if enough food is available many thousands of millions of bacteria can be produced in a day.

Some bacteria live freely in water or in soil, whereas others are parasites which need hosts such as human or animal bodies to live in. Many of the parasitic bacteria are of the type that cause illness. Examples of illnesses produced by bacteria are *salmonella*, a type of food poisoning, *tuberculosis* and *leprosy*.

Enzymes

Enzymes are types of proteins which speed up chemical changes. They are present in all living cells, whether of plants or animals and they play an important part in the reproduction and growth of cells. Enzymes also destroy dead cell tissue and in fact it is enzymes that cause meat, which is a type of dead cell tissue, to decay. An enzyme called *lactase* occurs in milk and it is this enzyme which converts the sugar or *lactose* into *lactic acid* and makes the milk sour. Enzymes are not destroyed by refrigeration but as the temperature becomes lower chemical reactions get much slower so that the enzymes are less effective.

Bacteria can only exist on food which has dissolved in water. This type of food is not always available and so most bacteria give off enzymes that alter the chemistry of the food to make it capable of dissolving. It is these enzymes which causes the decay of food by bacteria. Most types of bacteria are killed off at temperatures below the freezing point of water and those that are not killed off stop reproducing.

Yeasts

Yeast is another organism that causes food to decay. Like bacteria, yeasts are single-celled plants, although they are larger than bacteria. Yeasts are very simple members of the fungus family, which includes mushrooms and toadstools. Some yeasts are parasites that cause certain diseases, such as skin and lung complaints, in human beings. Other yeasts are used to make alcoholic drinks, such as wines and beers. Yeast is also used in the baking of bread.

Under the right conditions yeasts can multiply very quickly. Some types multiply by the splitting of cells, others by the growth of buds at the side of cells, which then get bigger and break away. Like bacteria, yeasts produce enzymes which cause decay in organisms. They also convert sugar to alcohol and this is why yeasts are used in wine and beer making. Freshly picked fruit goes rotten quickly, particularly in hot climates, because of yeast which was originally carried to the fruit, while it was on the tree, by the wind or by insects. Rotten fruit often smells of alcohol.

Moulds

Other organisms that produce decay in food are **moulds**. Like yeast they are fungi, but unlike yeast they do not consist of single cells. Moulds have many cells that arrange themselves in the form of long fibres. Some of these fibres acts as roots and grow into the food that the mould is growing on. Mould seeds or *spores*, as they are called, are carried by the wind and so can settle on any object, including items of food, such as fruit, jams and bread. The spores grow and the mould starts to cover the surface of the food. The blue or green mould common on oranges and lemons is called *penicillium* and from penicillium comes the drug penicillin.

Moulds grow particularly well where it is dark and damp. When the temperature is lowered during refrigeration, mould growth slows down. It stops completely at temperatures below −12°C.

Preservation by refrigeration

High temperatures are particularly effective in destroying bacteria, yeasts and moulds, provided that the high temperature is applied for long enough. The low temperatures used in refrigeration are not nearly so effective. Fruit and vegetables are much easier to preserve than, say, meats. This is because fruit is still alive after picking and refrigeration merely slows down the activity of the enzymes. Meat consists mainly of fat and dead muscle fibres and because of chemical activity within the fat, meat deteriorates much more easily. Meat is best preserved for long periods by using air-tight plastic packaging.

If food, whether meat or vegetable, is to be stored for a long time, then very low temperatures have to be used: the lower the temperature, the longer the period of storage. Shops and supermarkets sell their food stocks fairly quickly, a *food store*, in which the food is chilled but not frozen, is employed. However, meat sometimes has to be stored for a longer period and so a *frozen food store* has to be used. Wholesalers are businesses that supply shops and supermarkets and these have to keep food for a much longer period, sometimes for many months. Occasionally deeply frozen food is stored for several years.

Storage temperatures depend greatly on the type of food being stored. Meats of various kinds are stored at temperatures between about −10°C and −25°C. Apples need to be stored at temperatures of around 0°C but some varieties suffer damage at these temperatures. The temperature has to be adjusted very carefully with these varieties. The skins of bananas are damaged at temperatures below 13°C, so they have to be stored at a higher temperature but not one so high that the bananas go rotten quickly.

How long food can be stored depends not only on temperature but also on the relative humidity of the air and the speed at which the air moves. The relative humidity of the air determines the rate at which water evaporates from the food. If the relative humidity is very high, the rate at which water molecules re-enter the food will be nearly as high as the rate at which molecules leave the food. This means that the food will retain its moisture and not become *dehydrated*. *Dehydration*, or loss of water, causes fruit to shrivel and meat to dry and lose vitamins. If the relative humidity of the air in the store is low, food will dry out quite quickly. Fast-moving air will cause evaporation to proceed even faster, as molecules above the surface, which might re-enter, are blown away and the net rate of loss of molecules increases.

To stop dehydration completely, a very high relative humidity, at or near 100% would have to be employed, in completely still air. Unfortunately, these are the conditions under which moulds grow best. Therefore a compromise has to be reached in

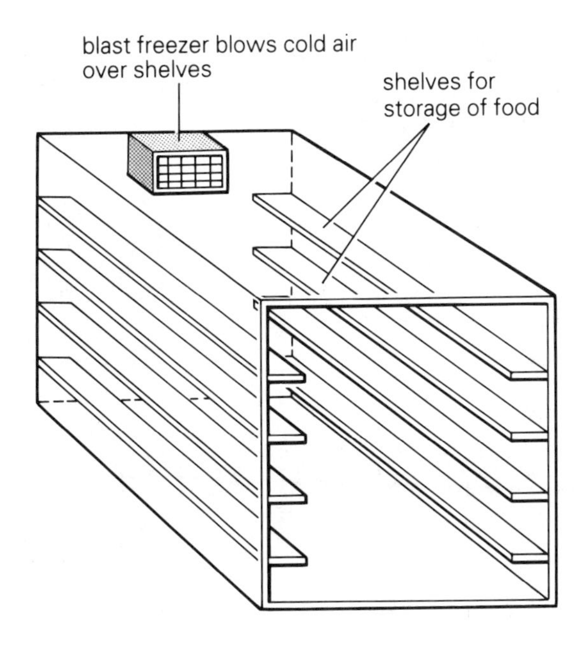

Figure 17.1 An air blast freezer.

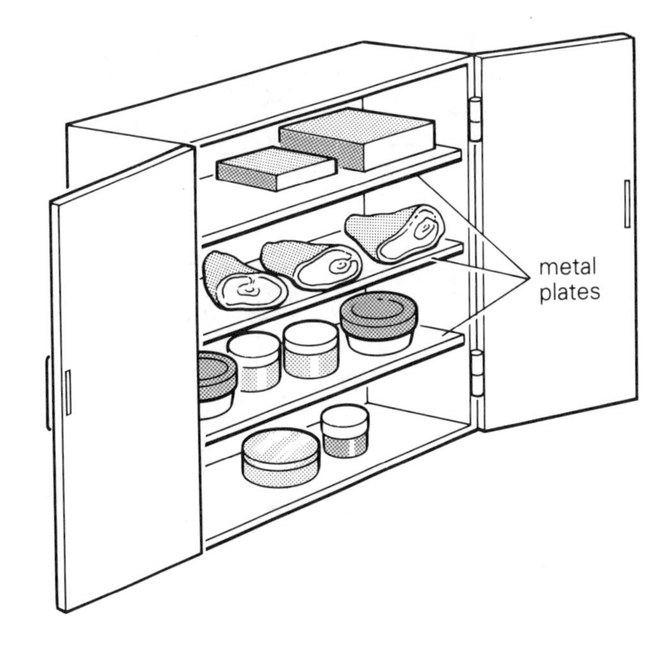

Figure 17.2 A plate freezer.

which the moisture loss is as low as possible but moulds cannot grow.

Sometimes products are stored in plastic containers that do not allow moisture to enter or leave. Then relative humidity and air speed are not critical.

Freezing methods

Food products can be frozen slowly, over a period of hours or even days, or they can be frozen quickly in a matter of minutes. Generally **quick freezing** is regarded as better, mainly because the ice crystals which form are smaller. Animal and plant cells have water inside them and any ice formation will damage the cells to some extent. Smaller crystals will cause less damage. Also, quick freezing does not allow the growth of organisms, such as bacteria, yeasts and moulds during the freezing process.

Slow freezing takes place in a cold room, where the temperature can be anywhere between about −20°C and −40°C, depending on the products being frozen. Usually, large items such as carcasses of meat and barrels of fruit are frozen in this way.

One method of quick freezing is by placing the product in a brine solution which has already been refrigerated to a low temperature. Brine is a good conductor, so that heat is conducted quickly away from the product and it is frozen within minutes. This process is called **immersion freezing**.

Air blast freezing employs high speed, low temperature air to reduce the temperature of the product quickly (see Figure 17.1). The freezer must be designed in such a way that air can move freely around the product.

In one design, trollies containing the food to be frozen are wheeled into a tunnel and cold air is blown through. The tunnel is insulated to prevent heat being conducted in. Sometimes a conveyor belt takes the product through the tunnel.

If fairly small quantities are to be quick frozen, the product can be placed on metal plates containing pipes through which refrigerant flows. Heat is conducted from the food into the metal plate. A **plate freezer** is shown in Figure 17.2.

Refrigerators in shops and stores

One common type of freezer used in shops is the *chest freezer*. Essentially, this is a very efficient refrigerator with good insulation and a transparent plastic door at the top. This has the advantage that customers can see the frozen goods displayed inside (see Figure 17.3).

Figure 17.3 Commercial chest freezers (courtesy of Iceland Frozen Foods plc).

Figure 17.4 Transparent doors allow drinks to be displayed (courtesy of Quest Refrigeration Manufacturing Ltd).

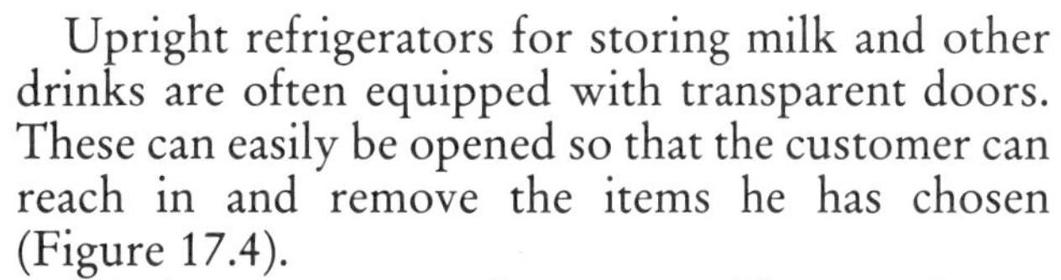

Upright refrigerators for storing milk and other drinks are often equipped with transparent doors. These can easily be opened so that the customer can reach in and remove the items he has chosen (Figure 17.4).

Display cases are refigerators with open fronts which are used to display dairy goods, such as cheese, butter and margarine, or ice cream and even cream cakes (see Figure 17.5).

CHECK YOUR UNDERSTANDING

- Living things are made up of cells.
- Bacteria are very simple plants that consist of just one cell.
- Bacteria can reproduce very quickly.
- Parasitic bacteria are the types which cause disease.
- Enzymes are chemicals which help in the growth of cells and also destroy dead cells.
- Bacteria give off enzymes and these cause decay in food.
- Yeasts are also single-celled plants (fungi) but they are larger than bacteria. Yeasts also give off enzymes and so cause decay.
- Moulds are a third organism that attack food. They are a simple type of fungi.

Figure 17.5 An open-fronted display case.

- Refrigeration slows down the process of decay caused by bacteria, yeasts and moulds.
- The length of time that food can be stored depends on the speed and relative humidity of the air.

- Different foods have different temperatures at which it is best to store them.
- If products have to be frozen it is generally better to employ quick, rather than slow, freezing.

REVISION EXERCISES AND QUESTIONS

1 What is meant by the term *bacteria*?
2 How do *bacteria* cause food to spoil?
3 What is meant by the term *yeast*?
4 How does *yeast* cause food to spoil?
5 What type of organism is a *mould*?
6 How does refrigeration stop food spoiling?
7 What problem occurs when food is kept under conditions where the relative humidity is low and the air speed is high?
8 Why should bananas not be kept in frozen storage?
9 Explain what is meant by *immersion freezing*.
10 Explain what is meant by *air blast freezing*.
11 What is meant by the term *slow freezing*?

18 Fans and pumps

Introduction

Fans are used in refrigeration and air conditioning to circulate air over condenser coils and compressors and also to move air along air-conditioning ducts. Pumps are used to move secondary refrigerants, such as water or brine, away from the evaporator to the place where cooling is needed.

Fans

When a fan causes air to move, a pressure above that of the atmosphere is set up in the direction in which the air moves. Different fans have different capabilities of setting up pressures. For example, Class I fans can exert pressures up to a maximum of about 1000 Pa G and these perform well in the average air-conditioning system. Class II and Class III fans exert higher pressures and Class IV types can develop pressures of above 4000 Pa G. The higher the class of fan the stronger is the construction because more work has to be done in order to produce greater pressure.

The pressure that a fan has to develop in an air-conditioning system depends on the resistance set up to the flow of air by the different components that make up the system. One factor is the size of the ducts through which the air moves. The greater the cross-sectional area of a duct, the smaller is the resistance to the air flow. Ducts of small cross-section have a large resistance. The type of inlet or outlet grille used at the end of the duct will have an effect on the air flow and the resistance of a wet cooling coil is greater than a dry one. If the fan is blowing air over a condenser to cool it down the fins will offer resistance to the air and so will the general design of the condenser.

Types of fan

There are two general types of fan used in refrigeration and air conditioning. These are:
1 the *axial flow* type, and
2 the *centrifugal* type.

AXIAL FLOW FANS

Axial flow means that the air moves or flows in the direction of the axis of the fan, as shown in Figure 18.1. Air is taken in at the front and leaves along the same line on the other side.

There are three types of axial fan: the *propeller fan*, the *tube axial fan* and the *vane axial fan*.

Propeller fans

Propeller fans are shaped broadly like the types of propellers or screws which are used to drive ships. The number of blades or vanes varies from two or three up to about five or six, according to the design. Some typical propeller fans are shown in Figure 18.2.

The air pressure that they can deliver is small compared with other types, but the volume flow per second is fairly large. As the resistance to the movement of air increases then the electrical power input to the fan must be increased to compensate. For example, if the surface of a cooling coil in a cold store becomes very wet and so has greater resistance to air flow, then the current input must be increased to increase the speed of the fan. Propeller fans are not designed to be mounted in air-conditioning ducts but to be fixed on walls or other suitable mountings for cooling, say, a condenser coil.

Tube axial fans

Tube axial fans are similar to propeller fans except that they are mounted inside tubes, as shown in Figure 18.3. The whole unit is then placed in an air-conditioning duct.

The disadvantage of this type of fan is its noise, so that it is used mostly in industrial air-conditioning rather than in the home.

Vane axial fans

These are similar to tube axial types, except that they have fixed vanes in addition to moving ones in order to produce a straighter flow of air. Like tube axial fans they are noisy.

CENTRIFUGAL FANS

Centrifugal fans blow air outwards, away from the centre of the fan, rather than along the axis. The centrifugal compressor works on similar principles (see Chapter 10).

Centrifugal fans are contained in housings that

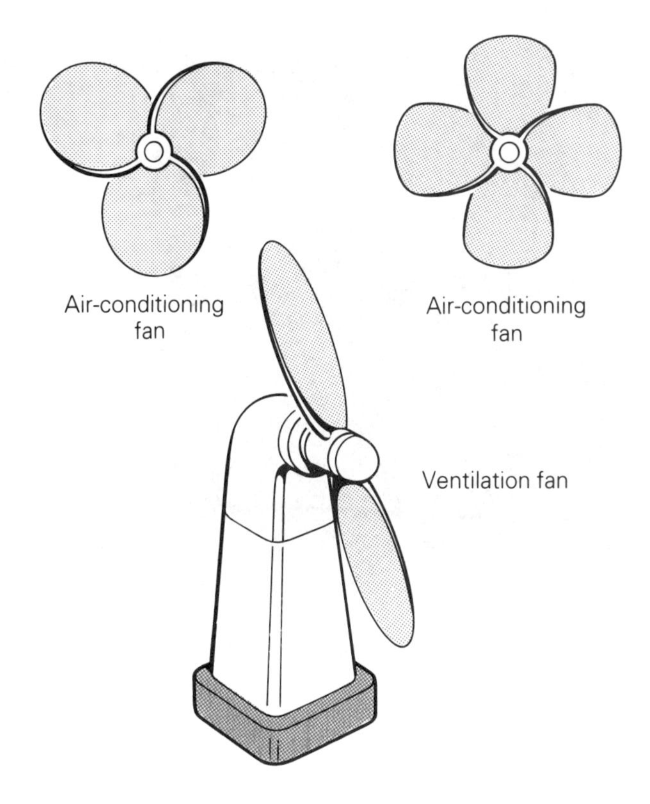

Figure 18.2 Some propeller fans.

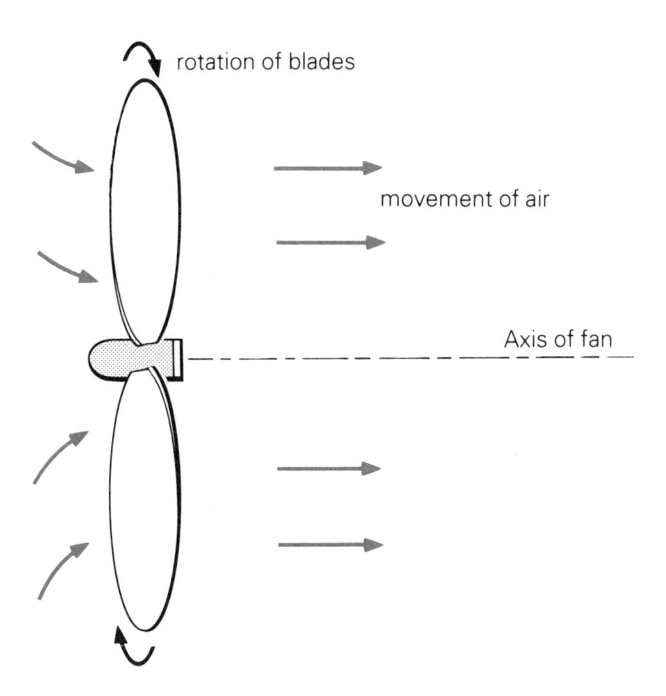

Figure 18.1 Movement of air caused by axial flow fan.

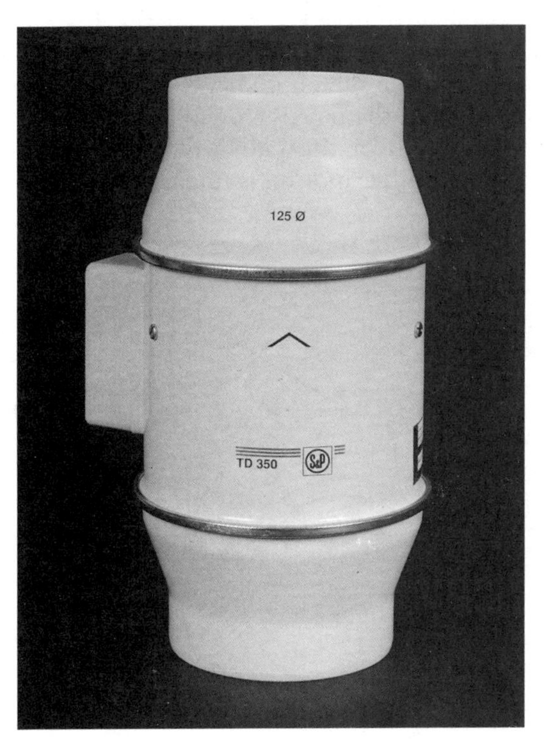

Figure 18.3 A tube axial fan (courtesy of Soler & Palan Ltd).

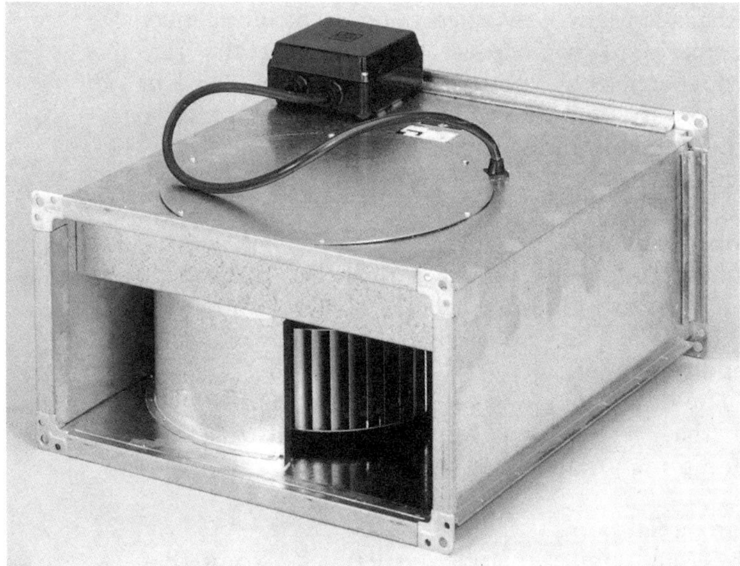

Figure 18.4 Some centrifugal fans: (left) single-inlet pedestal-mounted, (right) square in-line single-inlet (courtesy of Soler & Palan, Ltd).

are designed to fix on to air conditioning ducts (see Figure 18.4).

There are three basic types, classified according to the shape of the blades. These are *forward curved*, *radial* and *backward curved*.

Forward curved

These blades are curved forwards in the direction in which the fan rotates. The shape of the blade imparts a motion which is slightly forward of that of the radius of the fan, as shown in Figure 18.5.

The direction of the radius is called the radial direction. Another motion is imparted by the rotation of the fan and the two motions add together to give a resultant or net motion of the air. Given equal speeds of rotation, the forward-curved fan produces greater air pressure and moves a greater quantity of air in a given time than either the radial or the backward curved types. Forward curved fans are therefore the preferred type for use in air conditioning ducts.

Radial blades

Radial blades, as the name suggests, are set in the radial direction so that the motion given to the air is also radial (see Figure 18.6).

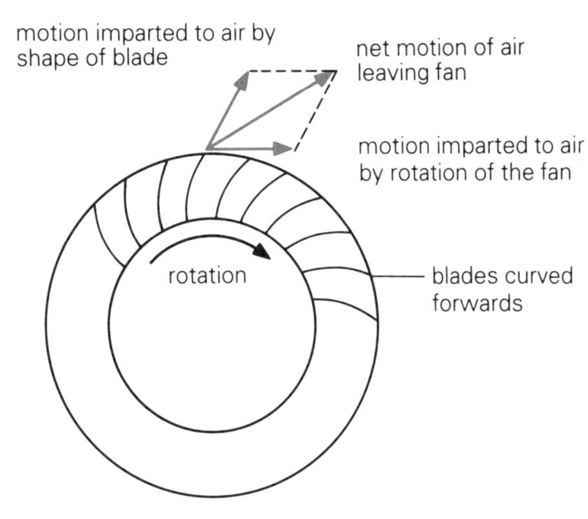

Figure 18.5 A forward-curved fan.

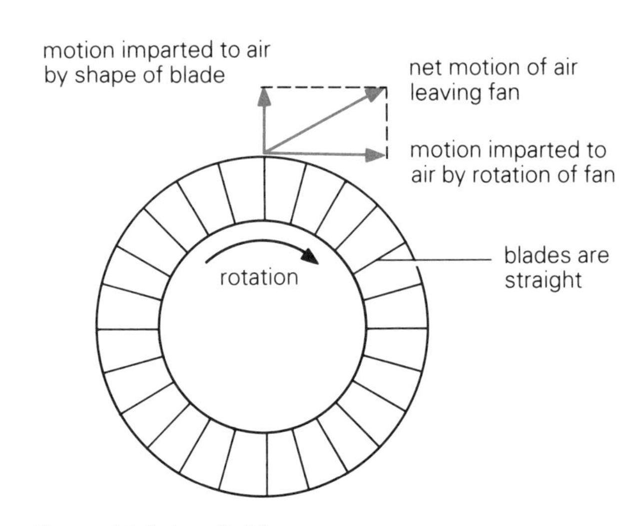

Figure 18.6 A radial fan.

The blades are straight and so they have no curvature. Added to the forward motion of the fan wheel, the resultant motion is as shown. Radial blade fans are often used to cool the electric motors that drive compressors.

Backward curved

Backward curved blades are curved backwards relative to the direction of motion of the fan. The resultant motion of the air is shown in Figure 18.7. These fans are often used for large air-conditioning systems.

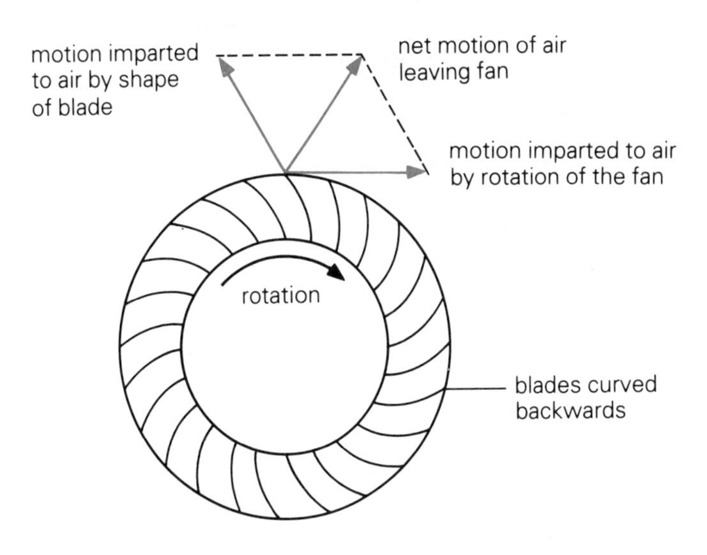

Figure 18.7 A backward-curved fan.

The fan laws

The fan laws are not exact but they are good enough for practical purposes and using these laws, manufacturers can produce fans with standard specifications.

> **The fan laws**
> - The volume of air delivered by a fan per second is directly proportional to the fan speed.
> - The pressure developed by a fan is directly proportional to the square of the fan speed.
> - The power required by a fan is directly proportional to the cube of the fan speed.

EXAMPLE 18.1

A fan is rotating at a speed of 15 revolutions per second and moves 2 m^3 of air every second. If the speed is increased to 30 revolutions per second, what is the new amount of air moved in a second?

Solution

The volume is directly proportional to the speed so that as the speed doubles so does the volume. Therefore the new volume is 4 m^3 per second.

More generally, since the volume is directly proportional to the speed then:

$$\frac{V_2}{V_1} = \frac{S_2}{S_1}$$

and

$$V_2 = \frac{30}{15} \times 2 = 4 \text{ m}^3 \text{ per second.}$$

EXAMPLE 18.2

The pressure developed by a fan is 500 Pa G at a speed of 20 revolutions per second. If the speed is increased to 40 revolutions per second, what is the new pressure developed?

Solution

$$\frac{P_2}{P_1} = \frac{S_2^2}{S_1^2}$$

and

$$P_2 = \frac{40^2}{20^2} \times 500 = \frac{1600}{400} \times 500 = 4 \times 500 = 2000 \text{ Pa G.}$$

EXAMPLE 18.3

The power required to drive a fan at 10 revolutions per second is 100 W. What is the power needed to drive the fan at 20 revolutions per second?

Solution

$$\frac{W_2}{W_1} = \frac{S_2^3}{S_1^3}$$

$$W_2 = \frac{20^3}{10^3} \times 100 = \frac{8000}{1000} \times 100 = 800 \text{ W.}$$

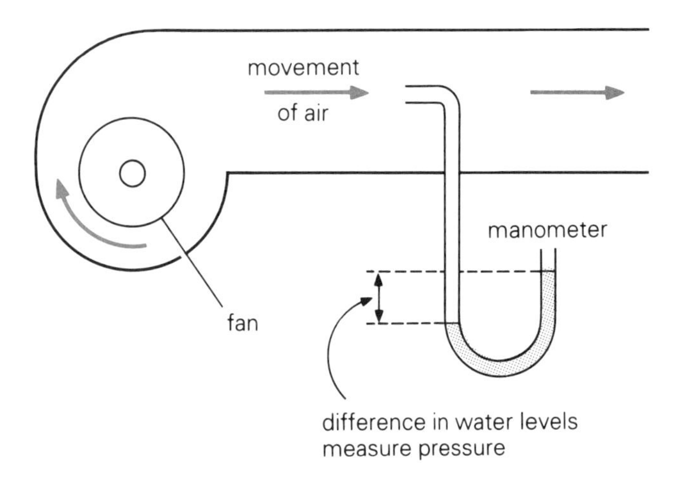

Figure 18.8 Pressure measurement.

Pressure measurements in ducts

The pressure of the air, caused by the fan, in air-conditioning ducts is measured by means of a manometer. Because the pressures involved, above that of the atmosphere, are small, water is used as the liquid instead of mercury. Because mercury is much more dense than water, the change in height of the mercury column would be too small to measure. The way in which the measurement is made is shown in Figure 18.8.

EXAMPLE 18.4

A water manometer is used to measure the pressure caused by a fan and the difference in water levels is found to be 25 mm. Calculate the fan pressure, taking the density of water as 1000 kg/m^3 and the acceleration of free fall 10 m/s^2.

Solution
Pressure = density × g × difference in levels
= 1000 × 10 × 0.025 = 250Pa G.

Liquid pumps

The uses of liquid pumps include circulating secondary refrigerants such as water or brines in air-conditioning or refrigeration systems and pumping water for water-cooled condensers. Pumps are generally of the centrifugal type, so that the refigerant is pushed outwards from the centre to the outer edge of the rotating impeller wheel that makes up the working part of the pump (see Figure 18.6). The impeller contains blades or vanes shaped in such a way that an outward force is exerted on the liquid.

The volume of water that a pump is capable of delivering every second depends on the pressure of water in the region of the pump. A water tower or a tank must be provided above the pump in order to provide a 'head of water' to give the necessary pressure.

Sometimes the pump and the electric motor that drives it operate from a single shaft and sometimes each has a separate shaft and the two are coupled together.

CHECK YOUR UNDERSTANDING

- There are classes of fan, classified according to the air pressure they can deliver.
- The pressure that a fan has to deliver in a system depends on the resistance set up by the system. Resistance is determined by factors such as the duct size, the grilles and the state of cooling coils and condensers.
- The two basic kinds of fan are the axial flow and the centrifugal types. Axial flow fans produce air flow along the axis while centrifugal fans push the air outwards from the centre.
- The kinds of axial flow fan are the propeller, the tube axial and the vane axial.
- Centrifugal fans are classified according to the way the blades are curved: forward curved, radial or straight, and backward curved.
- The volume of air delivered per second is directly proportional to the fan speed.
- The pressure developed by a fan is directly proportional to the square of the fan speed.
- The electrical power required by a fan is directly proportional to the cube of the fan speed.
- Most liquid pumps are of the centrifugal type.
- The volume of liquid delivered per second depends on the liquid pressure around the pump.

REVISION EXERCISES AND QUESTIONS

1 Name some of the factors which cause resistance to air which is blown by a fan.
2 State the *fan laws*.

3 Briefly describe the three main types of *centrifugal fan*.
4 Distinguish between *axial* and *centrifugal* fans.
5 Why is a water manometer used in preference to a mercury one in order to measure fan pressure in an air-conditioning duct?
6 What is a *propeller fan*?
7 There are different classes of fan, what factor distinguishes the different classes?
8 A fan is rotating at a speed of 20 revolutions per second and moves 3 m^3 of air every second. If the speed is increased to 40 revolutions per second, what is the new amount of air moved in a second?
9 The pressure developed by a fan is 600 Pa G at a speed of 15 revolutions per second. If the speed is increased to 30 revolutions per second, what is the new pressure developed?
10 The power required to drive a fan at 12 revolutions per second is 60 W. What is the power needed to drive the fan at 24 revolutions per second?
11 A water manometer is used to measure the pressure caused by a fan and the difference in water levels is found to be 50 mm. Calculate the fan pressure, taking the density of water as 1000 kg/m^3 and the acceleration of free fall 10 m/s^2.

19
Thermal insulation

Introduction

Cooling load is measured in watts and it is the rate at which heat must be extracted from a refrigerated space in order to maintain the desired temperature. If no heat is transferred into the space from outside it would only be necessary to achieve the right temperature, a few minutes after the refrigerator is switched on, and then the compressor could be switched off. However, heat is transferred in from a number of sources and so the compressor must continue to operate in order to maintain the temperature. Of course, the thermostat does switch the system off when the temperature is low enough but when the temperature begins to rise again it switches back on (see Chapter 21).

One way in which heat is transferred into a domestic refrigerator is by conduction through the walls. Also, every time the refrigerator door is opened, warm air gets in. In an air-conditioning system, heat is given off by people and by electric lights and other equipment. Cooling load can be divided into a number of separate loads: the **wall gain load**, the **air change load**, the **product load** and the **supplementary load**.

Wall gain load

Wall gain load 'Q' is the rate at which heat is conducted in through the walls of the refrigerator. It is given by the formula:

$$Q = A \times U \times TD$$

where A is the total area of the walls in m^2, U is the insulation factor or overall heat transmission coefficient in $W/m^2\,K$ and TD is the temperature difference across the walls in K or °C. U is normally known simply as the U factor and it depends on the insulating materials that make up the wall and on the thickness of the wall.

EXAMPLE 19.1

A wall of a refrigeration system measures 2 m by 1.5 m, the inside temperature is 2°C and the outside temperature is 25°C. If the U factor is 0.5 $W/m^2\,K$, calculate the rate of heat transfer through the wall (wall gain load).

Solution

$A = 2 \times 1.5 = 3\ m^2$.

$TD = 25 - 2 = 23°C$.

$Q = 3 \times 0.5 \times 23 = 34.5\ W$.

In an efficient refrigeration system the U factor should be as low as possible in order to stop heat getting in. This means using materials with a low ability to conduct heat; that is, insulators. Examples of such materials are expanded polystyrene, expanded polyurethane and glass fibre. The U factor can also be decreased by making the wall as thick as possible. Thick walls made of concrete blocks and, say, expanded polyurethane are used for large cold stores. However, in domestic refrigerators, the walls cannot be too thick, otherwise the appliance becomes too bulky. The important factor is the material, which is often expanded polystyrene.

One other effect that sometimes has to be taken into account, when determining wall gain load, is that of radiation from the sun. Metal surfaces when left in the sun become very hot and have temperatures much higher than the air. If a refrigerator is placed in direct sunlight then the metal cabinet will become very hot and the wall gain load will become very much higher than expected just from a measure of air temperature. All surfaces absorb some radiation and reflect the rest. It is the absorption of radiation at a surface that makes objects hot. White surfaces reflect more radiation and absorb less, so they do not become as hot as dark surfaces. In order to reduce wall gain load it is therefore advisable for refrigerator cabinets to be painted white, or at any rate a light colour.

Air change load

In domestic refrigerators and freezers, fresh air will only enter the cabinet when the door is opened. Provided the plastic or rubber seals round the edges of doors are in good condition, no air will enter at any other time. Air change load will be small as long as people do not repeatedly open the doors. This means that it will only be a significant factor in places such as busy shops which employ freezers and also in cold stores where the door is being opened frequently to bring out produce.

Any large air-conditioning system has to use outside air which is mixed with return air. Also most buildings will have some windows open and air comes in as doors are opened. Under such circumstances, the air change load makes up a large proportion of the total cooling load.

Product load

Every time warm food or food at room temperature is introduced into a refrigerator, heat must be extracted from it and there is a product load. In some cases this load is very small and in others it is significant. In liquid chillers, for example, where brine is being used to chill products the whole time, the brine itself is warmed by the products and must be kept cool. The product load then becomes the most important part of the the cooling load. In storage freezers in the butchery departments of large stores it can also be important and where food is being frozen, the latent heat (of fusion) needed for freezing makes the product load high.

EXAMPLE 19.2

Poultry is to be chilled in a refrigerator, starting from a room temperature of 27°C, and then stored. If the mass of the poultry is 200 kg and the temperature falls to 3°C in 5 h, calculate the product load. The specific heat capacity of poultry is 3.18 kJ/kg K.

Solution
Heat removed from the poultry = mass × specific heat capacity × temperature fall.
Temperature fall = 27 − 3 = 24°C.
Therefore, heat removed = 200 × 3.18 × 24.
Time taken = 5 × 60 × 60 s.

$$\text{So that product load} = \frac{200 \times 3.18 \times 24}{5 \times 60 \times 60} = 0.85\ \text{kW}.$$

Supplementary load

The supplementary load takes in all those sources of heat gain not included above. For example, it includes those people occupying the refrigerated space and also electrical equipment in the space. Electric lights are regarded as electrical equipment.

In air conditioning, people and electrical equipment in the air-conditioned space are important factors and they must be taken into account. However, they are too central to air conditioning just to be considered as a supplementary load.

CHECK YOUR UNDERSTANDING

- Cooling load can be divided into a number of separate loads: the wall gain load, the air change load, the product load and the supplementary load.
- Wall gain load (Q) is the rate at which heat is conducted in through the walls of the refrigerator. $Q = A \times U \times TD$, where A is the total area of the walls in m^2, U is the overall heat transmission coefficient in W/m^{2}K (U factor) and TD is the temperature difference across the walls in K or °C.
- Wall gain load can be affected by the absorption of the sun's radiation. White paint reflects a greater proportion of radiation than darker colours.
- Air change load is the load put on the system

when air comes in from the outside and has to be cooled. Sometimes it is not significant but it can be significant in large air-conditioning systems.

- Product load is the load which occurs when a warm product has to be refrigerated.
- Product load = mass × specific heat capacity × temperature fall per unit time, provided the temperature of the product does not go below the freezing point of water.
- The supplementary load takes in all those sources of heat that are not wall gain load, air change load and product load. It includes people and electrical equipment.

REVISION EXERCISES AND QUESTIONS

1. A wall of a refrigeration system measures 4 m by 2 m, the inside temperature is 0°C and the outside temperature is 27°C. If the U factor is 0.4 $W/m^2 K$, calculate the rate of heat transfer through the wall.
2. Some pork is to be chilled in a refigerator, starting from a room temperature of 25°C. If the mass of the pork is 300 kg and the temperature falls to 1°C in 3 h, calculate the product load. The specific heat capacity of pork is 2.90 kJ/kg K.
3. Explain the term *cooling load.*
4. Name four ways in which heat can transfer into a refrigeration system.
5. Explain the term *wall gain load.*
6. How does heat from the sun affect wall gain load?
7. Explain the term *air change load.*
8. What is meant by the term *product load*?
9. Upon what factors does the *U factor* of a wall depend?
10. Under which set of conditions will heat conduction be greater.
    i) where the wall is thick and filled with expanded polystyrene, or
    ii) where the wall is thin and is made from steel?

20 Lubrication

Introduction

Moving parts in a compressor, or in other machinery, are kept apart by lubricating oil. This ensures that the parts move freely over one another, with a minimum of friction. When this happens the compressor works efficiently.

Heat is always generated in a compressor and so cooling is necessary. The generated heat increases the temperature in the cylinder and it can cause moving parts to sieze up. Oil in the hot places of the compressor gets hot too. To avoid damage, the oil has to be kept moving so that once it has become heated, it is replaced by fresh oil. Compressor oil is used for both lubrication and cooling. It is specially designed for refrigeration compressors.

Viscosity

One property that compressor oil must have is **viscosity** of the right value. Viscosity is liquid friction between the layers within a liquid. The thicker a liquid is, the greater is the viscosity. Thick oil does not run easily and it has high viscosity. Thin oil is runny and has low viscosity. Very viscous oil will not be able to penetrate between surfaces and so lubricate them. Very thin oil will penetrate but will not protect the surfaces as they rub together. Also, it is oil which forms a seal between piston rings and cylinder and thin oil will be unable to form such a seal.

Viscosity changes with temperature and thick oil becomes much thinner as the temperature is raised. As we saw in Chapter 10, it is inevitable that some oil is carried through the piping to both the condenser (hot) and the evaporator (cold). It changes temperature as it passes through the system and the grade of oil is chosen so that it flows freely over a wide range of temperatures.

There are a number of ways in which viscosity can be measured. However, the viscosity of lubricating oil is determined by placing it in a tank and allowing it to flow out through a hole of fixed size. The time taken for all the oil to flow out is measured and the unit is the **Saybolt Seconds Universal (SSU)**. For example, if it takes 200 s for the oil to flow out at 30°C then the viscosity is 200 SSU at 30°C. A more viscous oil that takes 250 s to flow out at the same temperature will have a viscosity of 250 SSU.

Pour point

Lubricating oils have a certain amount of mineral wax mixed in with them. Because of this, although two oils may have the same viscosity at room temperature, this is not necessarily true at lower temperatures. The **pour point** is the lowest point at which oil will flow or pour. The greater the wax content, the higher is the pour point. When a lubricating oil is selected, it is important that the pour point is not too high, otherwise it will become slow moving in the low temperatures of the evaporator, stick to the surfaces and reduce efficiency.

Cloud point

As the temperature of a lubricating oil is lowered, the wax will start to go solid and separate from the rest of the oil. This means that wax gets deposited in the evaporator, again reducing efficiency. The temperature at which wax begins to separate is called the **cloud point** and the cloud point should be as low as possible.

Floc point

Refrigerant passing through a refrigeration system contains a certain amount of oil, usually, much less than 10%. **Floc point** is the temperature at which wax starts to separate from a mixture of 90% refrigerant R12 and 10% lubricating oil. This mixure allows for the worst possible set of conditions and the floc point should be as low as possible.

Chemical stability

Sometimes the same oil remains in a compressor for several years and, while the compressor is running, high temperatures are produced. High temperatures can cause chemical changes in oil and it is important that such changes do not occur in compressor oil. Compressor oil should have high chemical stability.

Dielectric strength

It is important that oil is as free of impurities as possible. One way in which the amount of impurities, including moisture content can be measured is by placing the oil between two electric plates spaced 2.5 mm apart. A high voltage is applied until an electric current passes between the plates. This type of current is called an arc. The higher the voltage that must be applied before the arc occurs, the greater is the **dielectric strength** of the oil. Contaminated oil will have a low dielectric strength and pure oil a high dielectric strength. Impurities can damage a refrigeration system and so dielectric strength is an important measure of impurity.

Acidity

Almost all lubricating oils are acid to some extent, but too large an acidity can damage the system. When acid is mixed with a substance called an *alkali* the acid is neutralised and no more damage is done. One example of an alkali is potassium hydroxide and the mass in milligrammes of potassium hydroxide needed to neutralise one gramme of oil is called the neutralisation number. Oil used in compressors should have a neutralisation number not greater than 0.05 mg/g.

Synthetic lubricants

Lubricating oils for use with refrigerants such as R12 and R22, and many others, are made of mineral oils which are taken from rocks beneath the earth. However, such oils are not used with R134a and instead chemicals called *synthetic esters* are employed. These esters are made by many manufacturers and those produced by ICI are known as Emkarate RL lubricants. These (and the esters made by other manufacturers) have much lower pour points than their mineral equivalents and so they perform better at lower temperatures. There is no floc point as there is no wax to separate out and they show a high level of chemical stability compared with mineral oils.

CHECK YOUR UNDERSTANDING

- Lubricating oil reduces friction in a compressor and also helps to keep it cool.
- Viscosity is a measure of how thick oil is and the higher the temperature the lower is the viscosity. Viscosity is measured in Saybolt Seconds Universal (SSU).
- Pour point is the temperature at which a lubricating oil begins to pour.
- Cloud point is the temperature at which wax begins to separate from the oil.
- Floc point is the temperature at which the wax in a mixture of 90% refrigerant and 10% oil, by volume begins to separate.
- Chemical stability is a measure of the resistance to chemical change of lubricating oil, at high temperatures.

- Dielectric strength is an electrical measure of the contamination of lubricating oil by impurities.
- Acidity is measured by the mass in milligrammes of the alkali potassium hydroxide to neutralise one gramme of it.

REVISION EXERCISES AND QUESTIONS

1 What are the two main functions that compressor lubricating oil has to perform?
2 If the viscosity of a lubricating oil increases from 500 SSU to 700 SSU does this indicate a rise or fall of temperature?
3 How is the amount of contamination in a lubricating oil measured?
4 How can the *acidity* of lubricating oil be measured?
5 What is meant by the *pour point* of a lubricating oil?
6 What is meant by the *cloud point* of a lubricating oil?
7 Explain the term *floc point*.

21 Refrigeration controls

Introduction

One type of refrigeration control is the throttling valve, which controls the rate of flow of refrigerant into the evaporator. Generally, these operate automatically, with the valve responding to some change in the system. Throttling valves act as flow controls and this topic was covered in Chapter 15.

Operating controls maintain desired conditions of temperature and humidity in the system. A temperature control is known as a thermostat. The temperature inside a refrigerator needs to be set to a suitable value. If the temperature of the evaporator starts to go below the set value, the thermostat switches off the compressor and the temperature of the evaporator starts to rise again. When the set value is again achieved the thermostat switches the compressor back on.

Bimetal strips

The simplest form of thermostat is the **bimetal strip**. This consists of a strip made of two different metals which have been riveted together. Brass and iron can be used and when the strip is heated the brass expands more than the iron. This causes the strip to bend and break an electrical contact. If the bimetal strip is placed close to the evaporator it can be used to switch off the compressor as the temperature changes (see Figure 21.1).

When the evaporator temperature decreases, the brass contracts more than the iron, the contacts open and the compressor switches off. The temperature then rises again, the bimetal strip straightens and the compressor switches on again.

Remote bulb thermostats

The **remote bulb thermostat** is the one commonly used in refrigeration (Figure 21.2). The bulb is filled with a liquid that easily evaporates, such as refrigerant. A capillary tube connects the bulb to a device called a *bellows*, which consists of a corrugated copper shell. Vapour from the refrigerant fills the bellows and as the temperature rises, the pressure exerted by the vapour increases. The bellows expand, push the lever, which is pivoted at the bottom and the contacts close. The spring is used to adjust the temperature range of the thermostat. Although, in domestic refrigerators the bulb is normally positioned in the evaporator, in larger systems it can be placed on or even in the product which is being refrigerated. In cold stores it can be several metres from the instrument itself.

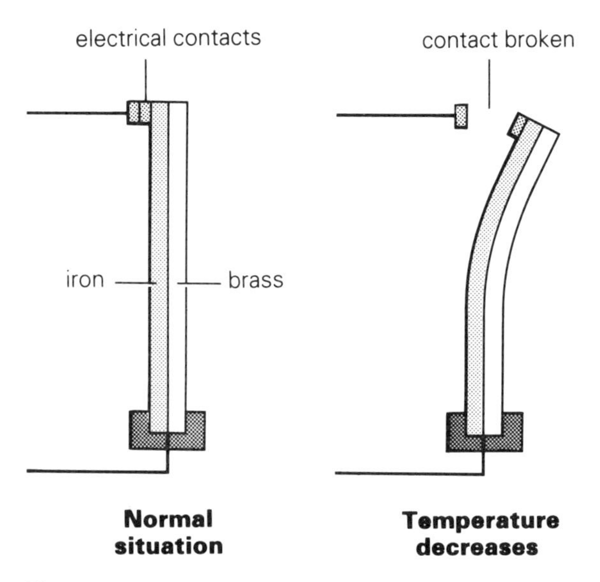

Figure 21.1 The bimetal strip.

Range and differential adjustment

The spring in the remote bulb thermostat is used to adjust the temperature range. Suppose that the thermostat switches off at −5°C (this is called the *cut-out temperature*) and switches back on at −1°C (the *cut-in temperature*) then the average evaporator temperature is −3°C. By adjusting the spring the cut-out and cut-in temperatures can be altered and the difference between the two (4°C), called the **differential**, kept the same. However, the differential cannot be changed without altering the cut-in and cut-out temperatures. The cut-in and cut-out temperatures are referred to as the **range**.

The thermostat in Figure 21.3 has separate screws for adjusting range and differential. If the range-adjustment screw is screwed inwards, the spring tension increases and the bellows must exert a greater force on the lever in order to close the contacts. By pushing the lever to the left, pin B at the top of the *armature* lever also moves to the left. An armature is a length of soft iron. By the action of the pivot the armature is pushed to the right, the permanent magnet attracts it and the contacts close. As a result of the increase in spring tension the cut-in and cut-out temperatures will both increase.

If the differential screw is turned clockwise, the bar A moves to the left and the pin B can move further to the left in the slot. This makes it easier for the bellows to close the contacts and the cut-in temperature increases. The differential also increases. An anticlockwise turn of the screw decreases the differential. By altering both controls the desired cut-in temperature, cut-out temperature and differential can be achieved.

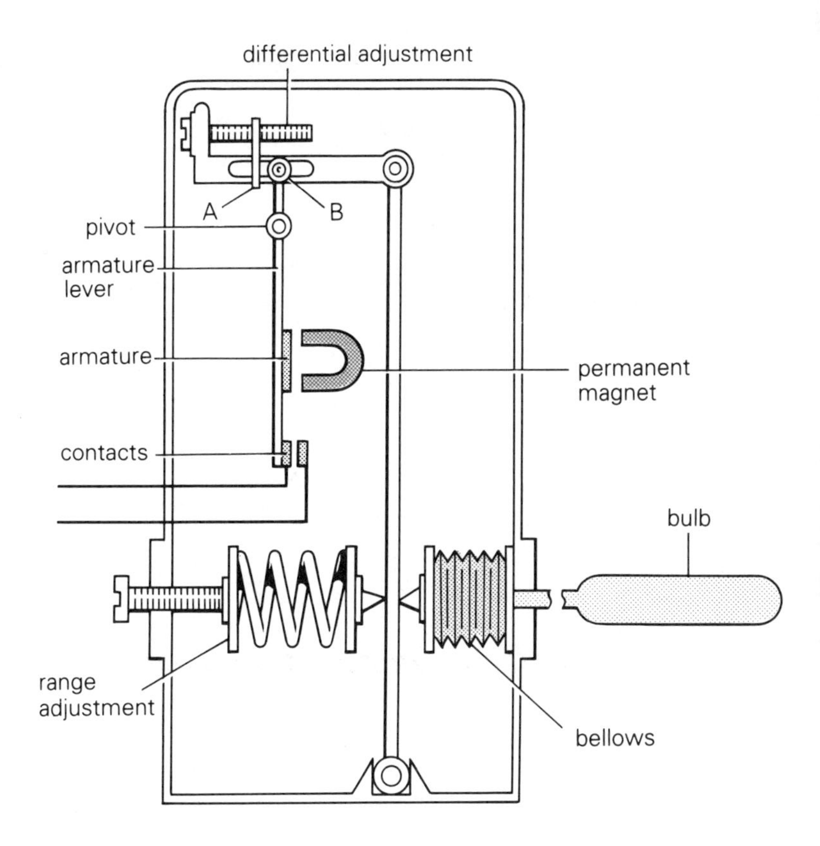

Figure 21.3 Range and differential adjustment.

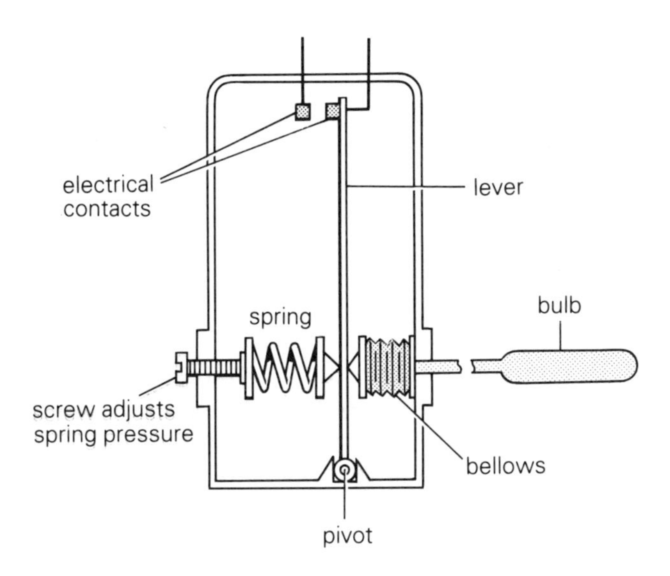

Figure 21.2 The remote bulb thermostat.

Low-pressure controls

Low-pressure controls have a similar design to the thermostat, except that the bellows are connected directly to the low-pressure part of the refrigeration system and not to a bulb. Usually, connection is made to the compressor end of the suction line. Because temperature rises as pressure rises, the low-pressure control can be used as a thermostat. If a low-pressure control is used in addition to a thermostat, the low-pressure control will cut out if refrigerant leaks out and so switch off the compressor. Without this the compressor would continue to run, taking in air and moisture, so causing far greater problems. A low-pressure control is shown in Figure 21.4.

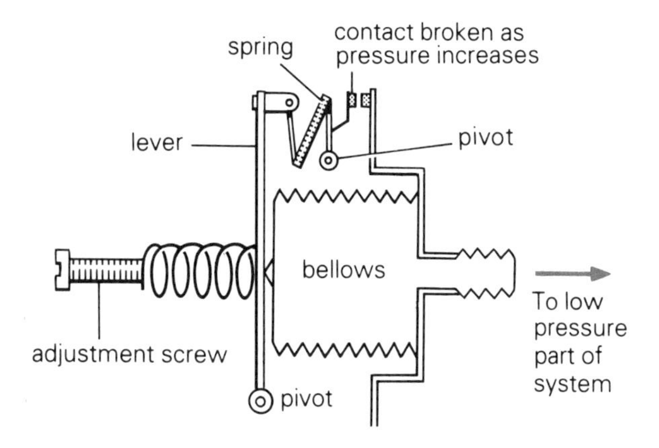

Figure 21.4 A low-pressure control.

High-pressure controls

High-pressure controls are very similar to low-pressure controls and they are usually connected to the compressor end of the discharge line. Their purpose is to cut out if the discharge pressure becomes too high. High-pressure controls are important where a water-cooled condenser is used, because if the water supply fails, cooling will stop, overheating may occur and the pressure may build up to dangerous levels. They are also important if the fan motor of an air-cooled condenser fails.

Dual-pressure controls

A dual-pressure control combines both high- and low-pressure controls. It is normal to have two bellows and only one set of contacts.

Compressor capacity controls

The compressor capacity is the amount of refrigerant that a compressor is capable of pumping. Capacity controls are necessary to ensure that the compressor does not pump more refrigerant than the evaporator and other parts of the system can cope with.

There are a number of ways in which this can be done. One way is to vary the speed of the electric motor and so vary the speed of the compressor. Another way is to lead the dischage vapour from one or more of the cylinders away from the discharge line and back into the suction line.

The amount of refrigerant can also be controlled by lifting the suction valve away from its seat. This means that as the piston moves upwards to compress the vapour, no compression occurs and the vapour is just pushed back into the suction line. The suction valve is lifted by a mechanism which responds to the oil pressure in the compressor. In compressors with a number of cylinders it can be arranged that one or more valves is lifted to reduce the capacity.

One other way is to connect two compressors in parallel and use pressure controls so that one cuts out when the compressors pump too much refrigerant.

Humidistats

Air-conditioning systems have to supply air of suitable relative humidity to a room or to a building. In order to adjust the humidity to a suitable value a humidistat is used.

The most common form of humidistat employs a nylon band in order to sense humidity. The nylon band absorbs moisture from humid air and as a result its length increases. When the air is dry, moisture leaves the band and it shortens. The band fits over three rollers, as shown in Figure 21.5.

At one end two rollers are attached to an idler lever. The idler lever is attached through a pivot to a control lever, which is in contact with the control knob cam. As the control knob is rotated, the cam rotates and alters the tension of the nylon band. As the tension increases, the bottom of the actuator lever is pulled to the right and by the action of the pivot, the top of the lever is pushed up. This causes the push rod to close the circuit, the humidifying spray comes on and the fan blows humid air into the room.

The humidity of the room now builds up and so the nylon band starts to become slack. The bottom of the actuator now moves to the left, the push rod moves down, the contacts open and the humidifying spray is switched off. No more moist air enters the room and so the band starts to tighten again. In this way a fairly constant moisture level is maintained in an air-conditioned space.

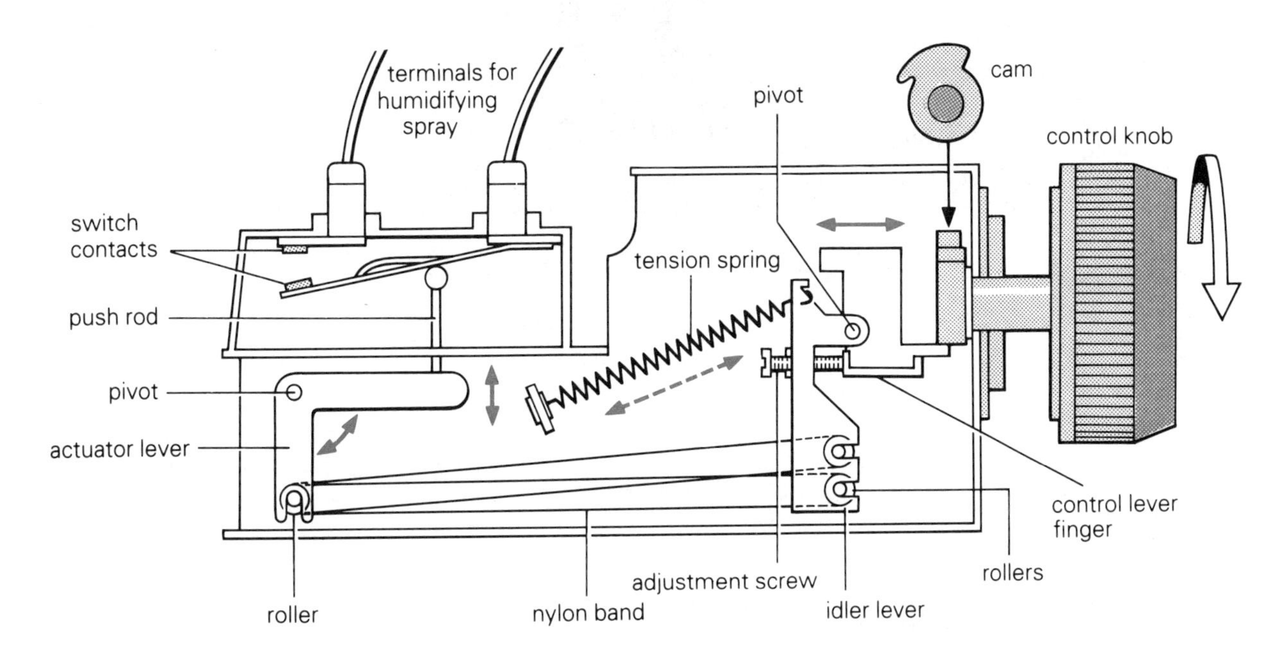

Figure 21.5 A humidistat.

Microprocessor controls

In recent years, control systems for use in refrigeration and air conditioning have been developed in which use is made of digital circuits. Digital circuits are used in computers and calculators, where in the form of *integrated circuits* or *silicon chips* they perform high-speed counting.

Microprocessor controls work on this principle and one microprocessor can control the air conditioning for a whole building or the refrigeration for a whole supermarket.

CHECK YOUR UNDERSTANDING

- A temperature control is called a thermostat. Thermostats switch off the compressor when the temperature goes too low.
- One type of thermostat is the bimetal strip, consisting of two different metals fixed together.
- Another type of thermostat consists of a bulb and bellows: the fluid in the bulb controls the bellows which in turn controls the electrical switch.
- A low pressure control can be used as a temperature control and it will also stop the compressor in the event of refrigerant loss.
- A high pressure control stops the compressor when the pressure becomes too high.
- A compressor capacity control controls the amount of refrigerant that the compressor pumps.
- Humidistats control the relative humidity of air-conditioned space. The most common sort uses a nylon band.
- Microprocessor controls, working on digital principles are used in modern air-conditioning systems.

REVISION EXERCISES AND QUESTIONS

1. Explain the operation of a *bimetal strip*.
2. What is meant by the term *pressure control*?
3. What is the purpose of a *humidistat*?
4. What is the effect of moisture on a nylon band?
5. What is the purpose of a *compressor capacity control*?
6. What is a *dual-pressure control*?
7. Explain the term *differential.*

22
Materials and hand tools

Introduction

It is necessary for the refrigeration technician to have a working knowledge of the materials used in refrigerators so that he can carry out repairs more successfully. Tubing of various sizes, in different materials, is used for several applications in refrigeration work.

Copper tubing

Copper tubing has the advantage that it is easily bent to shape and is easily joined using compression fittings. It can be used anywhere, either on the high or the low side of a refrigeration system. It does not corrode easily, it is easy to join by brazing or silver soldering but it does have the disadvantage that it is more expensive than steel tubing.

Steel tubing

Steel tubing comes in two main types. It may be either soft-drawn or hard-drawn and the term drawn refers to the way the tubes are pulled out or extruded in the factory where they were made. Soft-drawn tubes are the softest and these are more easily bent by one of the processes described below.

Steel tubing is used in the manufacture of condensers for domestic refrigerators. It is not such a good conductor of heat as copper but steel condensers are fastened in close contact to the body of the refrigerator and this, in effect, increases the surface area of the condenser. Lengths of steel tubing can be joined by silver soldered joints.

Aluminium tubing

Aluminium tubing is used in the manufacture of evaporators for domestic refrigerators. Like steel, aluminium is not such a good conductor of heat as copper, although it is cheaper. One advantage is that it is easy to bend.

Stainless steel tubing

The advantage of stainless steel is that it is strong and does not rust. Stainless steel tubing and fittings can be joined together by silver soldering, just as for other types of steel.

Flexible hoses

Air-conditioning systems for cars use flexible rubber or plastic hoses rather than metal tubing, as hoses withstand the vibration of moving vehicles better. Hoses are also employed in large refrigerated trucks and also in refrigerated vans.

Tube cutting

One method of cutting metal tubing is by means of a hacksaw (see Figure 22.1).

Hacksaws are mostly used for larger diameter tubing, which should be held in a clamp so that when the cut is made it is straight and square. The tubing should be tilted down slightly so that the small splinters of metal produced by the sawing fall out. After sawing, any splinters left inside should be removed, so as not to contaminate the refrigerant when the tubing is installed.

Another method of cutting is by a **tube cutter** (see Figure 22.2). The sharp jaws of the tube cutter are placed in contact with the tube, and then the adjustment knob is tightened slightly, so that the sharp cutting wheel bites into the metal. The tube cutter is then moved around the tube until a groove is cut into its surface. The knob is tightened a little bit more and the process is repeated in order to make the groove deeper. This is done several times until the tube is cut completely.

> Do not try to tighten the knob too much in one go as the tube may become squashed where the cut is being made.

Once tubing has been cut there will be a ridge of sharp metal on the inside of the tubing. This is known as a *burr* and burrs cannot be left, otherwise they will impede the flow of refrigerant through the system. Some tube cutters are fitted with a sharp blade known as a *reamer* and this should be run around the inside of the tubing in order to remove the burr. Alternatively, a half-round file may be used (see Figure 22.3). Remove any metal filings from the inside of the tubing, using a clean rag.

The process of removing burrs is known as **deburring**. Once tubing has been cut to length and deburred the lengths of tubing are ready to be fixed together by means of fittings. Some common types are **sweat**, **flare**, **compression** and **hose** fittings.

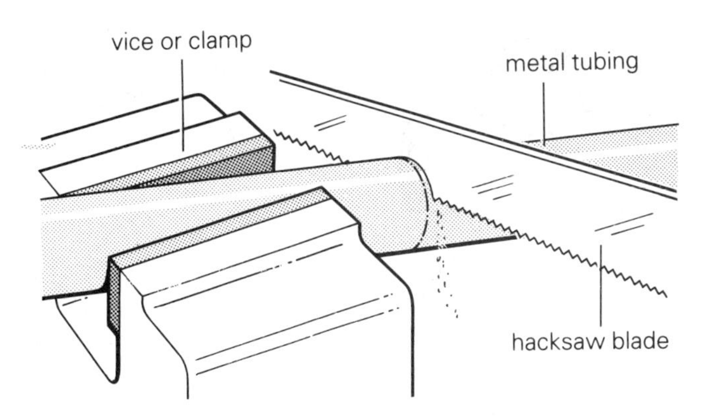

Figure 22.1 Cutting with a hacksaw.

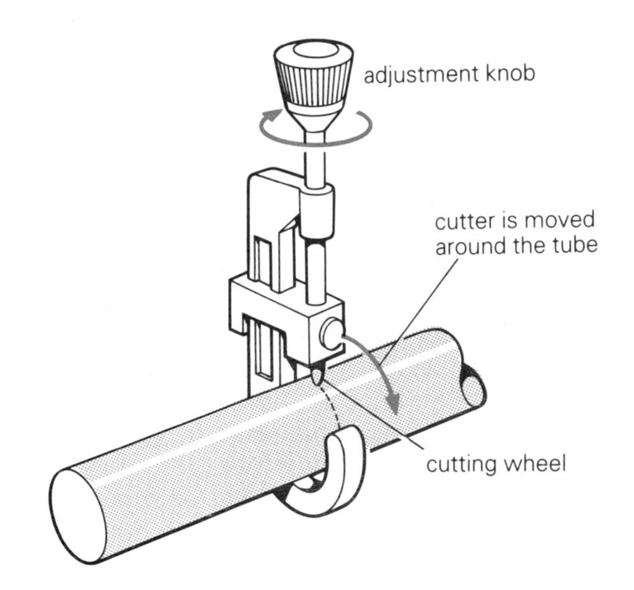

Figure 22.2 A tube cutter.

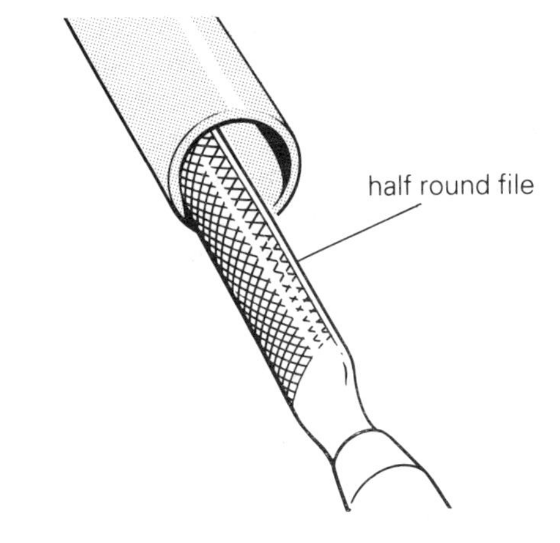

Figure 22.3 Deburring with a file.

Sweat fittings

Sweat fittings are designed to be soldered to the metal tubing and a selection are shown in Figure

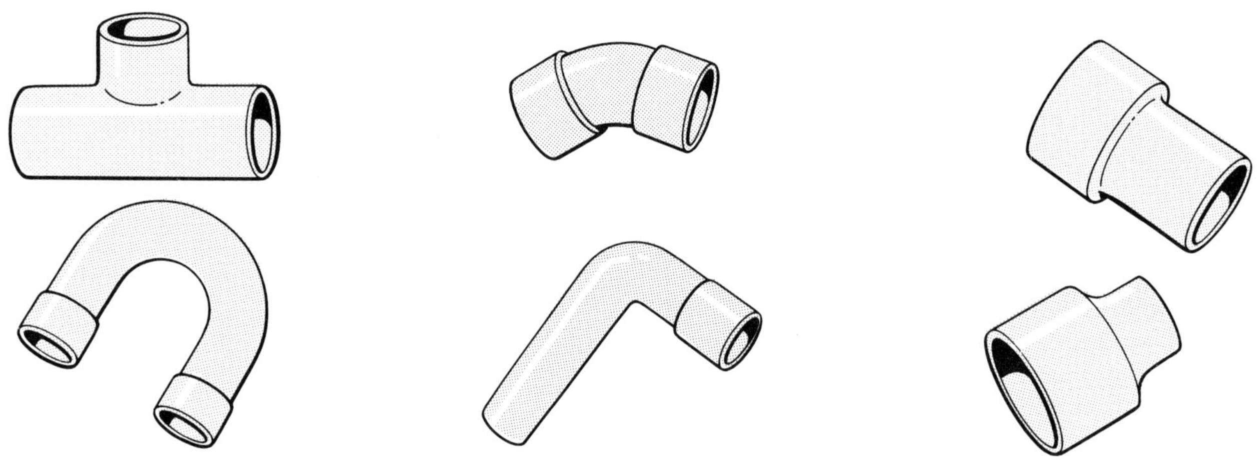

Figure 22.4 Some sweat fittings.

22.4. Sweating is another word for soldering. Soldering should be performed very carefully to make sure that there are no leaks and no solder blobs on the inside to impede the flow of refrigerant.

1 Cut the tubing and remove the burrs as explained previously.
2 Thoroughly clean both the tube and fittings to remove rust or other corrosion, oil, grease and general dirt, as all of these will prevent the formation of a proper joint. Rust and corrosion should be removed with sandpaper (Figure 22.5).

   Oil and grease are dissolved by applying an organic cleaning solvent with a piece of rag. All traces of the solvent should then be wiped away to allow for a good joint and to prevent contamination of the refrigerant. Before soldering the metal must be shiny and completely clean.
3 Immediately before soldering, clean the inside of the fitting with a stiff wire brush. Make sure that you do not touch the freshly-cleaned surface with your hands.
4 Two types of soldering are employed in refrigeration systems: **soft soldering** and **silver soldering**. Soft soldered joints cannot withstand such high temperatures and pressures as those formed by silver solder. This means that silver soldering is used far more often for refrigeration and air-conditioning work. The instructions given here apply to both types of soldering.

   The first step is two select the correct **flux** for the job. For soft soldering use soft-solder flux and for silver soldering use silver-solder flux. Never try to make do with the wrong flux. Brazing rods, consisting of silver solder with flux inside, can now be obtained.

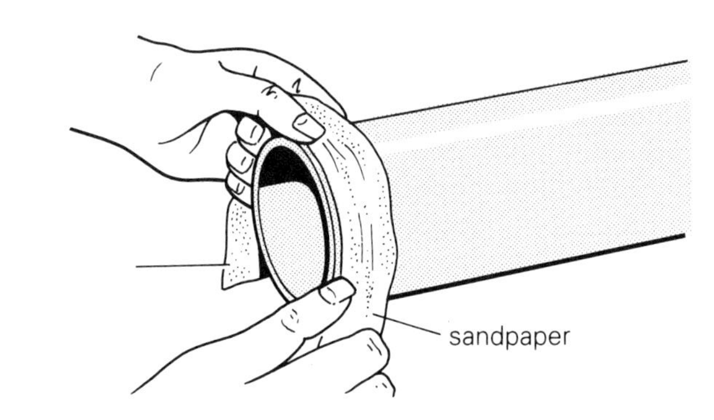

Figure 22.5 Sanding to produce clean surfaces.

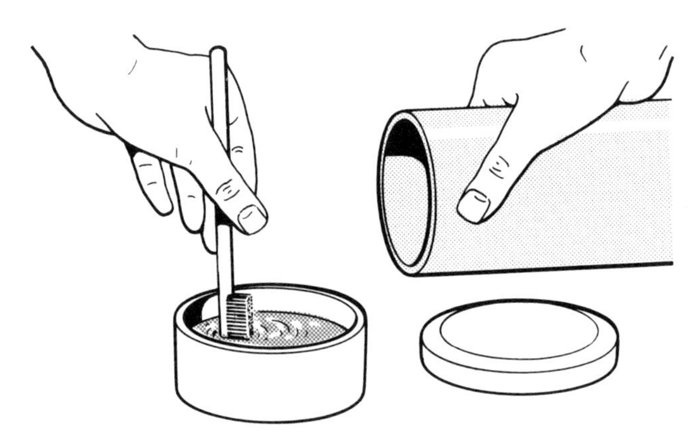

Figure 22.6 Stirring the flux.

Flux can be in the form of a paste or in the form of a liquid. Both perform the function of a flux which is to set up a barrier between the freshly cleaned work and the air. Without the flux, oxygen from the air would attack the cleaned surfaces and produce a thin layer of corrosion.

All the while you are making soldered joints keep the flux stirred by using the brush (see Figure 22.6). This stops some of the chemicals in the flux from settling to the bottom.

Push the tubing a little way into the fitting and using the brush apply flux on the outside surface of the tubing, where the joint is to be made. Do not use so much flux that it drips down inside the joint.

Now push the tubing fully into the fitting, making sure that the flux is spread uniformly around the joint.

At this stage, the joint can be soldered either by soft soldering or silver soldering, depending on the conditions the joint has to withstand. Soft soldered joints cannot be used in the main parts of a refrigeration system, as leakage may occur. They can only be used on peripheral equipment. The instructions for soft soldering and silver soldering joints are different.

Soft soldering

Soft soldering is low-temperature soldering. Soft solder is an alloy of mainly tin and lead but there is also a small amount of antimony. The type of soft solder used in refrigeration work does not have a single melting point but instead has a wide melting range between about 183°C and 250°C. This makes it easy to mould or shape. Soldering irons, employing a hot metal tip or bit, are used for some soft-soldering jobs but for tubing joints, of the type used in refrigeration, a *blow-torch* is better. A blow-torch is a device that produces a hot flame, sufficient to melt solder. Butane is commonly used as a fuel.

First, direct the flame on to the thickest part of the fitting and then move it towards the joint. Be careful not to touch the flame on to the flux, otherwise it will burn and the joint will have to be fluxed all over again. Move the flame all around the fitting, so that the joint is raised to a high enough temperature to melt the solder (see Figure 22.7).

The temperature may be tested by touching the solder on to the joint from time to time. When the joint is hot enough the solder will melt on contact with the metal.

Keep the fitting hot with the flame and melt the solder on to the joint. Move the solder round the joint until it is filled with just enough solder to make up a **fillet** (see Figure 22.8). The solder is sucked into the space between the fitting and the tube by a process known as capillary action. Capillary action occurs whenever a liquid is contained in a narrow space or in a narrow tube, such as a capillary tube.

Do not be tempted to use too much solder as this adds no strength to the joint. Do not heat solder directly using the flame, because the metal fitting and the tube will not get hot enough and the joint will be weak.

Silver soldering

Silver soldering is a form of high temperature soldering known as brazing. Originally brazing was done with brass (hence the name) but today there are a number of materials that can be used. Silver solder is one such material and it is made from silver, copper, zinc and sometimes, cadmium. It melts at temperatures varying from about 600°C to 800°C, depending on the exact mixture of metals.

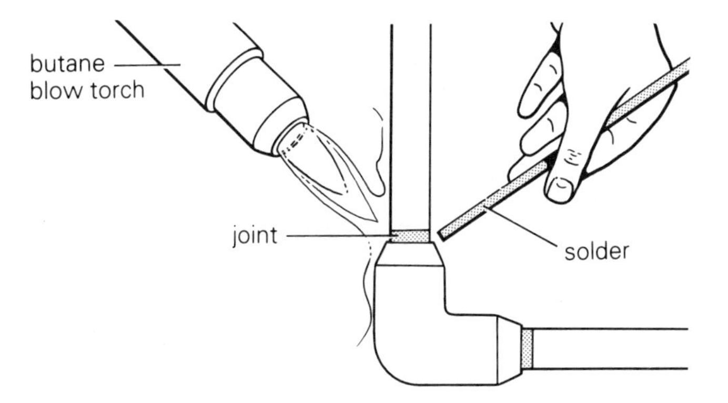

Figure 22.7 Soldering with a blow torch.

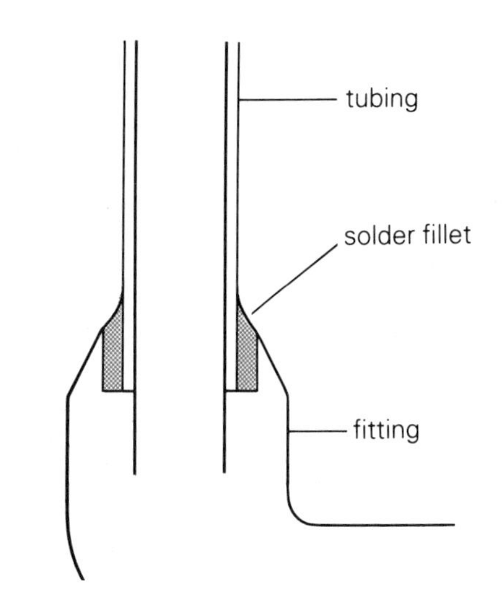

Figure 22.8 A solder fillet.

Because the temperatures are so high a special high-temperature torch, known as an **oxy-acetylene torch**, is used.

Because of the high temperatures the fitting and the tube should be positioned on special bricks, known as fire bricks, if possible. Apply the flux in the same way as for soft soldering. Then move the flame from the tube to the fitting and back again, until they are both hot enough for the silver solder to melt. Apply the solder all round the joint, being careful not to apply too much. At the right temperature the solder will flow into the joint.

Flare fittings

Flare fittings employ screw threads and they are fixed to the end of a piece of tubing that has been expanded or flared. Once the flare has been pushed on to the fitting a flare nut is screwed into position over the joint (see Figure 22.9) A selection of different flare fittings is shown in Figure 22.10.

A number of steps are necessary in order to produce a good flare fitting.

1 Cut the tubing and deburr the end, as described in the section on tube cutting.
2 Slide the flare nut over the tube, making sure the threaded end is towards the end of the tube to be flared (see Figure 22.11).
3 Now place the end of the tube in the *flare clamp*. The amount of tube which protrudes above the surface of the block determines the amount of flare. If the tube sticks up too much the flare will be too large and if it sticks up too little, the flare will be too small. Once the tube protrudes the right amount tighten the wing nut to clamp the tube in position (see Figure 22.12).

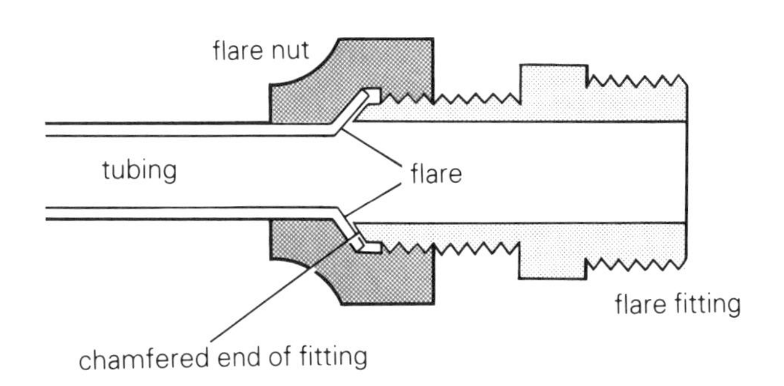

Figure 22.9 Connection with a flare fitting.

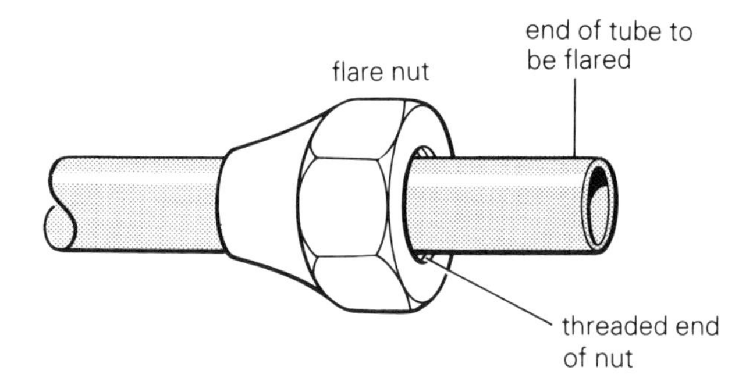

Figure 22.11 Positioning the flare nut.

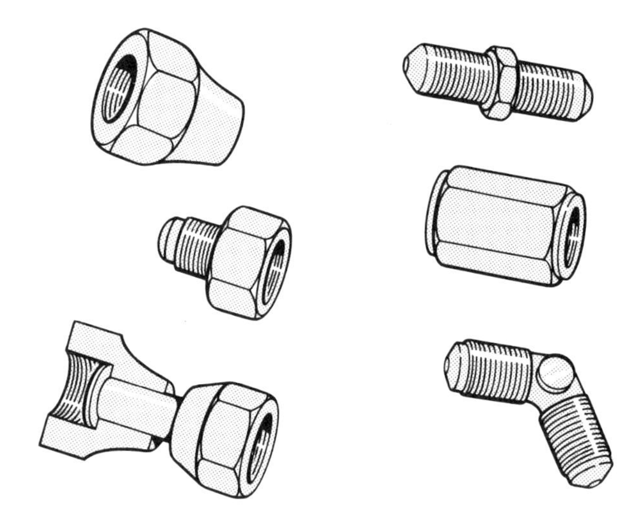

Figure 22.10 Some flare fittings.

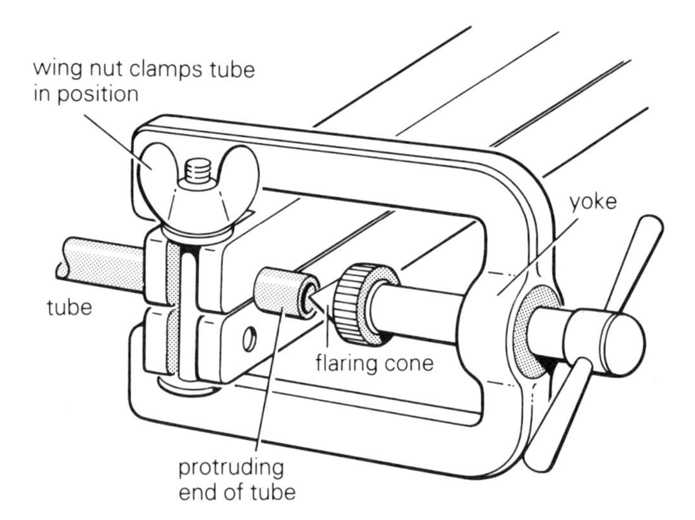

Figure 22.12 Clamping the tube.

Figure 22.13 Releasing the tube.

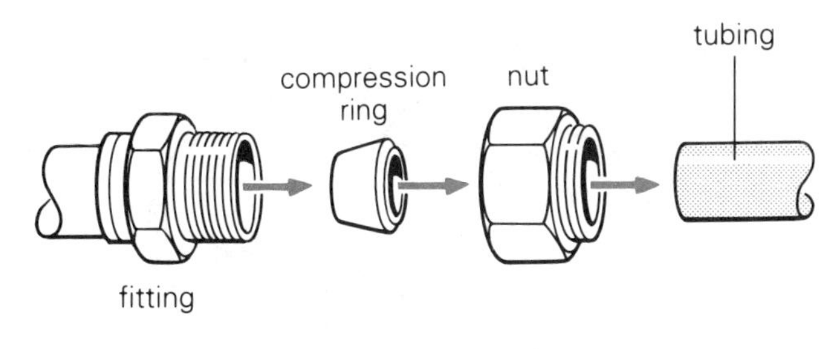

Figure 22.14 A compression fitting.

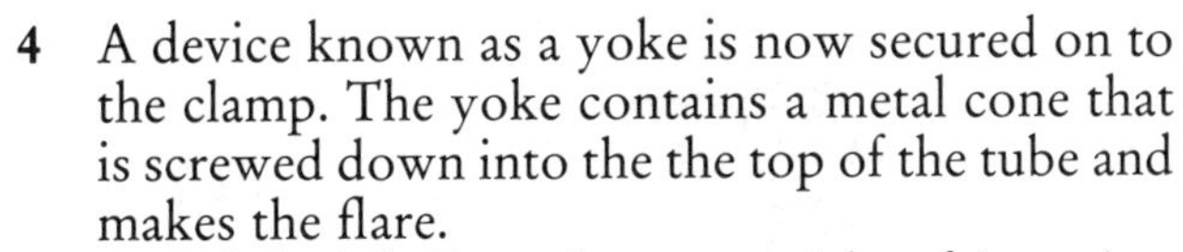

4 A device known as a yoke is now secured on to the clamp. The yoke contains a metal cone that is screwed down into the the top of the tube and makes the flare.

Lightly lubricate the cone with refrigeration oil. Once the cone makes contact with the tube, turn the screw several times. Do not over-tighten the screw as the end of the tube may become damaged. About five turns is usually enough.

5 Unscrew the cone from the tube. This process gives a shiny finish to the inside of the flare.

6 Remove the yoke and then unscrew the wing nut to release the flared end of the tube from the flare clamp (see Figure 22.13).

7 Before making the fitting, it is a good idea to put a small amount of refrigeration oil on both surfaces. Then place the end of the flare against the chamfered end of the fitting. Using the fingers, tighten the nut over the end of the fitting. Give a single turn with a spanner. If the joint is tightened too much the flare may be damaged and as a result, refrigerant may leak out when the tubing is in use.

Compression fittings

Compression fittings are used to a limited extent in a refrigeration system. After the tubing has been cut and deburred place first the nut and second the compression ring over the end of the tubing. Make sure that the screw-threaded end of the nut is facing towards the fitting (see Figure 22.14).

Now push the end of the tube into the fitting a short distance until it comes to a stop. Push the compression ring along the tube until it makes contact with the fitting. Then tighten the nut over the fitting using your fingers. Finish tightening with a spanner, taking care not to apply too much pressure.

Hose fittings

Hose fittings are used to fix hoses to water pipes. The simplest form of hose fitting is the *worm drive clip*. First of all cut the hose to length using a sharp knife while taking care that the end is square.

Select a worm drive clip of the correct size, place it in position over the hose and then push the hose over the tubing or over the fitting. Make sure there is sufficient overlap for a strong joint once the clip is tightened. Move the clip to the middle of the overlap (see Figure 22.15). Finally, secure the clip by tightening with a screwdriver.

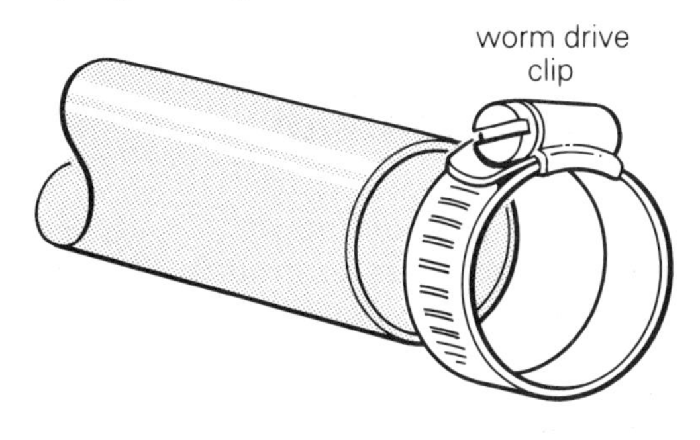

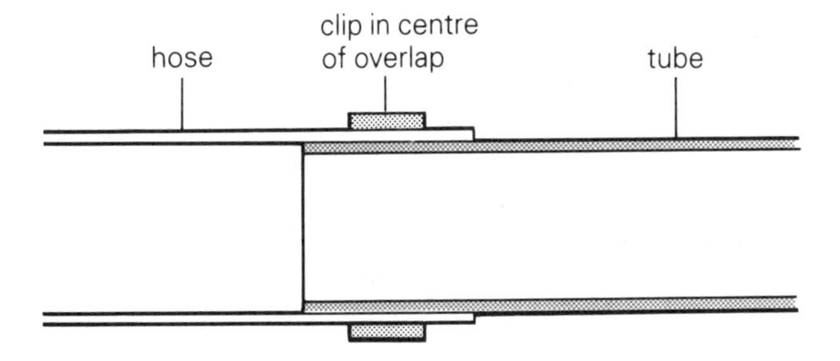

Figure 22.15 Fitting a worm drive clip.

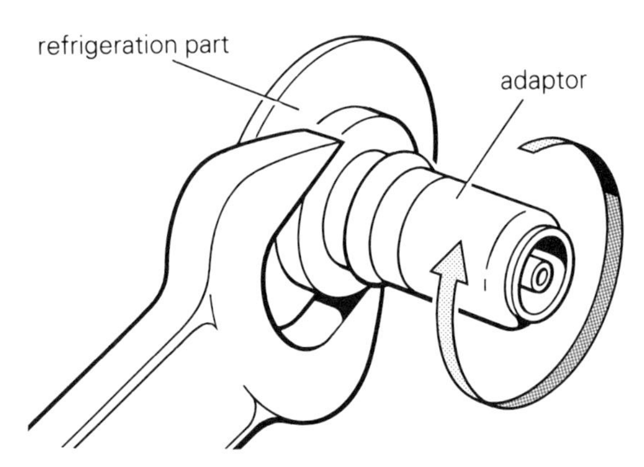

Figure 22.16 Fitting the adaptor.

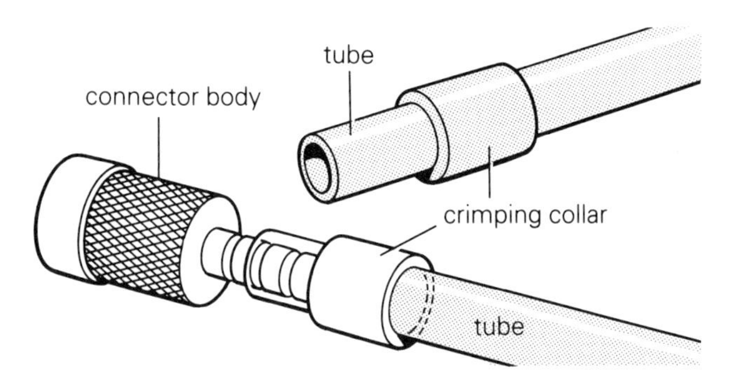

Figure 22.17 Fitting the adaptor.

Another fitting is the snap-on connector. One part of such a fitting is called the adaptor and this has an 'O' ring fixed around it. Another part is the connector, which fixes to the hose.

Take the adaptor and screw it into the refrigeration part that the hose is to be fitted to (see Figure 22.16). Slide a collar on to the hose and then push the end of the connector body into the hose (see Figure 22.17).

Push the crimping collar up to the connector, place the crimping tool over the collar and crimp it in position. Crimping is making dents in the collar which push down into the soft surface of the hose and hold the collar in position (see Figure 22.18). Push the connector body over the adaptor until the 'O' ring holds it in position (see Figure 22.19).

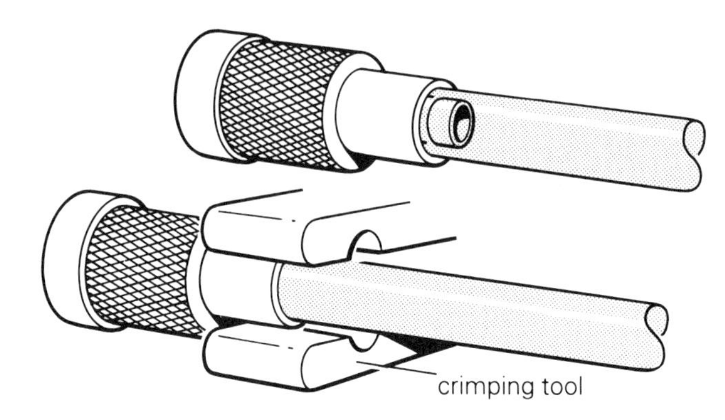

Figure 22.18 Crimping the adaptor.

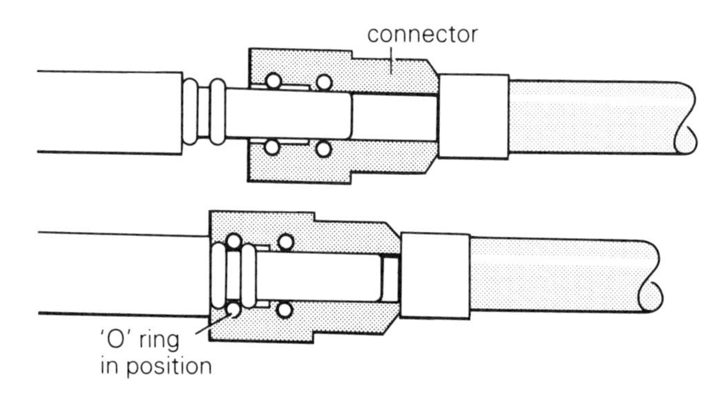

Figure 22.19 Making the connection.

Tube bending

In working with refrigeration tubing, as with any type of tubing, it is necessary to bend the tube to the required shape. The simplest way to bend tubing is by hand.

Hand bending can only be done on thin tubing. Take one end of the tube in each hand and bend it to a radius which is greater than that which is actually needed (see Figure 22.20). Then gradually reduce the radius to the required value. If you try to bend the tube to the correct radius in one attempt you may cause the walls of the tube to collapse at the bend.

Larger diameter tubing can be bent by hand by using a bending spring. Bending springs are only suitable for large-radius bends and the advantage that they have is that they stop the tube from collapsing.

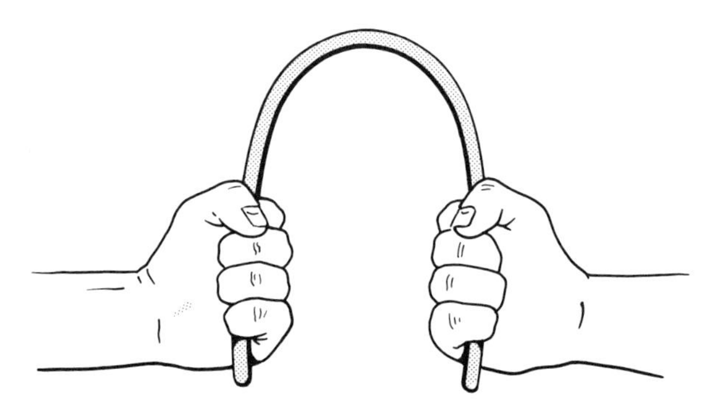

Figure 22.20 Bending by hand.

Select the spring of the right diameter and length and push it along the tube until it reaches the section which is to be bent (see Figure 22.21(a)).

Bend the tube around the knee pushing strongly on the centre point of the bend (see Figure 22.21(b)).

After bending, twist the spring in the direction of the spiral and pull it free using the tommy bar (see Figure 22.21(c)). External bending springs are also available. They have the advantage that they stand no chance of contaminating the inside of the tubing.

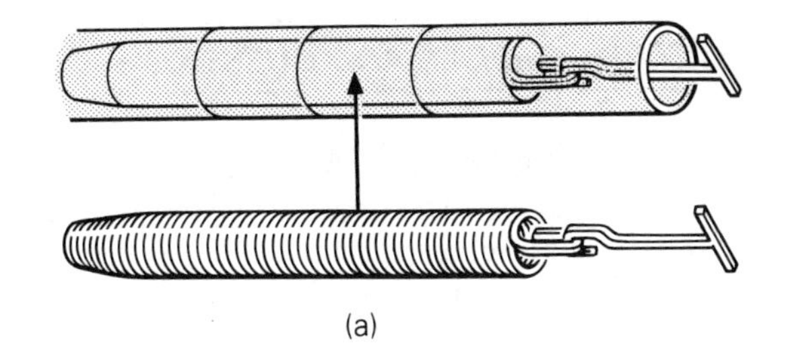

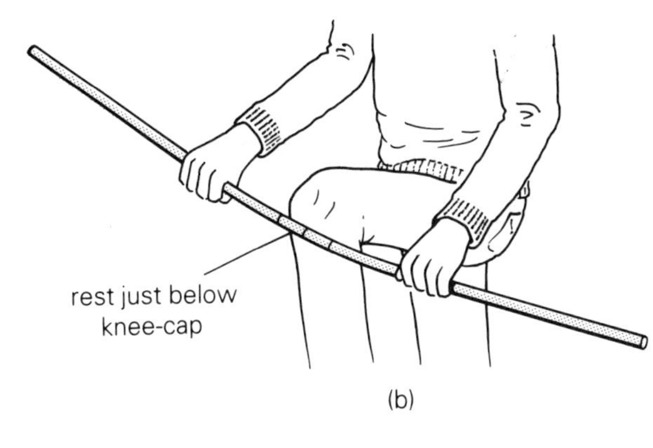

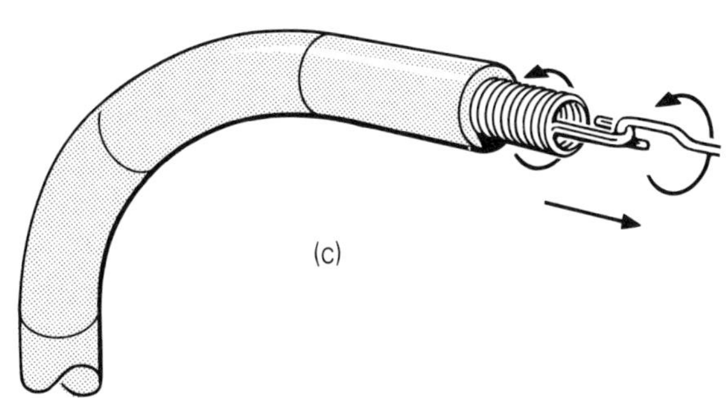

Figure 22.21 Bending with a spring.

Tubing benders

First of all, mark the length of the bend required, on the tubing. Then place the tubing in the bender (see Figure 22.22).

The bender is fitted with long handles in order to provide plenty of leverage for bending. When the handles are pulled together, the bending jaws exert pressure on the tubing. Bend the tubing to an angle which is slightly greater than the desired one, because once the tubing is removed it will straighten a little.

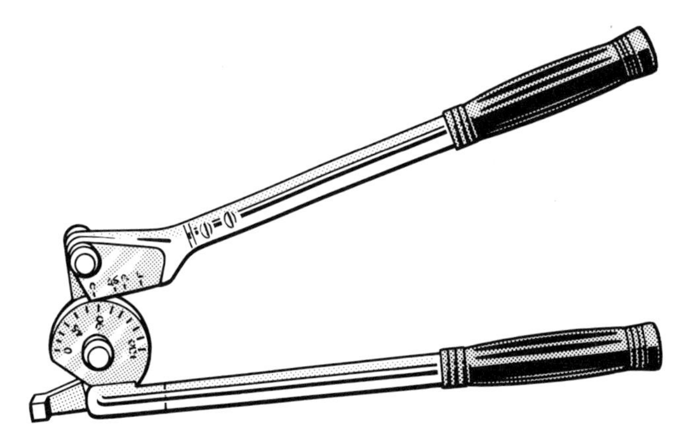

Figure 22.22 A tubing bender.

CHECK YOUR UNDERSTANDING

- Metal tubing used in refrigeration can consist of copper, steel, aluminium or stainless steel. Non-metal hoses are used for car air conditioning and for refrigerated transport.
- Metal tubing must be cut to size before it can be used. It can be cut using a hacksaw or with a tubing cutter. After cutting it must be deburred.
- Important tubing joints are sweat (or soldered), flare and compression fittings. Hose fittings include the worm drive clip and the crimped, snap-on connector.
- Soft soldering is low temperature soldering using a (butane) blow lamp and lead–tin–antimony solder.
- Silver soldering is a type of brazing using an oxy-acetylene torch and silver–copper–zinc (sometimes cadmium) solder.
- Tubing can be bent by hand, on its own; by hand using a spring or by using a tube bender.

REVISION EXERCISES AND QUESTIONS

1 What is meant by the term *soft soldering*?
2 What is meant by the term *silver soldering*?
3 Name four materials used for refrigeration and air-conditioning piping, listing their specific uses.
4 Explain how to cut a piece of metal using a *tube cutter*, without crushing the newly-cut end.
5 How may the inside edge of a piece of metal be *deburred*?
6 What is meant by a *flare fitting*?
7 Name three ways in which metal tubing can be bent.
8 What is the purpose of soldering *flux*?
9 What is the simplest kind of *hose fitting*?
10 Explain the term *capillary action*.
11 Why must burrs be removed from the inside of refrigeration piping?

23 Commissioning equipment

Introduction

Refigerating and air-conditioning plants are designed, in the first instance, by a design engineer who will produce plant layout drawings of the system. Installation engineers then use the drawings, together with other instructions, to install the equipment in buildings. Plant layout drawings tell the engineers where to place compressors, condensers, piping, ducts and other items of equipment. Installation drawings indicate how equipment is fixed to walls, floors, roofs and so on.

Once the equipment has been correctly placed and secured in position, it has to be thoroughly checked. There are a number of checks that can be made, some of them quite simple, before switching on and testing the plant.

1. If the compressor and electric motor are separate items, rotate the shafts of each to make sure that they both run freely. If they have a single shaft, make sure that they both turn without friction. Fans and water pumps should be checked for free movement.
2. Make sure that all bearings on moving parts are well greased.
3. Inspect motor windings for brick dust after holes have been drilled in brickwork. Remove any with a compressed-air blower.
4. Electric motor windings should be tested. If there is any doubt, engineering drawings should be consulted. Some types, however, are fairly straightforward and on the single-phase motor shown in Figure 23.1, there are three terminals. The terminal marked C is known as common, the terminal marked M is the **main winding** and the terminal marked S is the **start winding**.

The windings are tested using an ohmmeter, which is an instrument for measuring electrical resistance. Often a multi-purpose meter or multimeter, switched on to the resistance range, is used (see Chapters 4 and 24).

Try each pair of terminals in turn. The lowest resistance is that of the main winding. When you read the lowest resistance between terminals, you know you are measuring between C and M. The highest resistance is that of the main winding connected in **series** with the start winding. Series connection is shown in Figure 23.2 and in series connection the resistances add together.

When you read the highest resistance between terminals, you are reading the sum of

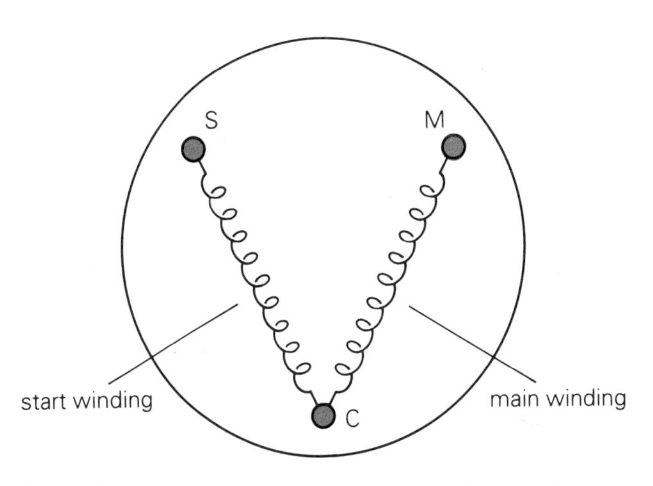

Figure 23.1 Compressor electrical motor terminals – single-phase motor.

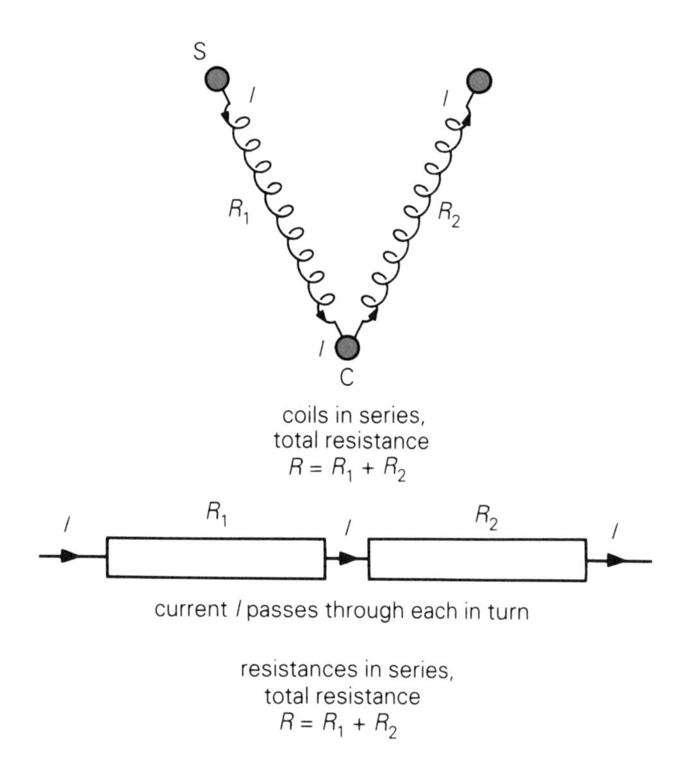

Figure 23.2 Series connection of windings.

the resistances of the main winding and the start winding, between S and M. The medium resistance, between S and C, is the start winding on its own. If the ohmmeter needle does not move at all (infinite resistance) when the instrument is connected between C and S or between C and M, then there is a break in the circuit and damage has occurred to the motor (see Figure 23.3).

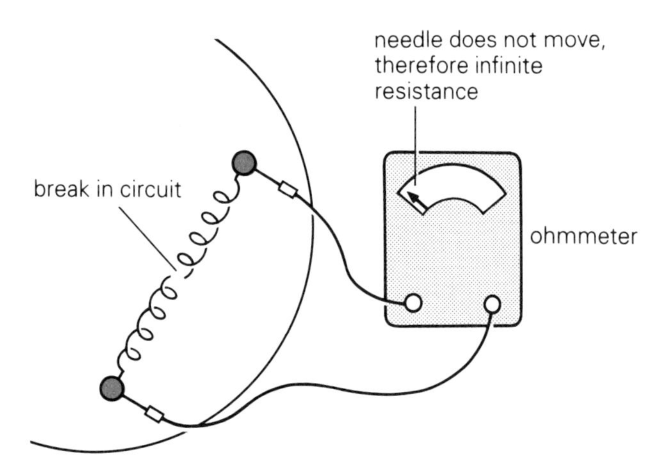

Figure 23.3 Damage to the circuit.

EXAMPLE 23.1

Three resistance readings of 40, 80 and 120 Ω are taken between the three terminals of a motor–compressor assembly. Identify the coils from the three readings.

Solution
The 40 Ω reading is for the main winding, the 80 Ω reading is for the start winding and the 120 Ω reading is for the two coils in series.

The resistance between the main winding and the earthed metal case and between the start winding and the case should be measured. This can be done with an ohmmeter but an **insulation resistance tester** is better. An infinite resistance should be recorded, showing if there is no short circuit between the windings and the case.

5 Check all electrical connections, making sure that none of them are loose. If there are soldered connections, make sure there are no *dry joints* which prevent an electric current flowing. Dry joints are weak joints that can often be broken just by pulling with the fingers.
6 If the motor and the compressor are separate units, run the motor on its own, without the compressor, just to make sure that the motor is working.
7 Make sure that the motor is correctly aligned to the compressor and that any fan or pump motors are also aligned.

> ▲ Before working on couplings, unplug the motor so that it cannot be accidently switched on.

One type of coupling between a motor and a compressor is the belt coupling. If the coupling is misaligned, as shown in Figure 23.4, there will be a strain on both shafts.

Usually, the motor will be bolted down on to elongated slots. Loosen the bolts and move the unit until the alignment is correct. Tighten the bolts.

Another type of coupling is by means of flanges connected to the ends of shafts. These shafts can be misaligned because they are

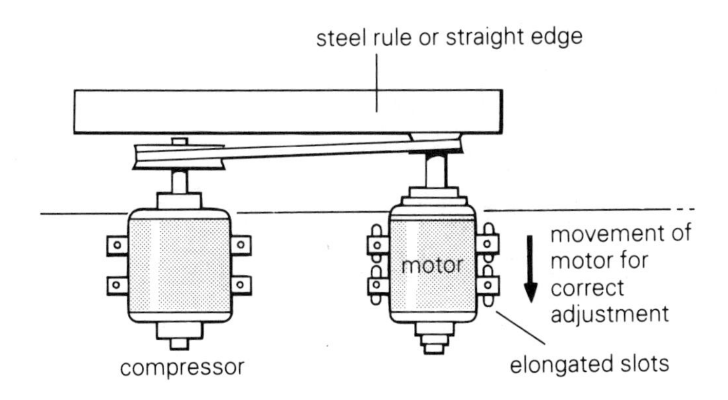

Figure 23.4 Alignment of belt coupling.

parallel to one another, instead of being along the same centre line. They can also be at an angle to one another. Both types of misalignment can damage shafts and couplings. Make sure that the shafts are straight and then tighten the bolts evenly to prevent angular misalignment (see Figure 23.5). Loosen the bolts that hold the motor to the base, then align it correctly in its elongated slots, before tightening, in order to prevent parallel misalignment (see Figure 23.5).

8 Fill the compressor crankcase with the recommended lubricating oil up to the specified level. Too much oil will cause the refrigerant to become contaminated. Too little oil will cause damage to the bearings and the crankshaft. Some compressors have a *sight glass* on the side of the compressor in order to get the amount of oil just right.

9 Fit a drier if the refrigeration plant requires one.

10 Conduct a pressure test on the system. Connect up the refrigerant vapour valve of the refrigerant cylinder to the central connector of the system analyser. Join the low-pressure gauge to the **suction service valve** of the compressor and the high-pressure gauge to the **discharge service valve.**

Large refrigeration systems have several service valves situated in various parts of the system. Their purpose is the monitoring of pressures during commissioning and servicing work and for shutting off parts of the system. Receivers often have service valves at both the inlet and the outlet.

Open both the system analyser valves and allow in a small amount of refrigerant until the pressure recorded by the low-pressure gauge is about, say, 0.3 bar G. Figure 23.6 shows the connection of the system analyser.

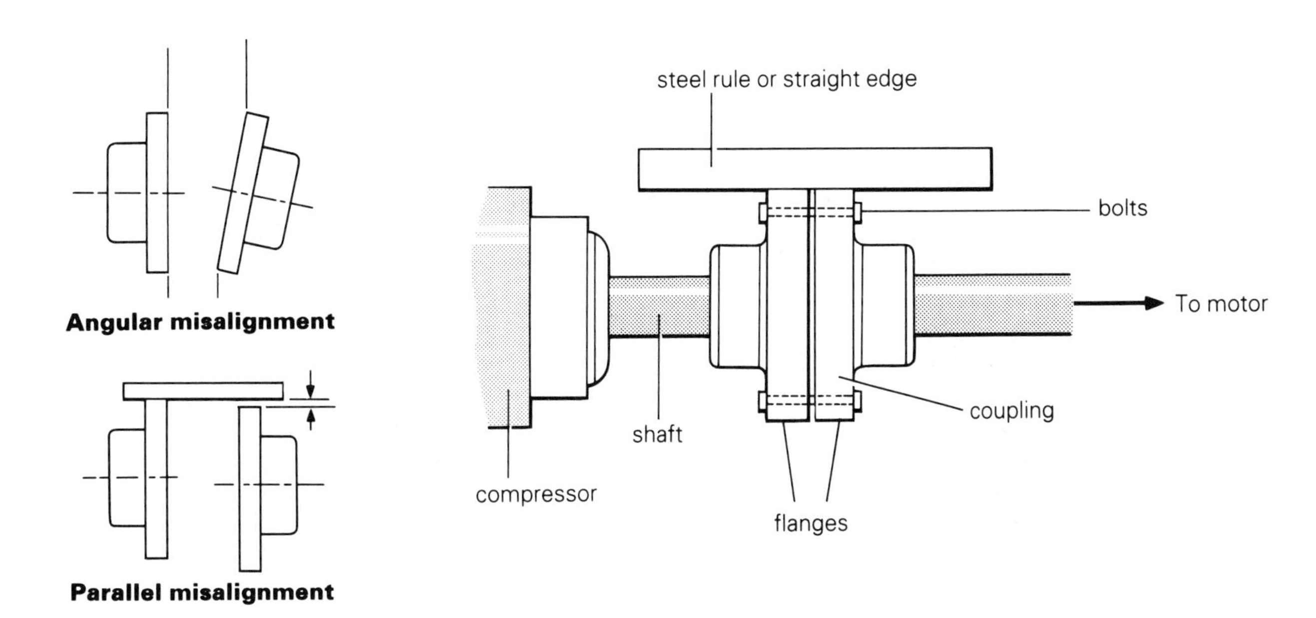

Figure 23.5 Alignment of flange coupling.

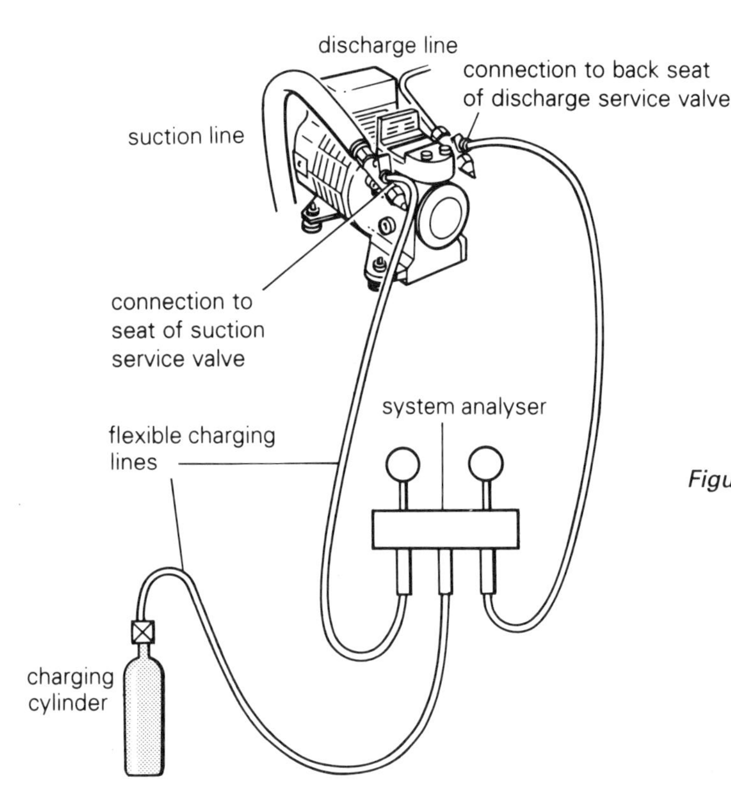

Figure 23.6 Charging the system with nitrogen.

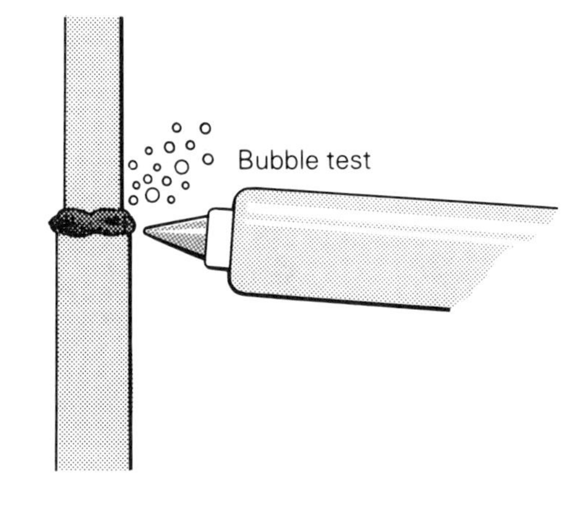

Figure 23.7 A liquid leak detector.

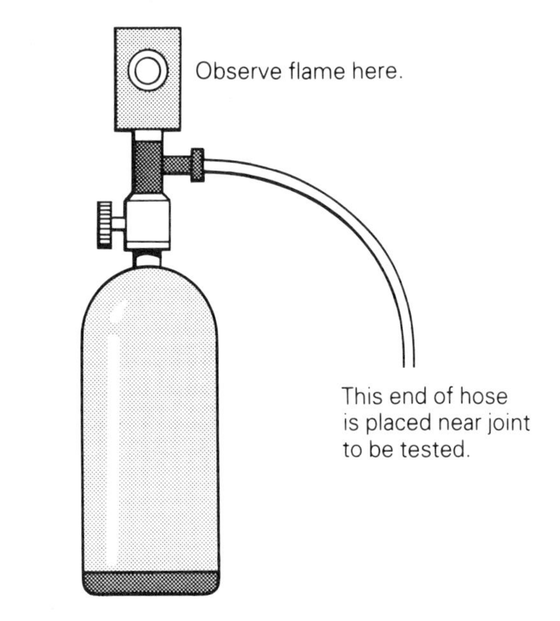

Figure 23.8 A halide torch.

Now connect up a nitrogen cylinder and admit nitrogen to increase the pressure. Allow the high side pressure to go up to about 25 bar G and the low side pressure to 15 bar G. Leave the system for 24 h, observing the pressure gauges from time to time. If either or both of the values falls then there is leakage and leak tests should be conducted.

11 One type of leak detector is a thick (or viscous) liquid which is applied to the joint being checked. A leak will cause the liquid to bubble. An alternative is to use soap solution or liquid detergent, but this has the problem that it tends to drip and so does not stay around the leak. A liquid leak detector is shown in Figure 23.7.

Another leak detector, suitable for CFCs and HCFCs, is the **halide torch**. This consists of a gas cylinder that produces a flame which burns with different colours according to the amount of refrigerant present. A hose is fixed just below the flame and the other end is applied to the possible leak (see Figure 23.8).

Any refrigerant present travels along the hose and affects the colour of the flame. The normal colour is blue and a small amount of refrigerant makes the flame turn green. A lot of refrigerant causes the flame to turn purple. Note that halide torches cannot be used with R134a or any other HFC refrigerant, as the method requires the presence of chlorine in the refrigerant.

A further leak detector uses a probe and the detection is done electronically. This is the **electronic leak detector** (see Figure 23.9).

The probe sucks in refrigerant from around the leak and the refrigerant is heated as it passes over a heating element. The heated refrigerant causes the current flow in the instrument to alter and the change in current indicates the size of the leak. When the probe finds a leak the instrument emits a loud noise and in some models a light also flashes.

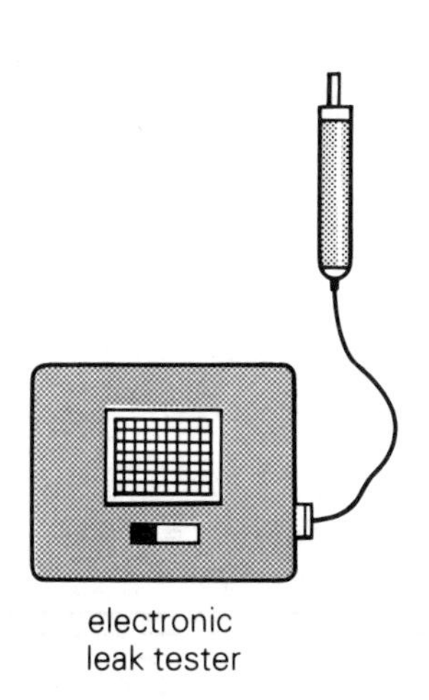

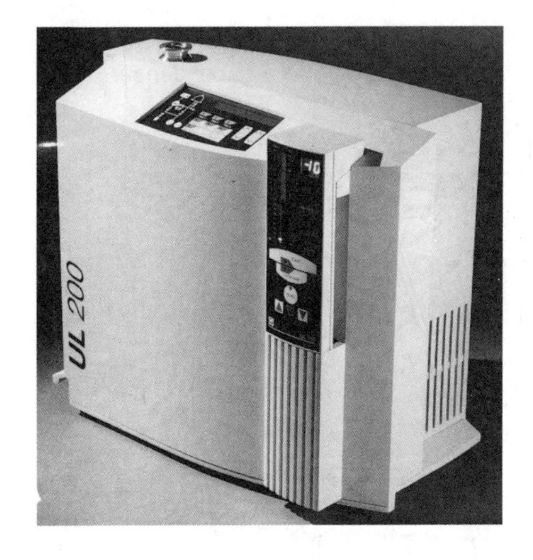

Figure 23.9 An electronic leak detector (courtesy of Leybold Ltd).

Electronic leak detectors are the most sensitive types and models for detecting CFCs, HCFCs, and HFCs can be obtained.

For ammonia refrigerant a burning *sulphur stick* is used. This gives off clouds of white fumes if ammonia is leaking. If the leak is large a fire may result, as ammonia is flammable. In this case use your sense of smell to find the leak.

12 Open the suction and discharge service valves to release the nitrogen and, when the pressure has been removed, repair any leaks by replacing, tightening or re-soldering fittings, or by replacing tubing. Once the process is complete, pressure test again for a further 24 h.

Now remove all fluids, including air, from the system by connecting it to a vacuum pump. This process is called *evacuation*.

Air, water and nitrogen in the pipes can have a bad effect on a refrigeration system. Any water in the refrigerant freezes in the low temperature parts of a refrigerator. For example, in a domestic refrigerator water may cause a restriction or even a blockage of the narrow capillary tube leading into the evaporator. A blockage will stop the refrigerating effect completely.

Water can also react with CFCs to form corrosive acids that damage the insides of the piping. Air in the refrigerant reduces the ability of the system to refrigerate.

To evacuate the system connect up the system analyser as in Figure 23.6 but with a vacuum pump instead of the nitrogen cylinder (see Figure 23.10).

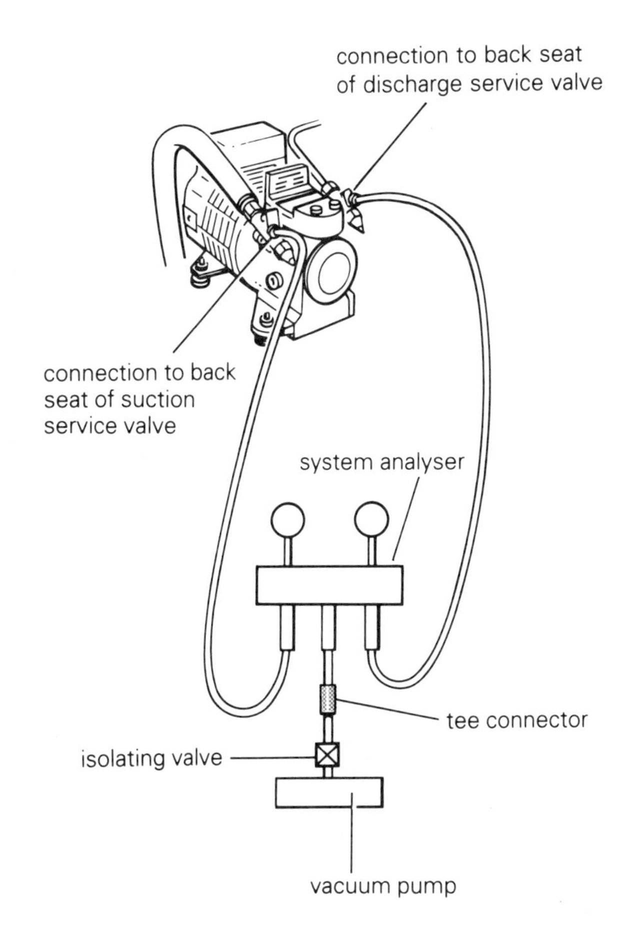

Figure 23.10 Evacuating the system using a vacuum pump.

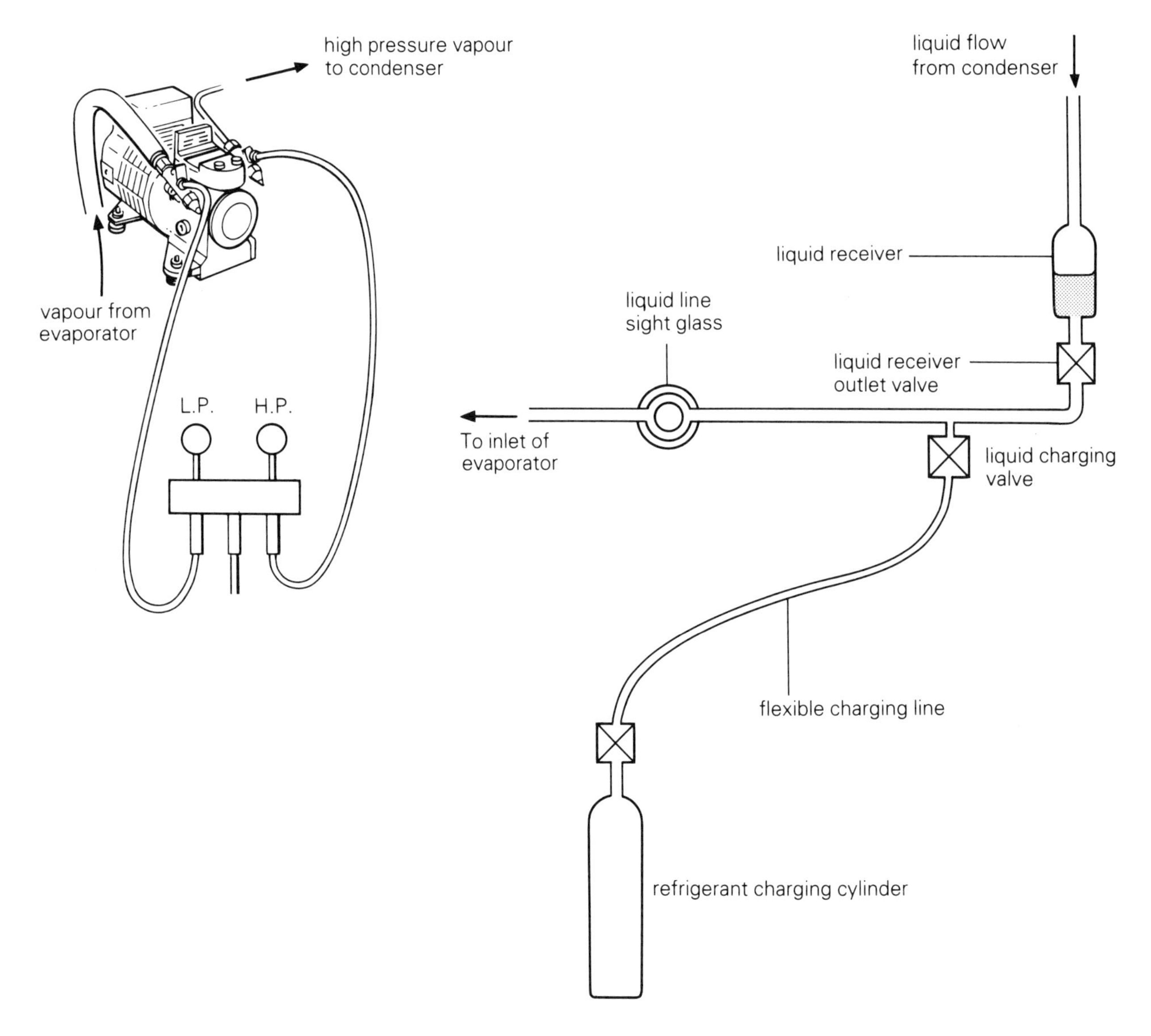

Figure 23.11 Charging the system with refrigerant.

When the pump is switched on the pressure falls, so the boiling point of water drops to a low value and the water in the system evaporates. Switch off when the vacuum reading is 759.9 mmHg of vacuum or nearly −100 kPa (−1 bar). The high vacuum removes other fluids too and the system is now ready for charging with refrigerant.

13 Charge the system with refrigerant by connecting the liquid valve of the refrigerant cylinder to the liquid-charging valve situated between the receiver and the evaporator. Connect the outer connections of the system analyser to the suction and discharge service valves and keeping both analyser valves open, allow refrigerant in until the pressure specified by the manufacturer is achieved (see Figure 23.11). Smaller systems, with no receiver, are charged through the suction and discharge service valves or even through the suction valve alone (see Chapter 24).

If a capillary tube is fitted, as in domestic refrigerators, the amount of refrigerant is critical. Make sure that the recommended amount is not exceeded.

Once everything has been checked and found to be in order, the system can be switched on. It must then be carefully tested to make sure that all the parts are working properly.

Testing

1 Monitor pressures, temperatures, oil levels, air or water flows over the condenser and evaporator and the working temperature of the electric motor.
2 Measure the superheat of the thermostatic expansion valve and adjust it if necessary (see Chapter 24).
3 Make sure that the piping is not vibrating too much.
4 Measure the current in the motor and compare it with the manufacturer's specification.
5 In an air-conditioning system, check the temperatures and pressures in the ducts and the temperatures in the air-conditioned space.

CHECK YOUR UNDERSTANDING

- Engineers install equipment in the correct places by referring to drawings made by the designer.
- Inspect rotating shafts for movement, inspect bearings, inpect motors for dust and test them electrically.
- Run the motor without the compressor.
- Line up the motor and the compressor in both belt and flange type couplings.
- Fill the compressor crankcase with lubricating oil.
- Fit a drier
- Conduct a pressure test.
- Conduct a leak test by means of a detection liquid, a halide torch, an electronic detector or a sulphur stick if the refrigerant is ammonia.
- Evacuate the system to remove all fluids, using a vacuum pump and a system analyser.
- Charge the system with refrigerant using a system analyser and a refrigerant cylinder.
- Switch on and conduct various tests on pressure, temperature and other important factors in the system to make sure that it is working properly.

REVISION EXERCISES AND QUESTIONS

1 Three resistance readings of 35, 70 and 105 Ω are taken between the three terminals of a motor–compressor assembly. Identify the coils from the three readings.
2 List two types of *coupling* between compressors and electric motors.
3 Name three types of *leak test* that can be used with CFC refrigerants.
4 What is the purpose of a *sight glass*?
5 Why do motors and compressors have to be carefully aligned?

Project 1
It is suspected that a domestic absorption refrigerator is leaking refrigerant. How would you find the leak?

Project 2
You are commissioning a refrigeration system which requires a drier. At what stage would you fit the drier?

24 Preventive maintenance and repairs

Introduction

Preventive maintenance means regularly inpecting the refrigeration system to see which parts are beginning to wear. These should be replaced before they wear any more. Sometimes parts must be repaired before they break down. This process minimises the number of times the system has to be stopped for major repairs. However, in spite of preventive maintenance, a refrigeration plant does sometimes break down. When this happens the technician must know how to carry out repairs.

Maintenance work scheduling

A list of parts that need to be inspected regularly, together with an inspection rota should be made up. Such a list is called a *schedule*. Some parts may only require inspection once a week, others once a fortnight or even once a month.

When a major repair is necessary, it must be reported and recorded as part of the maintenance system. From the report, and making use of the manufacturer's servicing instructions, such jobs can be scheduled in such a way that the working of the refrigeration plant is interrupted as little as possible. A record should be kept of all servicing work done and this should include carrying out the manufacturer's instructions. The records can then be used to improve the maintenance work schedule.

General tools

Some of the tools used in maintenance and repair work have already been described in Chapters 22 and 23. However, it is a good idea to make a list, so that the technician can make up a complete tool kit with which to carry out his responsibilities. The suggestions given do not include specialised tools that may be needed with some equipment.

Spanners include: open ended and adjustable spanners, self-gripping spanners (mole grips) and a socket set.

You should have a selection of flat bladed and Phillips type *screwdrivers*. Always make sure that you use the right sized blade for the job. When working with electrical connections use a screwdriver with an insulated handle.

There are many sizes of *pliers* but for general refrigeration work those about 15 cm long are the most satisfactory. Side-cutters, for cutting wire and stripping insulation; long nose; insulated handle electrician's and circlip removing pliers are all useful.

A selection of *hammers*, rubber or plastic faced, which avoid damaging delicate surfaces, in the range 250 g to 500 g are needed.

Files, 15 cm up to about 20 cm long, with strong handles are required for a variety of tasks. Suggested types are flat fine, round fine, flat medium, round medium and half round medium. The terms fine and medium refer to the roughness of the cut.

Hacksaws that can cut copper, steel, stainless steel and other metals of various strength are necessary. The blades vary in the number of teeth per centimetre and blades that are capable of performing all tasks should be available. Small hacksaws for working in confined spaces are useful. *Woodsaws* are needed for cutting boards and beams.

Other useful equipment includes an electric hand *drill*, metal *snips* for cutting metal, *Allen keys* for grub screws, hardened steel *chisels* for cutting metals, a *centre punch*, a wire *brush* for general cleaning, a softer brush with bristles for cleaning condenser fins, a range of *drill bits*, a pump action *oil can*, a *knife* with relaceable blades, an *extension lead* and an *inspection lamp*.

Special equipment

- *Bending springs* of different sizes for bending piping.
- *Pipe cutters* of different sizes.
- *Flaring tool*.
- *Capillary tube cleaner*. This consists of a tube containing oil with a handle that turns and pressurises the oil. The oil transmits the pressure to the capillary tube through an adaptor.
- *Silver soldering* and soft soldering equipment.
- A *portable vacuum pump*.
- A *refrigerant charging cylinder*.
- A *nitrogen cylinder*.
- *Fin tools* for straightening bent evaporator and condenser fins.
- A *refrigerant recovery machine* (see below).

Refrigerant recovery machine

Refrigerant recovery machines consist of a compressor and a condenser, contained in a metal case, together with a filter to remove water and an oil separator to remove oil from the recovered refrigerant. A cylinder or tank, connected to the machine, is used to store the refrigerant. Depending on factors, such as the size and price of the equipment, gauges on the case give the operator information on the pressure of refrigerant in the cylinder, moisture content and acid content.

Most machines can recover the common refrigerants such as R12, R22, R500, R512 and R134a and a button or knob is used to change settings for the different types. Some recovery machines are portable and fitted with handles and even shoulder harnesses for ease of carrying, whereas others are larger and more difficult to move.

Usually, small machines are for recovering refrigerant vapour while other, larger devices recover both vapour and liquid. It is a slower process to recover vapour than liquid and if a machine can remove, say, 5 kg of liquid in a minute its rate for vapour may be only 1 kg over the same period.

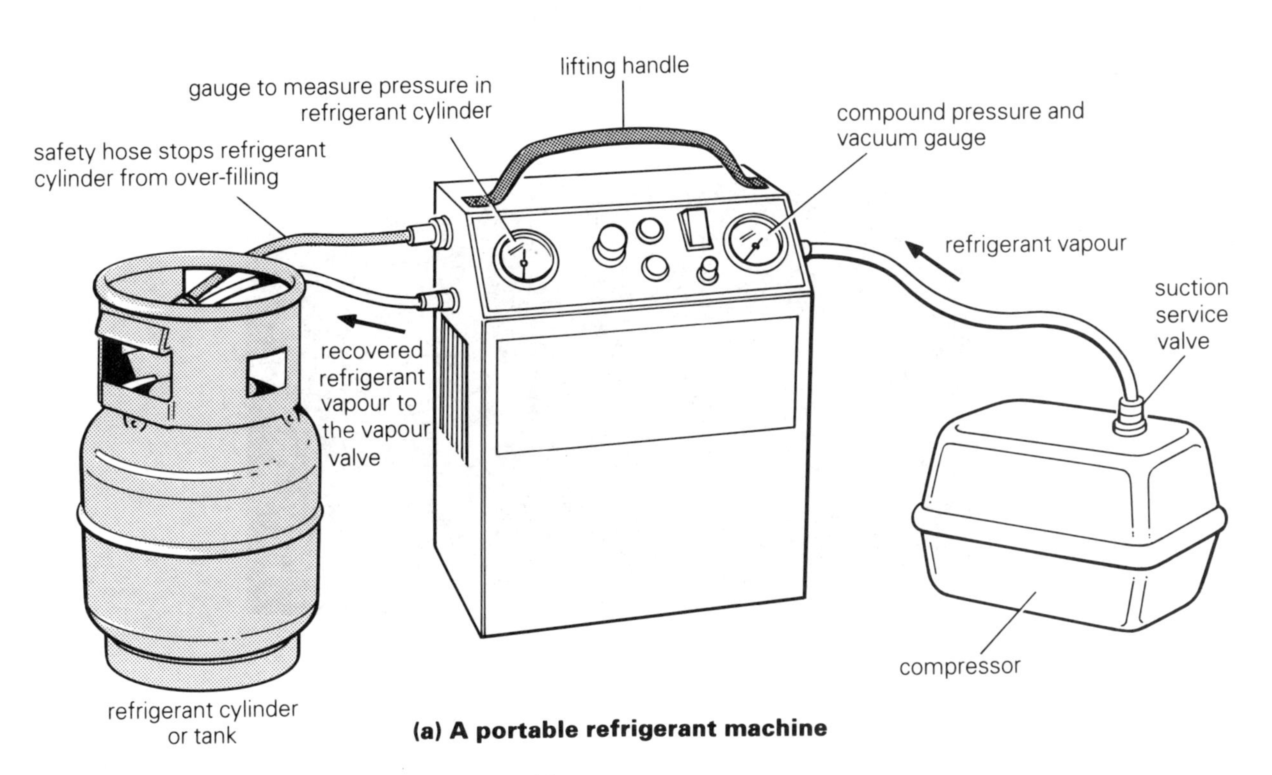

Figure 24.1 (a) A portable refrigerant recovery machine.

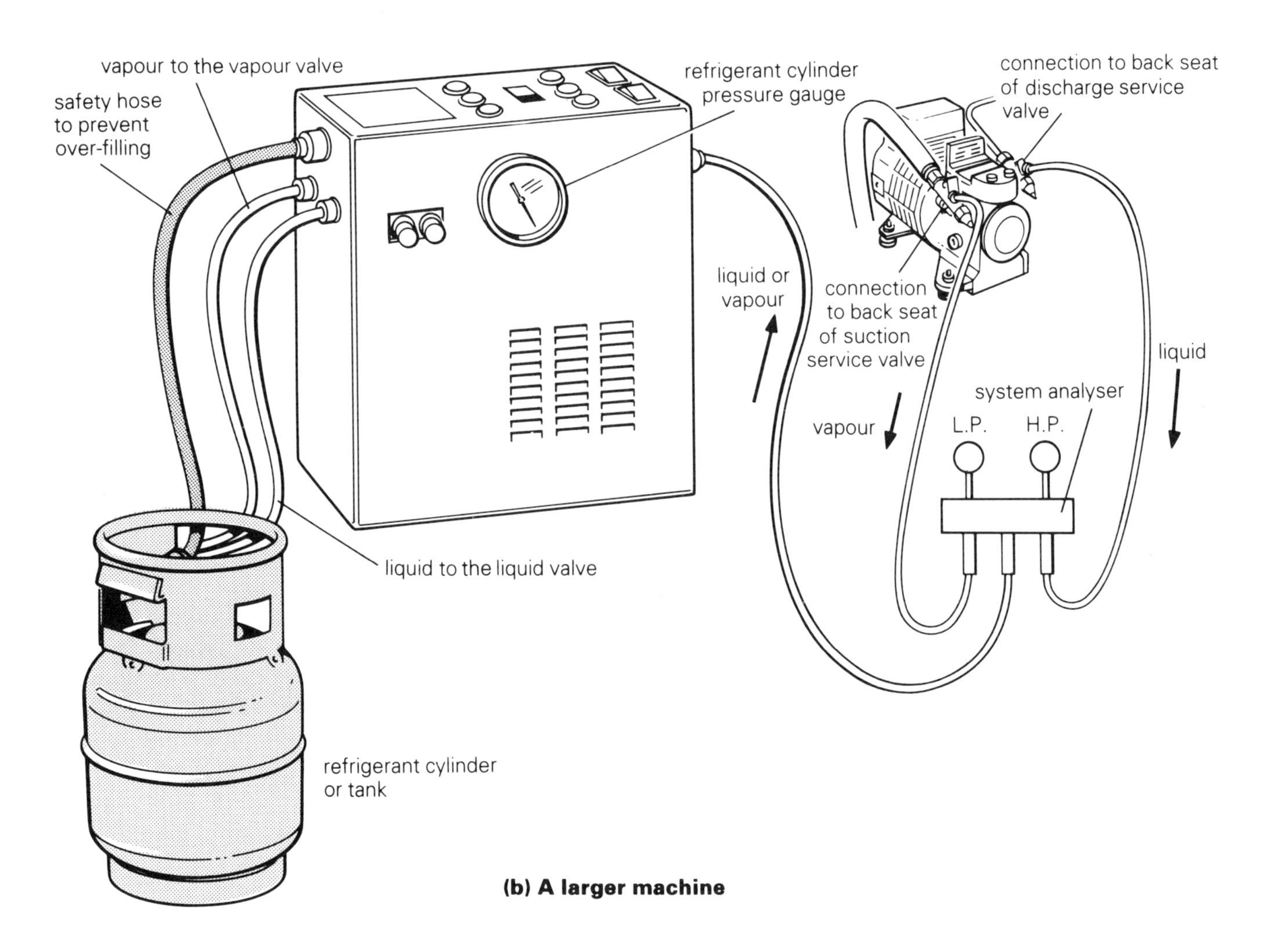

(b) A larger machine

(c)

Figure 24.1 Continued (b) a larger machine; (c) the controls of a recovery machine with liquid crystal display (courtesy of Carrier Air Conditioning).

A small machine is shown in Figure 24.1(a). One of the hoses connected from the device to the cylinder is part of a safety mechanism which prevents the cylinder from over-filling and it does this by stopping the compressor when a certain refrigerant level is reached. The other hose goes to the vapour valve of the cylinder and the recovered refrigerant vapour is pumped through it to the cylinder. A hose from the other end fixes to the suction service valve of the refrigeration or air-conditioning system.

When the compressor is switched on refrigerant vapour is pumped through the machine, where water and oil are removed, to the cylinder. Provided the refrigerant is not contaminated it can be re-used. This type of device can usually produce a vacuum of about 500 mmHg (67 kPa), shown by a gauge fitted to the body of the machine. If desired a system analyser can be used with the central connector to the recovery machine and one other side to the suction service valve.

One way of recharging is by connecting the refrigerant cylinder to the suction service valve of the refrigeration system and switching on the system compressor to suck in the vapour. A system analyser or other gauges can be used to make sure that the high and low side pressures are right. The other method is to leave the system compressor switched off and pump the refrigerant in using the 'recharge' setting of the recovery machine.

Larger machines have a liquid hose, in addition to the one for vapour, and it is connected to the liquid valve of the cylinder. The central connector of a system analyser goes to the suction end of the machine, while the two side connectors go respectively to the suction service valve and either to the discharge service valve in smaller systems, where there is no receiver, or to the receiver outlet valve in larger systems (Figure 24.1(b)). In this way liquid refrigerant can be removed first, followed by the remaining refrigerant, which is in vapour form. The most modern machines employ a microprocessor which switches from liquid to vapour removal automatically.

Liquid crystal displays (LCDs) are now quite commonly used to show information such as the type of refrigerant being recovered and the mode of recovery (either liquid or vapour). Larger machines can usually produce a vacuum of between about 600 mmHg (80 kPa) and nearly 760 mmHg (101 kPa) depending on their size.

Some machines have a distillation chamber to remove most of the impurities from the used refrigerant. Such refrigerant is said to be *recycled.* Recharging can be done directly from the cylinder or by using the recovery machine, just as for smaller machines. Figure 24.1(c) shows the controls of a commercial refrigerant recovery machine.

Measuring and testing equipment

- A sling hygrometer or *psychrometer* with a conversion table for measuring relative humidity.
- A *system analyser* or separate high and low pressure gauges.
- A *temperature gauge* with probes that can be attached to the outsides of pipes.
- A small *thermometer* that can be carried in the pocket.
- A *multimeter,* which is a multi-purpose electrical instrument for measuring current (ammeter), voltage (voltmeter), resistance (ohmmeter).
- An *insulation resistance tester.*
- An *electronic leak detector.*
- A *spirit level.*
- *Vernier calipers* for measuring the external and internal diameters of pipes.
- A *micrometer.*
- A *steel rule* and a *tape measure.*

Safety equipment

> ▲ Safety equipment should include: protective gloves, safety goggles, ear protectors, first aid kit and a fire extinguisher. The safety goggles and gloves are for use when handling refrigerant or contaminated oil, and the ear protectors for use with noisy refrigeration plant.

Repairing refrigerators

This section explains the principles behind the repair of domestic refrigerators and other small refrigeration systems. The same principles apply to the refrigeration sections of room air conditioners.

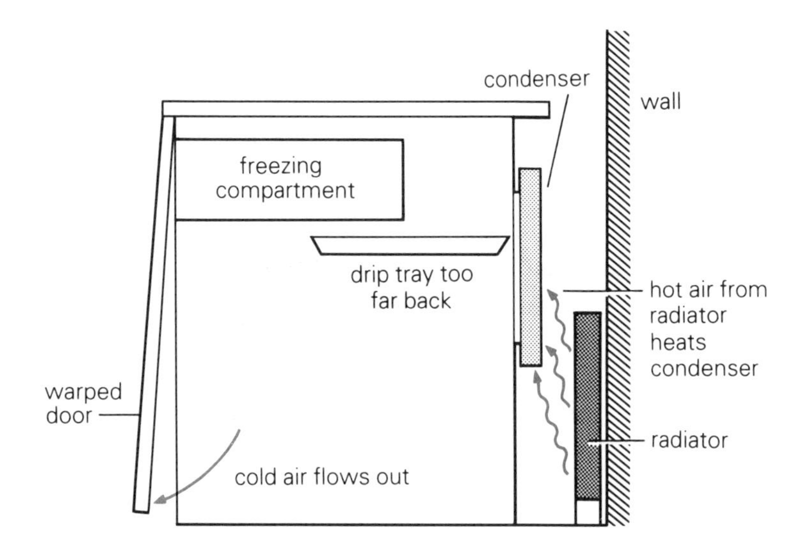

Figure 24.2 Freezing compartment too warm.

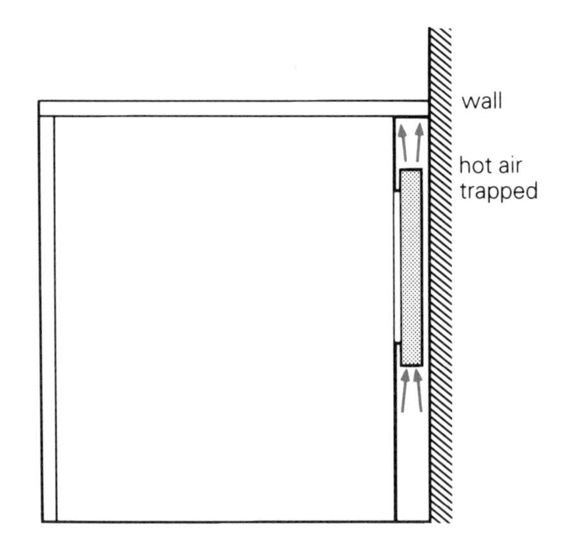

Figure 24.3 Refrigerator too close to a wall.

Not all problems that can occur are described but some of the more common ones are described in detail.

Simple problems

Some problems may be cured by simple investigation and require little or no repair work. For example, the freezing compartment of a domestic refrigerator is too warm and the compressor may run continuously for a number of reasons that have nothing to do with the system itself. Domestic freezers may run at too high a temperature and so they may not freeze very well.

1 The door may be opened too often.
2 The door may be warped and must be replaced.
3 The soft plastic door seal may be twisted or damaged.
4 The condenser is placed too near to a heater and the refrigerator must be moved.
5 The refigerator may be overloaded and the consumer may have to put less in.
6 There may be a **winter/summer control** that the consumer is not aware of. Set the control correctly and show it to the consumer.
7 The *drip tray* under the freezing compartment may be pushed to the back wall of the refrigerator so that air cannot circulate. Pull it forward.
8 The refrigerator may be pushed up against a wall so that heat cannot escape from the condenser. Pull the refrigerator forward.

These points are illustrated in Figures 24.2 and 24.3.

9 A refrigerator or freezer may over-freeze if the drip tray is too far forward, so that air inside circulates too easily.

Other problems are more difficult to solve. Some of these are explained below.

A total blockage in the pipes

This has a number of symptoms, all caused by the fact that refrigerant does not circulate and so refrigeration cannot take place.

1 There is no frost on the evaporator and if you listen at the capillary tube end the refrigerant cannot be heard to make its familiar hissing and gurgling noise.
2 The suction line, the discharge line and the drier are all at room temperature.
3 Because the temperature is high, the compressor will run continuously without the thermostat switching it off.
4 A vacuum gauge connected to the suction service valve will measure a high vacuum. Most hermetic compressors do not have service valves so **line tap valves** have to be screwed to the pipe. These make a hole in the pipe so that when a gauge is connected, pressure can be measured (see Figure 24.4).
5 A pressure gauge connected to the discharge service valve will measure lower pressure than normal. Use a line tap valve with hermetic compressors.

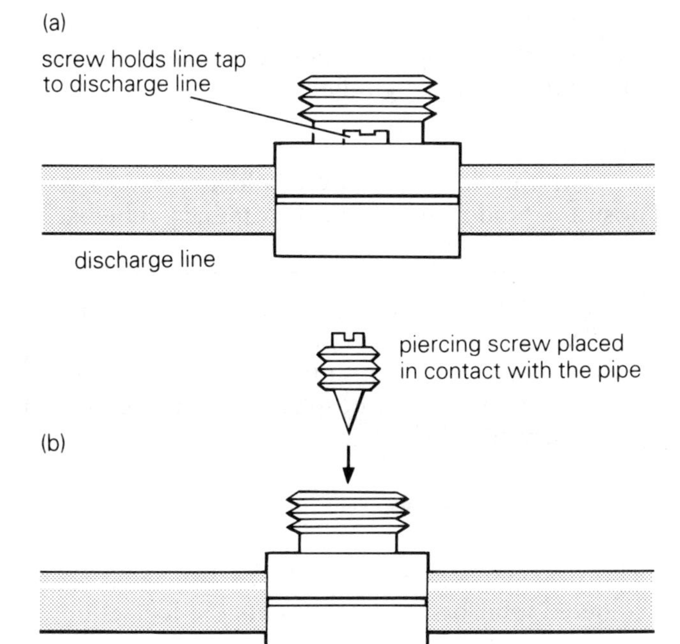

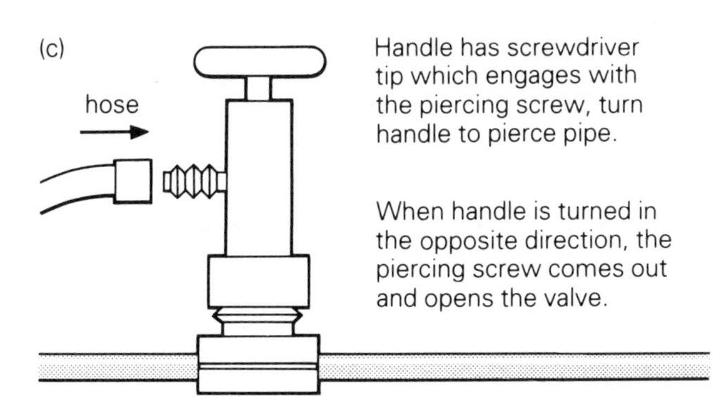

(d) When the line tap is no longer needed a cap is screwed in place.

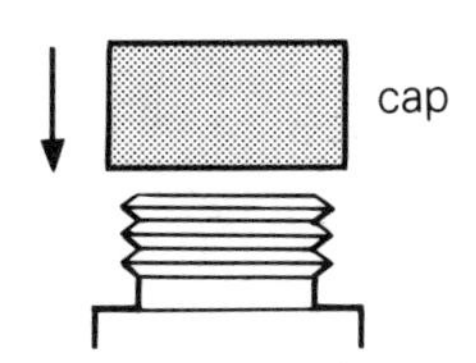

Figure 24.4 A line tap valve.

6 When the compressor is switched off the pressures on the high and low sides will not become the same. This is because the blockage isolates the two sides from one another.

Figure 24.5 shows a refrigerator with a blockage.

CLEARING THE BLOCKAGE

Step 1

Switch the compressor on and examine the point where the capillary tube enters the evaporator. Make sure that no frost forms there. If frost does form there may be moisure in the system. One method of removing moisture was described in Chapter 23.

Step 2

Assuming that no frost has formed continue investigating. It may be that the capillary tube is blocked. A blockage cannot be removed until the refrigerant is removed from the system. At one time it was permissable to open a valve or cut the tubing to allow refrigerant to disperse to the atmosphere.

> In view of the environmental damage caused, opening a valve or cutting tubing is no longer allowed. Instead, a refrigerant recovery machine must be used. Always put on goggles and gloves before using the recovery machine and switch off the power to the refrigeration system before connecting the machine up to the system.

On small domestic refrigerators and freezers, there is usually no suction service valve and so a line tap valve should be attached to the suction line near to the compressor. Connect a small refrigerant recovery machine to the service valve or line tap, as already described and remove the refrigerant.

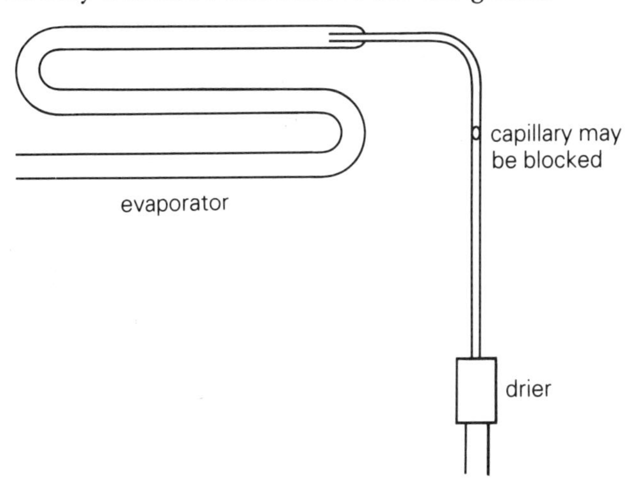

Figure 24.5 A refrigerator with a blockage.

> The service manual should be read carefully before using the machine, as each machine will have a prescribed set of operations which must be followed if refrigerant loss or mechanical damage are to be avoided.

Draw a vacuum and this may be enough to remove the blockage. Recharge with fresh refrigerant and the system may work properly.

If the pressure drops very slowly when the recovery machine is switched on, it is probable that the blockage is almost complete. In this case put a line tap on the discharge side or use the discharge service valve to connect up one side of the system analyser. The other side of the analyser is connected to the suction line tap or service valve. The central connector goes to the recovery machine and this time refrigerant will come out much more quickly because a quantity of liquid refrigerant will be drawn out. Usually, even small machines are capable of sucking some liquid.

If, after drawing a vacuum and recharging, the blockage is still there, remove the refrigerant again and cut into the tube, near the drier, using a small file with a sharp edge and then break the tube (see Figure 24.6). As an alternative a sharp knife can be used. Do not use a hacksaw.

Step 3
Connect the capillary tube cleaner to the open end and turn the handle until enough pressure is built up to remove the blockage (see Figure 24.7).

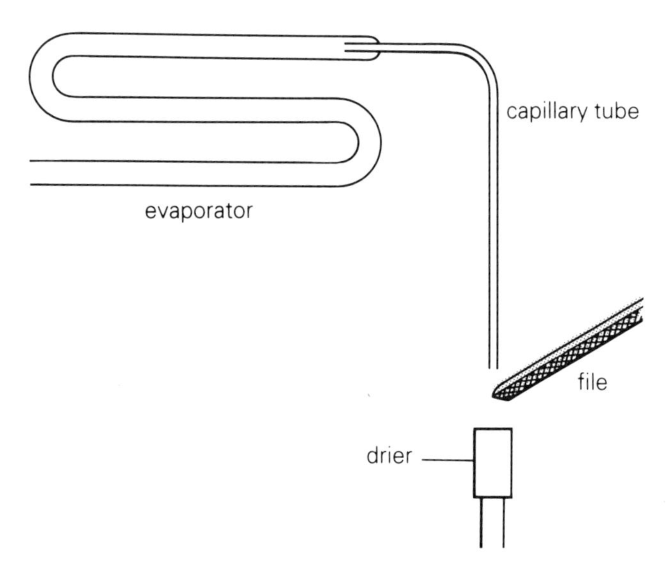

Figure 24.6 Cutting the capillary tube.

Step 4
Connect the nitrogen cylinder to the open end and blow nitrogen through the tube.

Step 5
Cut off the drier and silver solder a new one in position. Solder the end of the capillary tube back.

> ▲ Before soldering it is best to connect up the nitrogen cylinder to the suction line and allow nitrogen into the system. This provides an inert atmosphere so that the high temperatures involved are not likely to cause a fire.

The presence of nitrogen also produces a better soldered joint because it prevents the formation of a hard material called 'scale' at the joint. Scale can break off, enter the system and cause damage to components, such as valves and the compressor.

Step 6
It may be that the capillary was blocked with a waxy deposit. If this was the case replace the oil in the compressor.

Step 7
Evacuate the system and recharge with refrigerant.

Step 8
If there is still a blockage it may be the condenser. After recovering the refrigerant cut the drier away from the condenser and connect the nitrogen cylinder to the discharge line.

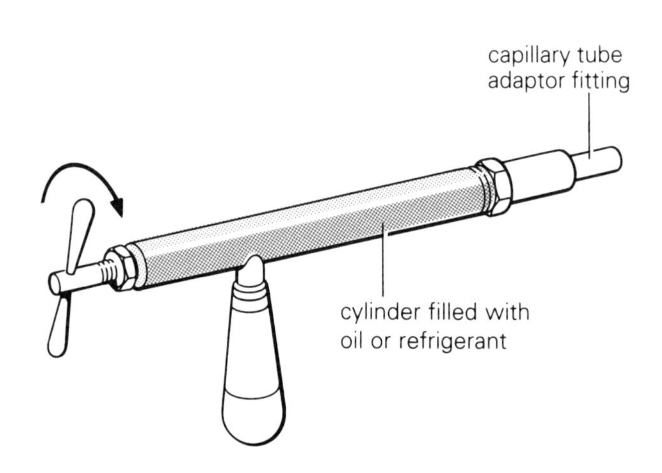

Figure 24.7 A capillary tube cleaner.

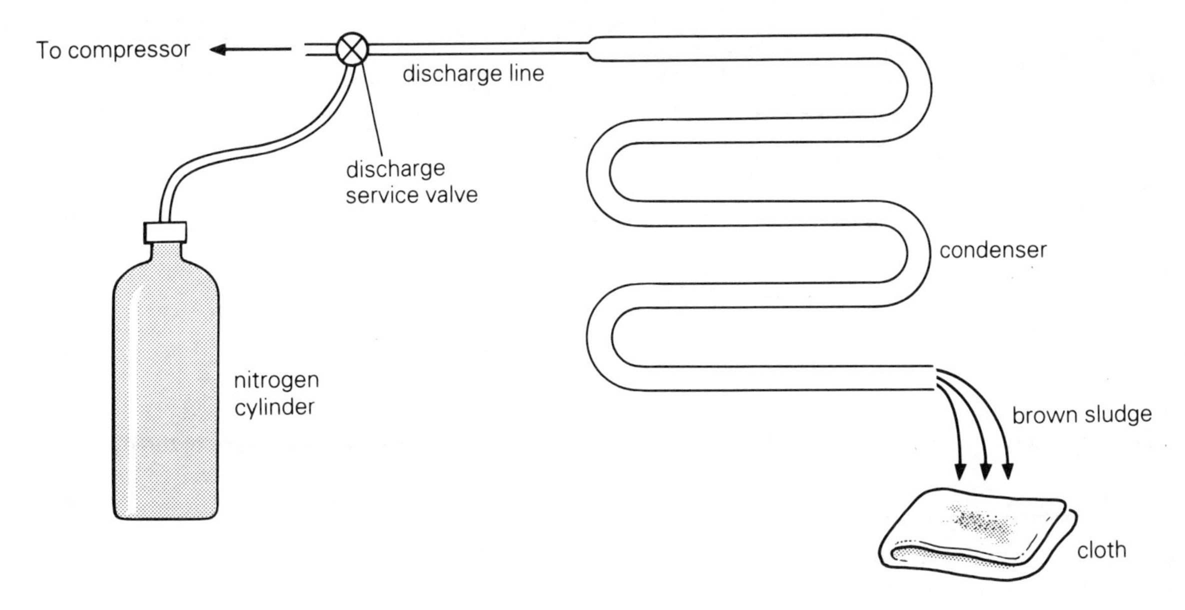

Figure 24.8 Clearing a condenser blockage.

Step 9
Open the valve on the cylinder slowly and place a clean cloth beneath the opening on the condenser where the drier was removed. If a brown sludge drops out on to the cloth and continues to come out after repeated pressure from the refrigerant, the condenser must be replaced (Figure 24.8).

A compressor burn out

A **burn out** is an electrical fault in which the motor wiring becomes damaged and the motor stops working. There are several symptoms that indicate a burn out. For example, because of the rise in temperature, the insulation may become damaged and there may be a **short circuit** between the windings and the earthed case. An insulation resistance tester or an ohmmeter measures zero resistance between the windings and earth. The windings themselves may also be short circuited and their resistance will then be zero. If the meter gives an infinite resistance reading then there is a break in the windings and this condition is known as **open circuit**.

 Switch off the power before making any resistance tests

REMOVING THE COMPRESSOR

Step 1

 Put on goggles and gloves and leave the system power off.

Use the refrigerant recovery machine to remove the refrigerant.

Step 2
Place a specially-designated 'waste oil' can under the drier. Cut the pipe beneath the drier, using a file or a knife. There may be oil discharged and this will collect in the can. When no more comes out, carefully remove the can.

Step 3
Using a spanner at the service valves, free the compressor from both the discharge and suction lines. With hermetic compressors use pipe cutters to cut both the discharge and suction lines. Unbolt the compressor and carefully remove it.

Step 4
Probably the oil will smell of burnt insulation.

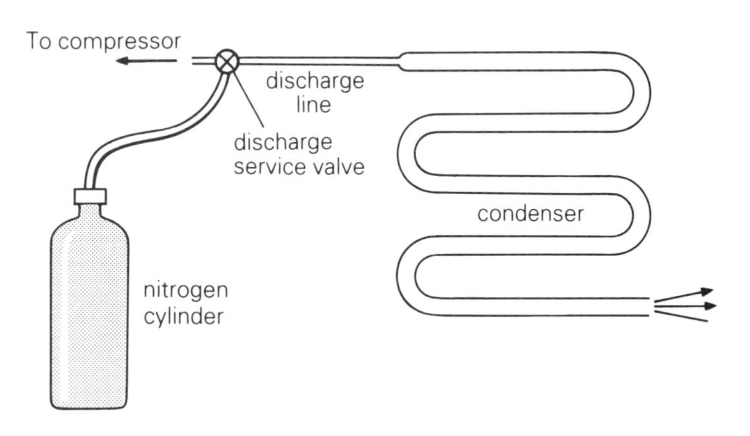

Figure 24.9 Cleaning the inside of the condenser.

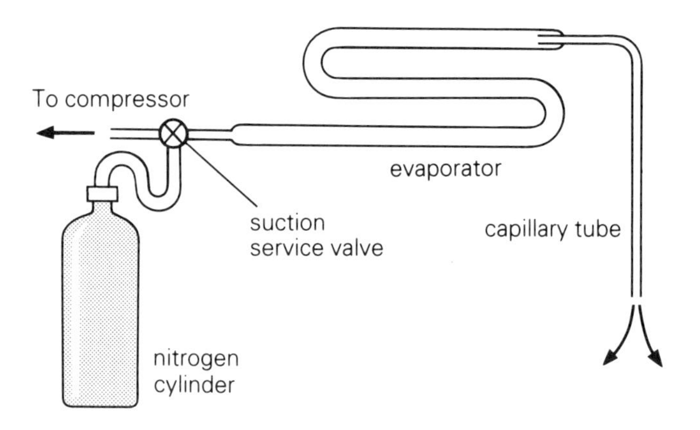

Figure 24.10 Cleaning the inside of the evaporator.

> Pour the oil into the 'waste oil' can making sure that you do not get splashed. Dispose of the oil carefully, according to environmental health regulations.

Step 5
Cut off the drier and connect up the nitrogen cylinder to the discharge line to remove contamination from the inside of the condenser (Figure 24.9).

Step 6
Connect up the nitrogen cylinder to the suction line to remove contamination from the inside of the evaporator and capillary (Figure 24.10).

Step 7
Bolt the new compressor down. Silver solder the new drier in position and then solder the suction and discharge lines to the compressor.

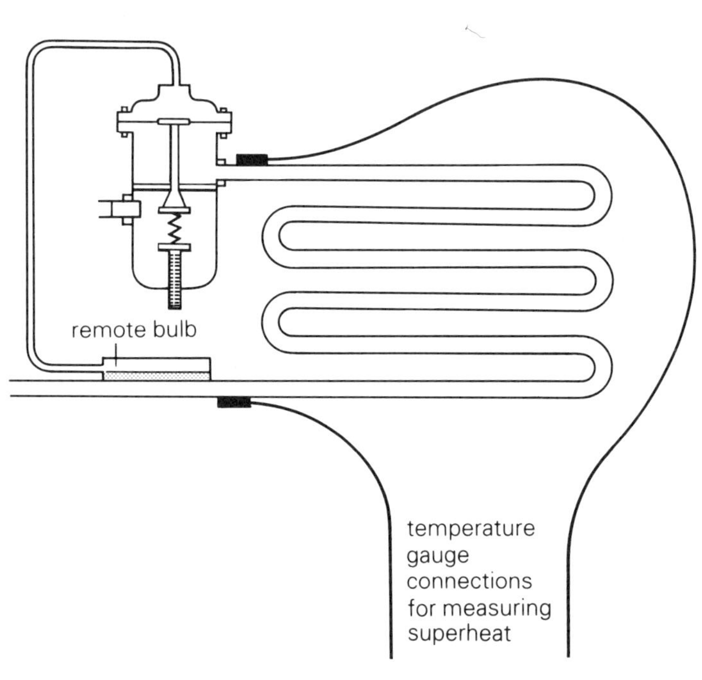

Figure 24.11 Connecting a temperature gauge.

Thermostatic expansion valves

While domestic refrigerators are normally fitted with capillary tubes, larger plants often have thermostatic expansion valves. These are set by the manufacturer but they need regular servicing to maintain good performance.

SERVICING THERMOSTATIC EXPANSION VALVES

Step 1
Connect the probes of a temperature gauge to the pipes as shown in Figure 24.11, with one probe near to the bulb and the other near the valve itself.

If the superheat temperature is too low, the valve is passing too much refrigerant and the temperature of the suction pipe is too low. It will either have a wet surface or it will frost up, depending on the evaporator temperature.

Step 2
Make sure the bulb (phial) is not loose or in a draught of warm air.

Step 3
By turning the screw at the bottom close the needle valve a little (see Figure 15.4). After a few minutes

read the two temperature gauges and make sure that the difference in temperature is the same as that recommended by the manufacturer. Mostly it will be between about 5°C and 8°C (see Chapter 15). If the temperature difference is still not correct, make further adjustments until it is.

If the superheat temperature is too high, the valve is not passing enough refrigerant and the evaporator will not be frosting properly. The compressor will keep running, or at least rarely switch off.

Step 1
Make sure that the filter at the valve inlet is not blocked.

Step 2
Make sure that the inside of the valve is not blocked with ice. If it is then change the liquid line, or high side, drier.

Step 3
If there are deposits of wax in the valve, change the oil and also the valve.

Step 4
Adjust the screw to open the needle valve more. Do this until the superheat temperature is correct.

CHECK YOUR UNDERSTANDING

- Parts of a refrigeration or air-conditioning system need to be inspected regularly as part of an inspection rota. All maintenance work should be recorded as part of a maintenance schedule.
- To do repairs properly you need a proper set of general purpose and specialised tools.
- There are a number of simple problems that can be solved with little or no actual repair work. These simple problems should be investigated first.
- One problem that can occur is complete blockage of the pipes. The symptoms of this should be learnt and it should be dealt with in logical sequence as explained in the chapter.
- Another common fault is the electrical one of compressor burn out and the symptoms of this should be learnt. The problem should be dealt with in the order described in the chapter.
- Larger systems often use thermostatic expansion valves. These need to be adjusted as described above.

REVISION EXERCISES AND QUESTIONS

Project 1
You are shown a domestic refrigerator in which the freezing compartment is too warm and the compressor is running continuously. There is no problem in the system. How would you find the fault?

Project 2
You are given a refrigerator in which the evaporator is not frosting over its full length and you are told that the problem is due to the lack of adjustment of the thermostatic expanion valve. The manufacturer says that the superheat temperature should be 8°C. Using a temperature gauge and two probes how would you correct the problem.

Project 3
You are presented with two motors, each with three terminals and each with a main winding and an auxiliary winding. You are told that one of them has burnt out. Using an ohmmeter or an insulation resistance tester, test which one has been damaged.

Project 4
You are shown a domestic refrigerator in which the freezing compartment is too cold and the compressor is running continuously. There is no problem in the system. How would you find the fault?

Project 5
The motor in a hermetic motor–compressor unit is burnt out. How would you remove the compressor and dispose of the oil? Explain any safety precautions you would take.

Project 6
You are given a refrigerator in which there is no frost on the evaporator and you are told that the capillary tube is blocked. How would you go about removing the blockage?

Project 7
It is suspected that a refigerator is losing refrigerant slowly due to a very small leak. How would you detect the leak?

Project 8
A natural-convection-air-cooled-condenser is suspected of not conducting heat away efficiently because the freezing compartment in the refrigerator is too warm. The condenser is not too near to a

wall or a radiator but it is noted that the condenser is dirty and some of the fins are bent. What is the likely cause of the problem and how may it be corrected?

Project 9
It is found that the flow of water from the nozzles in a cooling tower is too slow and that a green slime has developed on and around them. Explain how you would go about treating the problem.

Project 10
In a deep freeze system, equipped with an evaporator fan for circulating cold air, thick frost has formed on the evaporator surface. The deep freeze employs hot water defrosting. How would you correct the problem?

Project 11
In a deep freeze system, employing hot gas defrosting, thick frost has formed on the evaporator surface. How would you correct the problem?

Answers to questions and answering hints

Introduction

This section provides you with all the answers to the variety of questions and exercises given in the book. Always try a question or exercise yourself before you look at the answer. This will increase your understanding of the topic and give you practice in answering questions. If you are not sure of a particular answer, re-read the relevant section or chapter in the book to revise the work. You need to understand why a question has a particular answer, so that you can apply your understanding to similar types of question or exercise in your examinations and course assignments.

The book contains a variety of types of question and exercise. Find out the types of question that you will be expected to answer and their pattern. If possible, obtain past papers to support your work and revision. Some of the questions in the book require longer answers. We have provided hints on how to tackle these questions, and on the range of topics that you should include. Practice giving full answers to these questions and then check the answering hints to see that you have included all the relevant topics.

To revise a topic quickly you can refer to the 'Check your understanding' sections given at the end of each chapter, and the list of key words and definitions given at the end of the book.

Hints to answering questions in examinations and course work

- Read all the questions carefully before you try anything. Make sure that you understand what each question is asking you to do.
- Plan the time that you will spend on each question. Use the marks as a guide: the more marks a question is worth, the more time it is worth spending on it.
- If you have a choice of questions, try to make your choice and stick to it. Don't change your mind half-way through the examination.
- Make sure that you earn all the 'easy'marks. Do not spend too long on a question you find difficult. Leave it; if you have time, you can try it again later when you have finished all the other questions.
- Keep an eye on the time. Make sure that you try all the questions you are required to answer.
- Always present your work as clearly as you can, whether you are writing or drawing. Make your work easy to follow for the examiner or assessor.
- Try and allow some time at the end to check your answers and improve them.
- In practical work, make sure that you understand what you are being asked to do by re-reading the question before you start. Follow all instructions carefully.

CHAPTER 2

1 Contractions occur in the muscles of the body, including the heart and burns are caused.
2 (ii).
3 A large current should flow in the circuit, causing the fuse to melt or blow.
4 The current rating of such a fuse is not known and in any case its value would be too high.
5 The hair may catch in moving parts of the machinery, causing injury.
6 To avoid the risk of fire caused by the high temperatures used in brazing.

7 A fire might result because of overheating in the cable.
8 It may have become acid because of contamination by the refrigerant and may therefore be corrosive.
9 Signs containing symbols which warn of explosive, toxic, corrosive, flammable and irritant chemicals.
10 Spinal and abdominal injuries.
11 The mouth-to-mouth method.
12 The position in which the casualty is lying face downward with his head tilted to one side and one knee drawn up to his chest, so that he may safely regain conciousness.
13 Two hands are placed on the lower half of the breastbone and compressions are given at the rate of 80 per minute. A cycle of 15 compressions to 2 inflations is used until the heart starts beating and breathing starts again.
14 Because water is a conductor of electricity and the person using the extinguisher may be given an electric shock.

CHAPTER 3

1 15 m/s.
2 3 m/s^2.
3 6 N.
4 600 N.
5 3.9 kg.
6 30 000 Pa or 30 kPa.
7 (i) 102 000 Pa, (ii) 1.02 bar, (iii) 1020 mbar.
8 4.5 bar.
9 95.5 kPa.
10 720 mmHg, 40 mmHg.
11 80 000 J or 80 kJ.
12 562 500 J or 562.5 kJ.
13 405 000 J or 405 kJ.
14 268K, 318K.
15 680 kJ.
16 i) 15 820 000 J or 15 820 kJ or 15.82 MJ.
ii) 4 032 000 J or 4 032 kJ or 4.032 MJ.
17 Convection is the movement of currents in the air due to changes in density brought about variations in temperature.
Conduction is transfer mainly by electron movement in conductors and by molecular vibration in insulators. The amount of heat transferred through insulators is very small.
18 By (electromagnetic) radiation.

CHAPTER 4

1 $V = IR$ (or $I = V/R$ or $R = V/I$), volt, ampere, ohm.
2 i) 10 Ω, ii) 20 kΩ.
3 9 V.
4 2 A.
5 In the forward direction (forward-bias) a curve is produced and not a straight line, therefore Ohm's law is not obeyed. In the reverse direction there is no current as the voltage is increased and so the current cannot be said to be proportional to the voltage. Therefore Ohm's law is not obeyed, the diode is non-ohmic.
6 100 Hz, 2.1 A.
7 i) Capacitors are used for storing electric charge.
ii) Transistors are used to amplify (amplifiers) and as switches in computers.
8 i) 6.8 kΩ (6800 Ω) ± 5%; ii) 7140 Ω, 6460 Ω.
9 The motor effect is the presence of a force on a current-carrying conductor which is placed in a magnetic field.
10 The current flows into one side of the coil and flows out of the other, so that the currents are in opposite directions in the two sides of the coil. This means that one side is pushed up while the other is pushed down.
11 Electromagnetic induction is the generation of an e.m.f., and hence a current, by passing a wire through a magnetic field.
12 As the rotating magnetic field cuts across the conductors an e.m.f. is induced causing a current to flow.
13 Three-phase a.c. or alternating current refers to three alternating currents from the same generator, which rise to peak values with short time intervals between.

CHAPTER 5

1 10 m^3.
2 The temperature at which a liquid changes to the vapour phase or a vapour changes to the liquid phase.
3 A saturated vapour is a vapour above the surface of a liquid. A saturated liquid is a liquid in contact with its saturated vapour.
4 A superheated vapour is one which has been heated above the saturation temperature without change of pressure. A subcooled liquid is

one at a temperature below the saturation temperature.

5 The critical temperature is the temperature above which a vapour cannot be liquefied by pressure alone.

6 Internal energy (U) is the sum of the molecular kinetic and potential energies.
Enthalpy $= U + pV$, where p is the pressure set up by molecular bombardment on the walls of the container and V is the volume.

7 A refrigeration cycle in which cold vapour from an evaporator is compressed and passed on to a condenser.

CHAPTER 6

1 i) 11.54 bar, 163.8 kJ/kg; ii) 8.84 bar, 149.0 kJ/kg; iii) 10.67 bar, 159.3 kJ/kg.

2 i) 3.49 bar, 106.8 kJ/kg; ii) 2.93 bar, 100.0 kJ/kg (by definition); iii) 2.62 bar, 95.97 kJ/kg; iv) 2.17 bar, 89.3 kJ/kg.

3 The heat absorbed by the refrigerant from the refrigerated space. It is the change of specific enthalpy going from part B to part C of the cycle.

4 It is a measure of the efficiency of the refrigerating cycle and it is defined as the ratio of the energy absorbed from the refrigerated space to the heat equivalent of the energy supplied to the compressor.

5 At the throttling valve there is an adiabatic expansion without change of enthalpy whereas at the compressor there is an adiabatic compression without change of entropy.

CHAPTER 7

1 Ram air is air taken in from outside the fast-moving aircraft in order to cool the compressed air inside a heat exchanger.

2 To expand and cool the air prior to passing it through the air-conditioned space.

3 A junction between two different metals or semiconductors.

4 When a current is passed through a circuit with two thermocouple junctions, one junction gets hot while the other cools. The effect is reversed when the current reverses.

5 p-type has a surplus of positive charge carriers while n-type has a surplus of negative charge carriers or free electrons.

6 Hot – condenser and compressor, cold – evaporator.

7 Advantage – no moving parts, easy maintenance. Disadvantage – expensive.

8 The absorber and generator.

9 Because, in an absorption system, the generator must be heated to release refrigerant from solution. This heating can be done by means of a gas flame. While larger systems use an electric pump, small domestic absorption refrigerators do not need one and gas heating is all that is required.

10 Ammonia (in the ammonia–water system) and water (in the water–lithium bromide system).

11 The generator is heated to separate the refrigerant from the absorbent.

CHAPTER 8

1 10°C.

2 37% and 46%.

3 RH = 30%, specific enthalpy = 36.8 kJ/kg, specific humidity = 0.0053 kg/kg, DP = 4.3°C, specific volume = 0.84 m^3/kg.

4 i) DP = 8.7°C, moisture content = 0.007 kg/kg, total heat added = 6.1 kJ/kg. ii) RH = 80% to 48%. iii) 1586 kg/min.

5 i) Increase in WB = 18°C to 21°C, DP = 14°C to 19°C, specific enthalpy = 51 to 61 kJ/kg. ii) RH = 50% to 70%. iii) 1.04 kg/min.

6 WB = 18°C, RH = 64% to 100%, DP = 24°C to 18°C, moisture content = 0.019 to 0.013 kg/kg, specific enthalpy = 80.7 to 51 kJ/kg.

7 DB = 27.7°C, WB = 24.3°C, RH = 77%, moisture content = 0.0178 kg/kg, specific enthalpy = 73 kJ/kg.

CHAPTER 9

1 The total amount of heat coming into a refrigerated space, made up of heat coming through walls, windows, through cracks, from equipment and from people, that the air-conditioning system has to deal with to produce a comfortable temperature.

2 Comfort air conditioning is air conditioning designed to make people feel comfortable at home or at work, whereas process air conditioning is designed to provide the right atmosphere for industrial processes.

3 The conditioned air supplied to the air-conditioned space is the supply air. Air which

has passed through the air-conditioned space is called exhaust air and the exhaust air returned to the air-conditioning system is return air. Air taken in from outside the building is outside air or fresh air.

4 Filters remove dust, fumes, smoke, pollen and bacteria from supply air.
5 An absolute filter removes nearly all contaminating particles from the air.
6 Air may be dehumidified by cooling it to below dew point.
7 By a suitable filter and by an ultraviolet lamp.
8 To stop the paper curling on low humidity and from saturating on high humidity.
9 A device for detecting and controlling humidity.
10 The removal of outer electrons from the atoms that make up the molecules to leave behind positive ions and free electrons.
11 A device that detects and controls temperature.

CHAPTER 10

1 16 kW.
2 7.2 kW.
3 Compression ratio = 6.
4 Compressor power = 1.8 kW.
5 Electrical power = 2.5 kW.
6 The compressor clearance is the space left between the top of the piston and the end of the cylinder when the piston is top dead centre.
7 i) The area of contact between the rings and the cylinder is small so that friction is reduced.
ii) Once rings are worn they can be replaced without replacing the whole piston.
8 The electric motor in a hermetic compressor is cooled by passing cold vapour from the suction line through the motor.
9 One kind of rotary compressor is the rotating piston type and another is the rotating vane type.
10 The rotating vanes of a centrifugal compressor are shaped in such a way that a centrifugal force acts on the refrigerant and pushes it outwards to the rim from where it goes to the condenser.
11 Refrigerant flow can be too great so that liquid refrigerant passes through the throttling valve and eventually drips into the compressor *or* when the system switches off refrigerant in the evaporator condenses and then enters the compressor.
12 Proper lubrication can be stopped and a corrosive mixture can be formed.
13 By means of a pump.
14 An oil ring stops oil from the crankcase from splashing up and mixing with the refrigerant.

CHAPTER 11

1 The medium or material which removes heat from the condenser.
2 Fins are used to increase the area of contact between the condenser and the cooling medium, in order to increase the rate at which heat is rejected.
3 Natural convection is the movement of air over the condenser surface due to the temperature difference between the surface and the air. Forced convection is the movement of air due to a fan.
4 Because a greater volume of air can be obtained outdoors, to cool the condenser.
5 It causes scale to form on the inside and this reduces the water flow and rate of heat conduction through the walls.
6 Air and water.
7 To cool water that has circulated through a condenser.
8 The rate at which the condenser can extract heat from the refrigerant and transfer it to the cooling medium. $Q = A \times U \times TD$.
9 The ratio of the heat rejected by the condenser to the heat absorbed by the evaporator.
10 Algae blocks nozzles and filters in condeners and cooling towers.
11 60 kW.
12 1.33.

CHAPTER 12

1 The pressure between the plates is very low, so the outside air pressure pushes them hard on to the metal tube, producing a good contact for heat conduction.
2 A refrigerant, such as water or brine, which is cooled by primary refrigerant in an evaporator and then pumped to another location to produce cooling.
3 To cool secondary refrigerant.
4 By the rapid expansion of refrigerant through

a throttling valve or capillary tube into the evaporator.
5 By controlling the level of refrigerant using a float valve which regulates the flow of refrigerant into the accumulator.
6 5.6 kW.
7 11.5°C.
8 Ice formed from water which has condensed on the evaporator surface.
9 Removing frost which is reducing the heat transfer into the refrigerant.
10 Water spray, electric element, compressor gas.

CHAPTER 13

1 Driers are used to remove moisture from refrigerant so that acids, sludge and ice are not formed.
2 High side driers are fitted in the liquid line.
3 As the moist refrigerant passes through the microscopic holes of the dessicant, water sticks to the surface.
4 The water in the refrigerant reacts with the dessicant to form another substance.
5 Low side driers are fitted in the suction line.
6 A moisture indicator is a device that indicates the presence of moisture in refrigerant by means of a chemical that changes colour.

CHAPTER 14

1 A refrigerant is a working fluid used in refrigeration. Its function is to evaporate and absorb heat and also to condense and reject heat.
2 Suggestions: non-flammable, non-explosive and not be poisonous. Flow easily and be able to conduct heat well. Freezing point lower than the working temperature of the evaporator. Should not dilute oil.
3 They may damage the ozone layer and cause global warming.
4 An agreement between countries to limit and then phase out CFCs and HCFCs.
5 Where the temperature does not go below 0°C.
6 A brine is a mixture of water and a salt, such as sodium or calcium chloride.
7 It does not corrode metal surfaces.

CHAPTER 15

1 Throttling occurs when a liquid is allowed to expand through a small hole, some of the liquid turns to vapour and the temperature drops.
2 A capillary tube is a tube of small diameter through which liquid refrigerant passes and expands into a vapour.
3 When the compressor is off the two pressures become the same.
4 A constant superheat temperature is maintained by means of a remote bulb at the suction line end of the evaporator.
5 An operator is needed to monitor and adjust the valve the whole time.
6 Because the receiver contains a considerable quantity of refrigerant which will be sucked into the evaporator when the thermostat switches the system off. This can heat up and spoil the refrigerated produce.
7 The pressure tends to decrease because of friction.
8 An externally equalised TEV.
9 265 kPa G.
10 An adjustable spring acting downwards on a diaphragm balances out the upward pressure from the vapour in the evaporator.

CHAPTER 16

1 12.6 m/s.
2 51 000 Pa = 51 kPa or 0.51 bar.
3 i) 19 m, ii) 133 000 Pa = 133 kPa = 1.33 bar.
4 i) $6.4 \times 10^{-3} m^3/s$ (6.4 L/s).
ii) 32 m/s.
5 Four from viscosity, density, the roughness of the inner surface of the pipe, length of pipe, pipe joints.
6 A manometer with its opening at right angles to the fluid flow measures static pressure, while a manometer with its opening along the direction of flow measures total pressure.
7 Static pressure is exerted equally in all directions, whereas velocity pressure is exerted only in the direction of flow.
8 A fluid is any substance that flows, such as a liquid or gas.
9 Viscosity is friction inside the fluid.
10 Because friction causes heat to be generated and heat is a form of energy.

CHAPTER 17

1 Bacteria are very small, single celled plants, some of which cause food to spoil.
2 By giving off chemicals called enzymes which break down dead cell tissue.
3 Yeast is a single celled plant of the fungus family.
4 By giving off enzymes and by converting sugar to alcohol.
5 A mould is a simple fungus made up of a number of cells.
6 Refrigeration stops food spoiling by slowing down the activity of bacteria, yeasts, enzymes and moulds.
7 The food will dry out or dehydrate.
8 Because skins of bananas are damaged by temperatures below 13°C.
9 Immersion freezing is a method of quick freezing in which the product is immersed in brine.
10 Air blast freezing is quick freezing by passing low temperature, high speed air over the food.
11 Slow freezing is freezing products over a period of several hours or even days.

CHAPTER 18

1 The greater the cross-sectional area of the duct, the smaller is the resistance and vice versa, the design of grille used, the wetness of cooling coils, the size and shape of condensers.
2 i) The volume of air delivered by a fan per second is directly proportional to the fan speed.
ii) The pressure developed by a fan is directly proportional to the square of the fan speed.
iii) The power required by a fan is directly proportional to the cube of the fan speed.
3 In the forward-curved fan, the tip of the blade is curved forward in the direction of rotation; the radial blade is flat and arranged in an axial direction and in the backward-curved blade the tip is curved backward. In all three air is pushed outwards from the centre.
4 Axial fans blow air along an axis at right angles to the blades whereas centrifugal fans blow air outwards from the centre to the outside of the fan wheel.
5 Because water is less dense than mercury and therefore the water manometer is more sensitive to small changes of pressure.
6 A type of axial fan which is shaped like a simple propeller, with two, three or more blades.
7 The pressure exerted by the fans.
8 $6\,m^3$.
9 2400 Pa G.
10 480 W.
11 500 Pa G.

CHAPTER 19

1 86.4 W.
2 1.9 kW.
3 Cooling load is the transfer of heat into a refrigeration system, so that the compressor has to continue working in order to keep the temperature low.
4 Heat can transfer in by conduction, by air change, by the warmth of products and by the warmth of electrical equipment.
5 Wall gain load is the transfer of heat through the walls of a refrigeration system, mainly by conduction.
6 Heat from the sun warms the outside of the walls to a temperature which is above that of the surroundings. The amount of conduction therefore increases.
7 Air change load is the heat gain caused by warm air entering the refrigeration system.
8 Product load is the heat gain caused by products that need to be refrigerated.
9 The U factor depends on the material and the thickness of a wall.
10 Conduction is greater for ii).

CHAPTER 20

1 Lubricating oil reduces friction between moving parts and keeps the compressor cool.
2 A fall in temperature causes a rise in viscosity.
3 The amount of contamination is determined by measuring the dielectric strength of the oil.
4 Acidity is determined by neutralising it with a measured amount of potassium hydroxide.
5 Pour point is the lowest temperature at which an oil will flow.
6 Cloud point is the temperature at which wax in the oil separates out.
7 Floc point is the temperature at which wax will begin to separate out from a mixture of 10% oil and 90% refrigerant R12.

CHAPTER 21

1 Two metals, such a iron and brass, are fixed together and when the strip is cooled the strip bends because the metals contract by different amounts. The bending of the strip switches off the circuit.
2 A pressure control is a control, used in either the low or high pressure parts of the system, which responds to changes in pressure. They can be used as temperature controls or devices to switch off the system when pressure values are incorrect.
3 A humidistat is used to control the humidity of an air-conditioned space.
4 When the relative humidity is high a nylon band increases in length and when it is low the length decreases.
5 A compressor capacity control controls the flow of refrigerant from the compressor.
6 A dual-pressure control is a combined high pressure and low pressure control.
7 The differential is the difference between the cut-in and cut-out temperatures.

CHAPTER 22

1 Soft soldering is low temperature soldering, employing lead–tin–antimony solder and a blow torch.
2 Silver soldering is high temperature soldering, employing silver–copper–zinc solder and an oxy-acetylene torch.
3 Copper – general purpose, steel – condensers, aluminium – evaporators, plastic/rubber hose – car air conditioning, refrigerated transport.
4 The sharp jaws of the tube cutter are placed in contact with the tube, and then the adjustment knob is tightened slightly, so that they bite into the metal. The tube cutter is then moved around the tube until a groove is cut into its surface. The knob is tightened a little bit more and the process is repeated in order to make the groove deeper. This is done several times until the tube is cut completely. Do not try to tighten the knob too much in one go as the tube may become squashed where the cut is being made.
5 Some tube cutters are fitted with a sharp blade known as a reamer and this should be run around the inside of the tubing in order to remove the burr. Alternatively, a half-round file may be used.
6 Flare fittings employ screw threads and they are fixed to the end of a piece of tubing that has been expanded or flared. Once the flare has been pushed on to the fitting a flare nut is screwed into position over the join.
7 By hand, if the diameter of the tubing is small; using a spring for larger tubing and by using a tubing bender for the largest sizes.
8 Flux keeps a joint clean ready for soldering, after it has been cleaned with steel wool or emery cloth.
9 The simplest hose fitting is the worm drive clip.
10 Capillary action occurs when liquid is sucked into a narrow space.
11 Burrs must be removed to stop them from impeding the flow of refrigerant in the system.

CHAPTER 23

1 The 35 Ω reading is for the main winding, the 70 Ω reading is for the start winding and the 105 Ω reading is for the two coils in series.
2 Belt coupling and flange coupling.
3 Liquid tester, halide torch, electronic leak detector.
4 A sight glass, which is set into the side of the compressor case, is there to measure the oil level.
5 To avoid damage to the shafts.

Project 1: Suggested procedure
Take a lighted sulphur stick and move it over the pipes of the system until you see the dense white fumes which indicate that the ammonia refrigerant is leaking.

Project 2: Suggested procedure
Fit the drier after filling the condensor crankcase with oil. Afterwards conduct a pressure test.

CHAPTER 24

Project 1: Suggested procedure
Check for the following problems:
door warped, gasket damaged, door opened too often, condenser positioned near heater, overloaded shelves, drip tray pushed back, winter/summer control setting wrong, condenser near wall.

Project 2: Suggested procedure
Place one probe near to the bulb and one at the output of the valve. Adjust the screw outwards from the bottom of the valve so that more refrigerant is allowed through and the temperature adjusts itself to the correct value.

Project 3: Suggested procedure
With the meter, test the resistance between each pair of terminals on both motors. One motor should give three readings; one of low resistance, one of medium resistance and one of higher resistance. The resistance between each terminal and the earth connection to the motor case will be infinite. The other motor will give only one resistance reading or the resistance between each terminal and earth will be very low.

Project 4: Suggested procedure
Check for the following problems:
The position of the drip tray; if it is too far forward move it back to restrict the flow of air.

The winter/summer control is wrongly set; adjust it to the correct setting, that is, if it is still on a summer setting in the winter, put it on winter setting.

Project 5: Suggested procedure
Put on goggles and gloves, turn the power off and place a line tap on the suction pipe. Use a refrigerant recovery machine to remove the refrigerant.

Place a specially designated 'waste oil' can under the drier. Cut the pipe beneath the drier, using a file or a knife. There may be oil dicharged and this will collect in the can. When no more comes out, carefully remove the can. Use pipe cutters to cut both the discharge and suction lines.

Unbolt the compressor and carefully remove it.

▲ Probably the oil will smell of burnt insulation. Pour the oil into the 'waste oil' can, making sure that you do not get splashed. Dispose of the oil carefully, according to the environmental health regulations.

Project 6: Suggested procedure
Put on goggles and gloves, turn the power off and use a refrigerant recovery machine to remove the refrigerant.

If the blockage is still there after recharging, remove the refrigerant again and cut into the tube, near the drier, using a small file with a sharp edge and then break the tube. As an alternative a sharp knife can be used.

Connect the capillary tube cleaner to the open end and turn the handle until enough pressure is built up to remove the blockage.

Project 7: Suggested procedure
Use an electronic leak detector which has both an audible and a visible alarm. Electronic leak detectors are the most sensitive and the best for very small leaks. Move the probe carefully over the piping until the alarm sounds and the light flashes.

Project 8: Suggested procedure
It is likely that the condenser is not conducting heat away quickly enough because it is dirty. Also because some of the fins are bent it may have been on the refrigerator for some time without maintenance.

With a soft brush remove as much of the dirt and grease as possible. Using a proprietary cleaner and a cloth dissolve away the remaining dirt, carefully cleaning between the fins. **If the cleaner is spirit based make sure there is plenty of ventilation.** Finally straighten the fins using a fin tool.

Project 9: Suggested procedure
The problem is caused by algae blocking the nozzles. Switch off the water supply and scrape away the algae using a stiff brush, taking special care to remove deposits from the nozzles. Use a proprietary chemical algaecide to dissolve away any that remains.

Project 10: Suggested procedure
Sometimes defrosting is automatic and it will occur at regular intervals. If it is not:

1 Close the liquid line valve and allow the compressor to pump refrigerant out.
2 Switch off the compressor and the evaporator fan to stop water being sprayed into the system.
3 Switch on the warm water spray for a few minutes until the frost has melted and the water has drained away.
4 Switch off the spray, switch on the compressor and open the liquid line valve, and then switch on the fan.

Project 11: Suggested procedure
Switch on the valve in the by-pass line, which runs from the discharge line to the evaporator, to release hot gas and melt the frost.

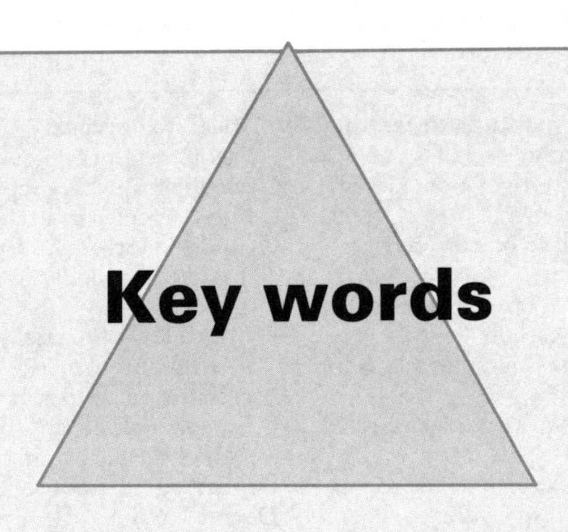

Key words

Absolute filter A very high efficiency filter that removes between 95 and 100% of dust.
Absolute humidity The mass of water vapour per unit volume of air.
Absolute pressure Total pressure of fluid in a refrigeration system, measured relative to that of a vacuum.
Absorbent In an absorption refrigerator, the liquid in which the refrigerant is dissolved.
Absorber The part of an absorption refrigerator which absorbs refrigerant vapour coming from the evaporator.
Absorption cycle The refrigeration cycle of the absorption refrigerator.
Absorption dessicant A chemical that dries refrigerant by reacting with it to form another chemical compound.
Acceleration Change of speed per unit time.
Acceleration due to gravity (acceleration of free fall) Acceleration of objects due to the earth's gravity.
Acidity A measure of how acid a lubricating oil is.
Adiabatic change A rapid change, in the pressure of a gas, that occurs together with a change of temperature.
Adsorption dessicant A chemical that dries refrigerant by allowing it to pass through microscopic holes where the water sticks to the surfaces.
Air blast freezing The use of high speed, low temperature air as a method of quick freezing.
Air change load The part of the cooling load caused by opening doors of freezers and refrigerators.
Air cooled condenser A condenser in which heat is removed from the outer walls by convection.
Air-conditioned space The room or rooms in which the air is conditioned by an air-conditioning system.
Alternating current (a.c.) Current that repeatedly changes direction under the influence of an alternating voltage.
Alternating voltage Voltage in which a neutral terminal remains constant at 0 V and a live terminal varies between a negative and a positive value.
Ammeter A meter which measures electric current.
Ampere The SI unit of electric current.
Antifreeze A compound such as propylene or ethylene glycol, which can be used as a secondary refrigerant.
Armature The soft iron rotating core, which holds the coils of an electric motor.
Atom Atoms are the microscopic particles that are the basic building blocks of nature.
Bacterium (plural bacteria) A single celled plant that is instrumental in causing food spoilage and some diseases.
Bar A unit of pressure used by weather forecasters. 1 bar = 10^5 Pa.
Bare tube evaporator An evaporator consisting of simple tubing through which heat is conducted.
Barometer An instrument for measuring atmospheric pressure.
Baudelot cooler A cooler with a series of parallel tubes, containing refrigerant, over which the liquid to be cooled is passed.
Big end The end of the connecting rod that is connected to the off-centre section of the crankshaft.
Bimetal strip A type of thermostat consisting of two different metals joined together.
Bleed-off The periodic removal of a small proportion of water from the bottom of a cooling tower in order to prevent scale formation.
Boiling point The temperature at which the pressure of the vapour produced by a liquid is equal to the pressure of the atmosphere or other surrounding pressure.
Bourdon gauge A pressure gauge consisting of a hollow metal tube made into a spiral which begins to open under the influence of the fluid inside it.
Boyle's law The law that states that the volume of a gas is inversely proportional to pressure for constant temperature.
Brine A solution of common salt, or some other salt, and water.
Brushes Parts of an electric motor, usually made of carbon, which make contact with the rotating commutator.
Burn out An electrical fault in which wiring is damaged by high temperatures.

Capacitor An electrical component used for storing charge.
Capillary tube A length of narrow metal tubing, used as a throttling device, which connects between the liquid line and the evaporator.
Central air handling unit A central unit containing all the important working parts of a large air-conditioning system.
Centrifugal compressor A compressor with a rotating

wheel which pushes the refrigerant outwards to the rim of the wheel and from there to the condenser.

Charging The process of filling a refrigeration system with refrigerant.

Chiller An evaporator used to cool secondary refrigerants.

Chlorofluorocarbon (CFC) A refrigerant made of a compound of chlorine, fluorine and carbon.

Circuit diagram A diagram which uses circuit symbols in order to explain electrical circuits.

Circuit symbol A standard symbol representing electrical components and quantities.

Clearance (clearance volume) The space left at the top of the cylinder when the piston is top dead centre.

Cloud point The temperature at which wax begins to separate from the rest of the lubricating oil.

Coefficient of performance The ratio of the refrigerating effect to the heat of compression.

Comfort air conditioning Air conditioning to provide comfort for people at home or at work.

Commercial air conditioning Special air conditioning for large buildings such as hotels, hospitals and other commercial buildings.

Commutator A ring, often of brass, cut into sections and connected to the coils that make up an electric motor.

Compression fitting A fitting which uses a compression ring and a threaded nut.

Compression ratio The ratio of the absolute discharge pressure to the absolute suction pressure.

Compound gauge A gauge that reads both above and below atmospheric pressure.

Compressor A type of pump which compresses refrigerant and circulates it round the refrigeration system.

Compressor power The theoretical power required to drive a compressor.

Condenser The part of a refrigeration system in which hot, compressed refrigerant is cooled.

Condensing unit A compressor, motor, condenser and discharge line all supplied as a single unit.

Conductance The ability to conduct heat (by a metal).

Conduction The transfer of heat by the movement of electrons or by the vibration of molecules.

Connecting rod The rod that connects the camshaft to the piston.

Constant pressure expansion valve A throttling valve which maintains a constant pressure in the evaporator.

Convection The transfer of heat by changes of density in a fluid.

Conventional current The convention that electric current flows from positive to negative.

Cooling coil A device used to produce cool air by the action of secondary refrigerant, in an air-conditioning system.

Cooling load The rate at which heat must be extracted from a refrigerated space in order to maintain the desired temperature.

Cooling tower A water conservation device used to supply water for cooling condensers.

Corrosive (chemical) A chemical that attacks laboratory surfaces and human tissue.

Crank pin The pin that connects the piston to the crankshaft.

Crankshaft The rotating shaft that makes the piston move up and down.

Critical temperature The temperature above which a vapour cannot be liquefied by pressure alone.

Cycle diagram A graphical representation of the state of the refrigerant in a refrigeration system.

Cylinder sleeve A replaceable sleeve which lines the inside of a cylinder in a larger compressor.

Dalton's law of partial pressures The law that states that in a mixture of gases or vapours: A) each one exerts a pressure equal to that which it would exert if it occupied the space alone; and B) the total pressure is equal to the sum of the partial pressures.

Deburring Removing burrs from the inside of piping.

Degree Celsius The everyday unit of temperature.

Dehumidification Reducing the humidity of air.

Density The property of a material, defined as mass per unit volume.

Desert cooler A simple air-conditioning system which uses a fan and a wet pad to cool and humidify dry desert air.

Dessicant A chemical used to dry refrigerant.

Dew point The temperature at which the water vapour in the air becomes saturated.

Dielectric strength An electrical measure of the amount of impurity in lubricating oil.

Differential The difference between the cut-in and cut-out temperatures in a remote bulb thermostat.

Diode An electical component which allows current to flow in only one direction.

Direct current (d.c.) Steady current, which does not change direction and flows from positive to negative.

Direct voltage A steady voltage from a battery or similar source, which does not change direction.

Discharge line The line between the compressor and the condenser.

Discharge service valve The valve on the discharge side of a compressor used for charging and discharging refrigerant.

Discharge valve The valve on a reciprocating compressor through which the compressed refrigerant leaves.

Discharging The process of removing refrigerant from a refrigeration system.

Double pipe cooler A cooler where brine flows through an inner tube while refrigerant flows in the opposite direction through an outer tube.

Double-tube condenser A condenser where cooling water flows through an inner tube while refrigerant flows in the opposite direction through an outer tube.

Drier A high or low side device that dries the refrigerant.

Dry bulb The thermometer bulb on a psychrometer which is kept dry and so gives the dry bulb temperature.

Dry expansion chiller A chiller where the flow of refrigerant is controlled by a throttling valve and vaporises in tubes contained in a metal shell which holds the secondary refrigerant.

Dry expansion evaporator An evaporator where the flow of refrigerant is controlled by a throttling valve.

Dry filter A filter which uses glass fibre or cotton wool with a sticky substance.

Duct A large pipe for carrying air in an air-conditioning system.

Electric current The movement of electrons through a wire, liquid or gas.

Electric filter A type of filter which uses a high voltage to attract charged dust particles.
Electric motor A rotating machine in which rotation is caused by the forces on current-carrying coils in a magnetic field.
Electromagnet A bar of soft iron, placed within a coil, that becomes magnetic when a current passes in the coil.
Electromagnetic induction The generation of electricity by passing a conducting wire through a magnetic field.
Electromotive force (e.m.f.) The voltage of a power supply.
Electron A small negative particle that orbits the nucleus of an atom and is also responsible for electrical conduction.
Electronic leak detector An electronic device which usually indicates a leakage of refrigerant by emitting a sound.
Energy The capacity to do work.
Enthalpy The sum of the internal energy and the product of pressure and volume.
Entropy Change of entropy is heat transferred divided by absolute temperature.
Enzymes Types of proteins which speed up chemical changes.
Evaporative condenser A condenser that uses both air and water as the condensing media.
Evaporator The hollow tube into which liquid refrigerant evaporates.
Evaporator capacity The ability of an evaporator to conduct heat into the refrigerant.
Exhaust air Air which has passed through the air-conditioned space.
Expansion turbine A rotating machine, used in an aircraft air-conditioning system, in which air is cooled by expansion.
Externally equalised TEV A thermostatic expansion valve with a narrow tube running from beyond the suction line to a point below the diaphragm in the valve.

Field coils Coils, wound on to a soft iron frame, which generate the magnetic field for an electric motor.
Fillet (solder) Solder that has moved into and closed a narrow gap.
Filter A device for preventing dirt and dust from entering an air-conditioned space.
Finned condenser A condenser fitted with metal fins to help conduct heat away from the hot refrigerant.
Finned evaporator An evaporator fitted with metal fins to help conduct heat in from the refrigerated space.
Flammable A chemical that easily bursts into flames is said to be flammable.
Flare fitting A fitting with an expanded end that is held in position by a flare nut.
Fleming's Left Hand Rule The motor effect rule in which the thumb, forefinger and centre finger indicate the directions of the force, magnetic field and current, respectively.
Floc point The temperature at which wax starts to separate from a mixture of 90% refrigerant R12 and 10% lubricating oil.
Flooded evaporator An evaporator where the flow of refrigerant is controlled by a float valve.
Flooded chiller A chiller where the primary refrigerant, controlled by a float valve, is contained in the shell, while the secondary refrigerant flows through the pipes.
Fluid A liquid or vapour (gas).
Force A force causes a body to accelerate.
Flux A material that sets up a barrier between freshly cleaned work, which is ready for soldering, and the air.
Force A force causes a body to accelerate.
Frequency The number of cycles per second of an alternating current or voltage.
Fuse A safety device, in an electrical circuit, which burns out when the current becomes too high.

Gauge pressure The pressure in a refrigeration system expressed in terms of the amount by which the pressure exceeds atmospheric pressure.
Generator The part of an absorption refrigerator which is heated to release the refrigerant from solution.

Halide torch A device, using a flame, which indicates leaks in a refrigeration system.
Hand expansion valve A throttling valve in which the flow of refrigerant is controlled by adjustments made by an operator.
Head A depth of water that causes a pressure and so can be used as a measure of pressure.
Heat That form of energy which transfers as a result of a temperature difference.
Heat capacity The heat required to heat a body through a temperature rise of 1°C.
Heat exchanger A device in an aircraft air-conditioning system which cools the compressed air.
Hermetic condensing unit A condensing unit, with the motor and the compressor having the same rotor shaft, contained in a totally closed shell.
Hertz The SI unit of frequency.
High-pressure control A pressure connected to the compressor end of the discharge line.
High side The high pressure side of a refrigeration system; includes the output of the compressor, the discharge line, the condenser, the receiver and the liquid line.
High side drier (liquid line drier) A type of drier placed in the liquid line of a refrigeration system.
Hose fitting A fitting which fixes a hose over tubing or a connector.
Humid Air with a high relative humidity is said to feel humid.
Humidifying and humidification Adding water to air.
Humidistat A device for controlling the humidity of an air-conditioned space.
Hydrochlorofluorocarbon (HCFC) A refrigerant made of a compound of hydrogen, chlorine, fluorine and carbon.
Hydrofluorocarbon (HFC) A refrigerant made of a compound of hydrogen, fluorine and carbon.
Hygrometer An instrument for measuring wet and dry bulb temperatures, dew point and relative humidity.

Immersion freezing Quick freezing by placing the product in refrigerated brine.
Induction motor A type of a.c. motor in which a rotating magnetic field induces currents in a rotor so that, by the motor effect, a force is exerted on the rotor.
Insulation resistance/continuity tester An instrument for measuring high resistances and for testing short and open circuits.

Internal energy The sum of the kinetic and potential energies of the molecules of a substance.
Ionised Atoms that lose one or more electrons are said to be ionised.
Isothermal change A change in pressure and volume of a gas that occurs without change of temperature.

Joule The SI unit of energy and work.

Kelvin The SI unit of absolute temperature.
Kinetic energy The energy of movement of a body.

Latent heat 'Hidden heat' which causes a change of phase and not a rise in temperature. *Latent heat of fusion*: latent heat when the phase change is from solid to liquid. *Specific latent heat of fusion*: latent heat of fusion per unit mass. *Latent heat of vaporisation*: latent heat when the phase change is from liquid to vapour. *Specific latent heat of vaporisation*: latent heat of vaporisation per unit mass.
Law of conservation of energy The law that states that matter cannot be destroyed, only converted from one form to another.
Light emitting diode (LED) A diode that emits light when it is connected into a circuit.
Line tap valve A valve that is fixed to refrigeration tubing and which makes a hole in the tubing for measurement or for charging and discharging refrigerant.
Liquid line The line between the receiver and the throttling valve.
Litre (L) A unit of volume equal to 1000 cm^3.
Live The terminal of an alternating supply which varies between a positive and negative e.m.f.
Low pressure control A pressure control where the bellows are connected directly to the low pressure part of the system.
Low side The low pressure side of a refrigeration system, which includes the input of the compressor, the suction line and the evaporator.
Low side drier (suction line drier) A type of drier placed in the suction line of a refrigeration system.

Main winding The stator coils of an induction motor.
Manometer A U-tube full of liquid used to measure the pressure difference between a fluid and the atmosphere outside.
Mean effective temperature difference A more accurate way of measuring than mean temperature difference, which takes into account the way that air temperature varies through the evaporator.
Mean temperature difference The average temperature difference between air passing through an evaporator and the refrigerant inside.
Mechanical draught cooling tower A type of cooling tower where water droplets are cooled by means of a fan.
Microprocessor control A refrigeration control working on digital electronic principles.
Mixture region On the Mollier diagram, the central region of phase change between liquid and vapour.
Moisture indicator A device, placed in the liquid line, with a glass viewing port which enables the presence of water in the refrigerant to be detected.
Molecule A combination of atoms which has different chemical properties from the atoms themselves.
Mollier diagram The pressure–enthalpy cycle diagram.
Montreal Protocol An international agreement to limit and then finally stop the production of certain types of refrigerant.
Motor effect The generation of a force on a current-carrying wire which is in a magnetic field.
Moulds Many-celled fungi that cause decay.
Multimeter A meter with the capability of measuring current voltage and resistance.

Natural draught (atmospheric) cooling tower A type of cooling tower where water droplets are cooled by the natural movement of air.
Neutral (i) The terminal of an alternating supply, has a permanent voltage of zero. (ii) A situation in which positive and negative charges exactly balance.
Newton The SI unit of force.
Non-ohmic Electrical components which do not obey Ohm's law are said to be non-ohmic.
n-type and p-type semiconductor n-type semiconductors contain a surplus of negative charge carriers (free electrons) while p-types contain a surplus of positive charge carriers.
Nucleus The positively charged central core of the atom which contains nearly all the mass.

Ohmic Electrical components which obey Ohm's law are said to be ohmic.
Ohmmeter An instrument for measuring electrical resistance.
Ohm's law The law which states that the current flowing in a wire is directly proportional to the applied potential difference, provided the temperature remains constant.
Oil ring A ring situated on the piston and designed to stop the mixing of refrigerant and oil.
Open circuit A circuit which is broken, so that no current can flow.
Operating control A control which maintains desired conditions of temperature or humidity in the system.
Outside air (fresh air) Air taken in by an air-conditioning system from outside the building.
Oxy-acetylene torch A type of high temperature torch used in silver soldering.

Pascal The SI unit of pressure.
Peltier effect The warming of one junction and the cooling of the other when a current is passed through a thermocouple.
Period The time taken for one cycle of alternating current or voltage.
Phase Solid, liquid and vapour (or gas) are the three phases of matter.
Piston displacement The difference in volume between top and bottom dead centre.
Piston ring A replaceable ring placed on a piston to establish a small area of contact between it and the cylinder in order to reduce friction.
Plate condenser A condenser to which a metal plate is fastened to improve heat conduction.
Plate freezer A freezer with metal plates that contain pipes which hold refrigerant.
Plate surface evaporator A type of evaporator where the large surface area of the plate improves heat conduction.

Positive ion An atom which has lost one or more electrons and so is positively charged.
Potential difference (p.d.) The voltage across the components in a circuit.
Potential energy Energy of position, either in a gravitational or an electric field.
Pour point The lowest temperature at which oil will pour.
Power Rate of doing work or rate at which energy is expended.
Pressure Force per unit area exerted by a solid, liquid or gas (vapour).
Pressure–enthalpy diagram A cycle diagram in which pressure is plotted against enthalpy.
Pressure gauge A gauge for measuring the pressure in a refrigeration system.
Preventive maintenance Regular inspection followed by repair or replacement of defective parts.
Process air conditioning Air conditioning to produce suitable conditions for the manufacture of certain goods.
Product load The part of the cooling load concerned with placing warm objects in a refrigerator.
Psychrometer An instrument for measuring wet and dry bulb temperatures, dew point and relative humidity.
Psychrometric chart A chart which shows details on dry bulb, wet bulb and dew point temperatures, relative humidity and the specific values of enthalpy, heat capacity, humidity and volume.
Psychrometry The study of air and its water vapour content for use in air conditioning.

Quick freezing Freezing that takes place in a matter of minutes to stop the growth of organisms.

Radiation Electromagnetic radiation (mostly infrared) which is responsible for the transfer of heat.
Radioactivity Radiation from radioactive material.
Range The cut-in and cut-out temperatures of a remote bulb thermostat.
Receiver The part of the refrigeration into which condensed refrigerant from the condenser collects.
Reciprocating compressor A compressor which uses a piston to compress the refrigerant.
Refrigerant The working fluid that circulates through a refrigeration system and produces both cooling and heating as it changes phase.
Refrigerant recovery machine A machine used to remove refrigerant from a system, so that environmental damage is avoided while maintenance or repair is carried out. These machines always clean the used refrigerant to some extent.
Refrigerating capacity The ability of a compressor to cause refrigeration.
Refrigerating effect The heat absorbed by the refrigerant from the refrigerated space.
Refrigerating rate The rate at which heat is taken in from the refrigerated space.
Relative humidity The ratio of s.v.p. at dew point to s.v.p. at air temperature expressed as a percentage.
Relay An electromagnetic switch which can allow one circuit to switch another circuit on or off.
Remote bulb (phial) A bulb containing refrigerant that is placed at the end of the evaporator or some other convenient place.
Remote bulb thermostat A thermostat which works from a bulb containing refrigerant that is placed in the evaporator or some other convenient place.
Resistance The ratio of voltage to current for a component or circuit. It is measured in ohms (Ω).
Return air Exhaust air returned to the air-conditioning system.
Room air conditioning The air conditioning of a single room by means of a room air conditioner placed in the room.
Root mean square (r.m.s.) A kind of 'average' value of alternating current and voltage.
Rotary compressor A type of compressor where compression is achieved by rotation rather than up and down (reciprocating) motion.
Rotating piston A roller attached to a rotating shaft which compresses the refrigerant in certain types of rotary compressor.
Rotating vane (compressor) A type of compressor with four spring-loaded vanes on a rotating shaft.
Rotor The soft iron rotating core, which holds the coils of an electric motor.

Saturated liquid Liquid which is in contact with its vapour, so that molecules re-enter the liquid the whole time.
Saturated liquid line The curved line on a Mollier diagram which separates the subcooled region and the mixture region.
Saturated vapour Vapour which is in contact with its liquid, so that molecules enter the vapour from the liquid the whole time.
Saturation temperature The temperature at which a liquid changes into a vapour or a vapour changes into a liquid.
Saybolt seconds universal (SSU) A way of measuring the viscosity of lubricating oil.
Scale (fur) A hard deposit left on the inside of evaporative condensers when water is heated, so releasing dissolved minerals.
Scroll compressor A type of rotary compressor, used extensively in air-conditioning systems, in which a rotating spiral or scroll compresses refrigerant against a fixed scroll.
Secondary refrigerant A liquid such as a brine or anti-freeze, used in some air conditioning and refrigeration systems, which are cooled by the main or promary refrigerant.
Semiconductor A material with the ability, somewhere between that of a conductor and an insulator, to conduct electricity.
Sensible heat Heat that can be detected as a result of a temperature rise.
Series connection A method of connecting resistances so that their values add together.
Shell-and-coil condenser A type of condenser in which the cooling water flows through copper tube wound into the shape of a coil and the refrigerant flows in the space between the tubes and the shell.
Shell-and-tube condenser A type of condenser in which the cooling water flows through a number of parallel copper tubes and the refrigerant flows in the space between the tubes and the shell.
Short circuit An electrical fault in which there is a direct

connection between a damaged winding and earth or a direct connection across the windings.

SI units, basic SI units, derived units The most advanced of the metric systems of units in which the basic units include the metre, kilogramme, second and ampere and in which the derived units are based on the basic units.

Silver soldering A type of high temperature soldering performed with an alloy of silver.

Simple air cycle A refrigeration cycle in which air is used as the refrigerant.

Slip ring A means of making an electrical connection to some sorts of induction motor rotors.

Slow freezing A method of freezing large items over a period of hours or days.

Soft soldering A type of low temperature soldering performed with tin and lead.

Specific enthalpy The enthalpy of a liquid or vapour per unit mass.

Specific entropy The entropy of a liquid or vapour per unit mass.

Specific humidity The mass of water vapour per unit mass of dry air.

Specific volume The volume of a liquid or vapour per unit mass.

Speed Rate of change of distance with time.

Split unit A unit larger than a room air conditioner, with the condenser mounted separately from the rest of the unit.

Squirrel cage A type of rotor, for an induction motor, consisting of a series of parallel aluminium bars connected to end rings.

Standard pressure The pressure corresponding to a column of mercury 760 mm high.

Start winding Induction motor winding designed to start the motor efficiently.

Static head The head of liquid corresponding to static pressure.

Static pressure The pressure exerted by a fluid which is not moving.

Stator The soft iron frame on which the field or stator coils of an electric motor are wound.

Subcooled liquid A liquid at any temperature below its saturation temperature.

Subcooled region On the Mollier diagram, region in which the refrigerant is in the form of a subcooled liquid.

Suction line The line between the evaporator and the compressor.

Suction service valve The service valve on the suction side of the compressor.

Suction valve The valve on a reciprocating compressor through which refrigerant vapour is taken in.

Superheat The amount of heat necessary to produce a superheated vapour from the original state of the fluid.

Superheat temperature The temperature difference between the saturated vapour in the outlet end of the evaporator and the superheated vapour further along.

Superheated region On the Mollier diagram, region in which the refrigerant is in the form of a superheated vapour.

Superheated vapour A vapour heated to a temperature above saturation temperature.

Supplementary load The part of the cooling load not included under wall gain load, air change load or product load. It includes items such as electrical equipment in the refrigerated space.

Supply air Conditioned air supplied to the air-conditioned space.

Sweat fitting A soldered fitting on a pipe or connector.

System analyser (Manifold gauge set) A device for testing, evacuating and charging refrigeration equipment.

Temperature A measure of the degree of hotness of a solid, liquid or gas.

Temperature–entropy diagram A cycle diagram in which temperature is plotted against entropy.

Thermocouple A device made up of two junctions of two different metals.

Thermoelectric refrigeration Refrigeration produced by passing a current through a thermocouple so that one junction becomes hot while the other becomes cold.

Thermostat A refrigeration temperature control.

Thermostatic expansion valve A throttling valve which works by maintaining a constant superheat temperature at the suction line end of the evaporator.

Three-phase alternating e.m.f. An alternating e.m.f. which produces three waveforms differing in phase by 120°.

Three-phase induction motor A type of induction motor which is driven by three-phase alternating e.m.f.

Throttling valve A valve which controls the rate at which refrigerant passes into the evaporator.

Total volumetric efficiency A measure of the actual volume of refrigerant vapour coming into a compressor cylinder compared with the piston displacement.

Toxic Poisonous.

Transformer A device for either increasing or decreasing an alternating voltage.

Transistor An electronic component that acts as both an amplifier and a switch.

Tube cutter A tool with jaws that grip and cut metal tubing.

Universal motor A type of electric motor that can operate on either a.c. or d.c.

Vacuum gauge A Bourdon gauge that reads pressures less than atmospheric.

Vaporisation The process by which liquid changes phase to a vapour at boiling point.

Vapour-compression cycle The refrigeration cycle in which the refrigerant is vaporised in an evaporator and condensed in a condenser.

Velocity Speed in a particular direction.

Velocity head The head of liquid corresponding to velocity pressure.

Velocity pressure The pressure exerted by a fluid which is moving, in addition to its static pressure.

Viscosity Liquid friction between the layers of a liquid.

Viscous filter A type of filter in which dust particles stick to oil which is on the surface of metal shavings.

Volt The unit of e.m.f. or p.d.

Voltage e.m.f. or p.d.

Voltmeter A meter which measures voltage.

Wall gain load The rate at which heat is conducted through the walls of a refrigerator.

Water cooled condenser A type of condenser in which the heat is removed by water.

Watt The SI unit of power.

Weight The pull of gravity on a body, given by the product of the mass and the acceleration of free fall.

Wet bulb The thermometer bulb on a psychrometer which is kept wet by a cloth wick dipped in water and so gives the wet bulb temperature.

Winter/summer control A domestic refrigerator control that alters the rate of freezing between summer and winter.

Wiredrawing The rapid expansion of refrigerant that occurs when it enters the evaporator from the throttling valve.

Work The product of work and distance, measured in joules.

Yeast A single celled plant, of the fungus family, larger than a bacterium, that causes food to decay.

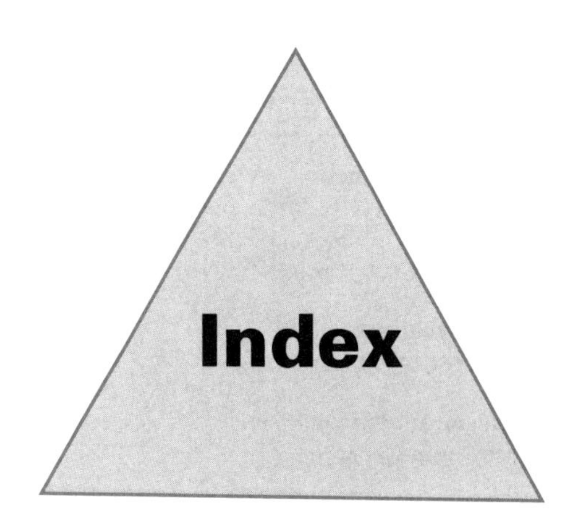

Index

(Page numbers in **bold** refer to illustrations)